Sub-Qu... Consciousness:

A Geometry of Consciousness Based Upon the Work of Karl Pribram, David Bohm, and Pierre Teilhard De Chardin

Shelli Renée Joye

B.S. Electrical Engineering
M.A. Indian Philosophy
Ph.D. Philosophy and Religion

Published by the Viola Institute
Viola, California

This book is dedicated to my many mentors including Dr. John Lilly, Alan Watts, Dr. Haridas Chaudhuri, and Dr. Brian Swimme, Dr. Allan Combs, and Dr. Dean Radin. However I would not have begun this work without the early encouragement and amazing input from my wife, Susanne Cathryn Rohner, who has encouraged, supported, motivated, and sustained me throughout this effort, and who made it possible for me to make a home with her in a cedar cabin in the majestic silence of Lassen forest, where this thesis has been developed. And finally, infinite gratitude and love to all of my family, teachers, friends, and ancestors in this journey that we share.

**Sub-Quantum Consciousness:
A Geometry of Consciousness Based Upon
the Work of Karl Pribram, David Bohm,
and Pierre Teilhard de Chardin**.

ISBN-13:   978-1-950761-00-5

TABLE OF CONTENTS

LIST OF FIGURES

By the same author:

The Little Book of Consciousness: Holonomic Brain Theory and the Implicate Order

Dr. Joye has not only created a map of consciousness; she has created a map of reality. Everything we call reality is experienced in consciousness, known in consciousness, and is in fact a modified form of consciousness. Reading this book will move you beyond physical materialism into better understanding the realities of consciousness.

——**DEEPAK CHOPRA, M.D.**,
Endocrinologist, founder of The Chopra Center, and author of
You Are the Universe with the physicist Menas Kafatos

Tuning the Mind: The Geometry of Consciousness

Shelli Joye's integrative masterpiece, *Tuning the Mind*, reads like insane science fiction—quantum black holes, a universal center that's everywhere and nowhere, the dark energy holoflux, and of course, the mysterious Teilhardian isospheres. But the strange thing is, it's not insane, nor is it fiction. It's a novel and refreshing scientific take on the role of consciousness in the physical world. Well worth the read.

——**DEAN RADIN, Ph.D.**,
Chief Scientist, Institute of Noetic Sciences (IONS), and author of
Supernormal: Science, Yoga, and the Evidence for Extraordinary Psychic Abilities

Chapter 1: Introduction

In this book a unique paradigm is presented which maps the underlying energy dynamics of consciousness in the cosmos. Through application of an integral methodology, and maintaining congruence with widely held principles of physics, neurophysiology, and electrical engineering, a holoflux theory of consciousness is presented.[1] This paradigm is developed as an extension of the holonomic mind/brain research of Karl Pribram, the quantum potential theory of David Bohm, and the hyperphysics of Pierre Teilhard de Chardin, mapping the dynamics of consciousness as an evolving process of energy.[2]

A New Theory of Consciousness

A new theory of consciousness is presented here as an extension of the theories pioneered by Pribram, Bohm, and Teilhard de Chardin. Core elements from their lifetime publications are examined and applied to construct a coherent, logical, and adequate model of consciousness that is in alignment with established principles of physics, mathematics, electrical engineering, and speculative philosophy.[3] The objective is to articulate a theory of

---

[1] The integral methodology used in this book is described later in this Introduction.

[2] Teilhard de Chardin, *Activation of Energy*.

[3] Whitehead, *Process and Reality*, 3; "Speculative philosophy is the endeavor to frame a coherent, logical, necessary system of general ideas in terms of which every element of our experience can be interpreted."

consciousness that can be characterized as "the simplest possible theory that explains the data," a challenge put forth by the Australian philosopher of consciousness, David J. Chalmers, in an essay describing an "Outline of a Theory of Consciousness":

> It is not too soon to begin work on a theory. We are already in a position to understand certain key facts about the relationship between physical processes and experience and about the regularities that connect them . . . . Finally, the fact that we are searching for a *fundamental* theory means that we can appeal to non-empirical constraints such as simplicity and homogeneity in developing a theory. We must seek to systematize the information we have, to extend it as far as possible by careful analysis, and then to make the inference to the simplest possible theory that explains the data while remaining a plausible candidate to be part of the fundamental furniture of the world.[4]

Integral Methodology: An Integral Perspective

This thesis is developed through application of an integral methodology that has been encouraged and developed within the California Institute of Integral Studies (CIIS) over the past forty years. The Australian psychologist Jennifer Gidley, President of the World Futures Studies Federation, comments on the approach fostered at CIIS in her article on the need for an imminent evolution of consciousness:

---

[4] Chalmers, "Facing Up to the Problem of Consciousness," 217.

Although there is an emergence of new integrative material from within both science and the humanities, there is still a predominance of researchers who do not refer to scholarly research from neighboring disciplines .... An exception is the California Institute of Integral Studies. By contrast, integral thought is less explicit and tangible in Europe—with the term *transdisciplinary* apparently favored over *integral.*[5]

The methodology applied here is more than simply transdisciplinary. While it does include the effort to discern patterns and elicit connections from a set of normally disparate academic and scientific disciplines, the integral method fully acknowledges the importance of participatory, experiential dimensions, particularly in any approach to consciousness studies. Thus the theories of Pribram, Bohm, and Teilhard de Chardin, are presented sequentially, in the context of their own unique life experiences. This methodology can be seen as a multiperspectival approach to the primary object of study, consciousness.

Integral Philosophy and Integral Theory

With ever-increasing information to assimilate, academic specializations have had to grow more focused. However, excessive focus and specialization has resulted in a human knowledge that is becoming increasingly fragmented. The archetypal pattern of the Tower of Babel comes to mind; each domain of knowledge has developed its own highly specialized language and conceptual framework,

---

[5] Gidley, "Evolution of Consciousness as a Planetary Imperative," 201.

such that cross-departmental dialog has been impaired. According to the systems thinker, Edgar Morin, the problem seems to be fragmentation and lack of integration:

> An influx of knowledge at the end of the 20th century sheds new light on the situation of human beings in the universe. Parallel progress in cosmology, earth sciences, ecology, biology and prehistory in the 1960s and 1970s have modified our ideas about the universe, the earth, life and humanity itself. But these contributions remain disjointed. That which is human is cut up into pieces of a puzzle that cannot form an image . . . . The new knowledge, for lack of being connected, is neither assimilated nor integrated. There is progress in knowledge of the parts and paradoxical ignorance of the whole.[6]

The integral methodological approach in this book assumes that valid data may be found significantly beyond the traditional domains of scientific methodology. An integral method examines information from multiple and often disparate domains, seeking to perceive correlations between them, resonances among disparate domains of knowledge which might lead to conceptual bridges between these otherwise relatively isolated, compartmentalized knowledge.

Aurobindo's Integral Perspective

Historically, this integral methodology stems from integral philosophy and integral theory.[7] The Cambridge-

---

[6] Morin, *Seven Complex Lessons in Education for the Future*, 21.

[7] Gidley, "Evolution of Consciousness as a Planetary Imperative," 224.

educated Indian philosopher, Aurobindo Ghose, was possibly the first writer to use the word "integral" extensively in his own writings on consciousness and evolution:

> Aurobindo is often credited as the first to use the term "integral" in connection with evolutionary philosophy. However, Harvard sociologist Pitirim Sorokin also began using the phrases "integral philosophy" and "integralist" in this connection at around the same time as Aurobindo. In fact, it appears that Sorokin, Aurobindo, and Gebser each originally adopted the term "integral" independently without knowledge of its use by others.[8]

In 1950, Dr. Haridas Chaudhuri traveled to the United States at the request of the Stanford professor of Asian Religions, Frederic Spiegelberg, who had approached the philosopher–sage Sri Aurobindo to recommend an Indian professor to head a center of East–West studies in San Francisco. Chaudhuri left India, where he had been Chair of Philosophy at the University of Calcutta, and eventually founded what is today the California Institute of Integral Studies.[9] In California, Chaudhuri developed his own version of integral philosophy, which he termed "integral panentheism," or "integral nondualism," based upon the writings of Sri Aurobindo, for whom evolutionary energy is to be found simultaneously manifest in the cosmos of

---

[8] McIntosh, *Integral Consciousness*, 180.

[9] Chaudhuri, *The Integral Philosophy of Sri Aurobindo*.

space–time as well as in a transcendent region, beyond time or space.[10]

Aurobindo Ghose (later known as Sri Aurobindo), academically trained at King's College, Cambridge, was banished by the British Raj to the predominantly French-speaking southeastern port of Pondicherry in 1910, after having spent a year in solitary confinement for his alleged part in a political act of terrorism in northern India. During his time in jail, Aurobindo spent much of the time practicing a contemplative technique of Indian yoga he had been taught; upon release, and to the surprise of his former revolutionary associates, Aurobindo dropped any involvement in the politics of independence. Instead, he spent the next four years reading philosophy and living the life of a contemplative in Pondicherry, then a French colony. [11] Having become fluent in the French language during his years at Cambridge, it is likely that during his Pondicherry years Aurobindo became acquainted with the writings of Henri Bergson, who in 1911 had published *Creative Evolution*.[12]

In *Creative Evolution*, Bergson argues for "intuition" as being of primary import in advancing any really new understanding of consciousness. He sees intuition as being clearly a mode of conscious awareness *beyond* the domain of an intellectual consciousness, and goes on to criticize modern epistemologies for discounting the efficacy of intuition while enforcing the primacy of intellect:

---

[10] Chaudhuri, *The Philosophy of Integralism*.

[11] Heehs, *The Lives of Sri Aurobindo*.

[12] Bergson, *Creative Evolution*.

In the humanity of which we are a part, intuition is, in fact, almost completely sacrificed to intellect . . . . Intuition is there, however, but vague and above all discontinuous. It is a lamp almost extinguished, which only glimmers now and then, for a few moments at most . . . feeble and vacillating, but which none the less pierces the darkness of the night in which the intellect leaves us.[13]

After four years of study, contemplation, and silence, Aurobindo once more began writing, and soon published, on a monthly basis, a wide-ranging collection of philosophical essays. In these essays, Aurobindo can be seen integrating his knowledge of Western evolutionary ideas with intuitive, experiential observations of consciousness obtained through direct contemplative experience.[14]

Gebser's Integral Perspective

A contemporary of Aurobindo, the German cultural historian and evolutionary philosopher Jean Gebser, writing in Switzerland in the 1940s, developed another approach to integral philosophy. Laying out his theory of integral consciousness, in *The Ever-Present Origin*, Gebser develops a theory of the evolutionary emergence of what he calls "the 'aperspectival (arational–integral)' consciousness."[15] Gebser's motivating objective was to foster what he called an incipient "integral aperspectival consciousness."

---

[13] Ibid., 152.

[14] Heehs, *The Lives of Sri Aurobindo.*

[15] Gebser, *The Ever-Present Origin*, xxix.

Gebser's own research focus was primarily within cultural anthropology, but his integral methodology is far ranging. In it can be seen a search for meaning through the discovery of transdisciplinary connections. In an essay entitled "Cultural Philosophy as Method and Venture," Gebser explains the importance of an integral effort for uncovering "meaning giving connections:"

> It is a scientific attempt, particularly distinctive of our epoch, to appraise the multiplicity of cultural endeavors, that is to say, to uncover meaning-giving connections . . . it could contribute toward the abolition of the feeling of isolation which today not only reigns in the various scientific disciplines but which is generally prevalent.[16]

The German philosopher Georg Feuerstein, in discussing Gebser's methodology, describes how Gebser's aim can be seen encapsulated in the term *synairesis*, "an intelligent realization of reality proceeding from the accomplished transparency of all modes of cognition."[17] In fact, Feuerstein tells us, it is this *synairesis* of Gebser's that can free us from the limited bounds of scientific realism. Feuerstein here comments:

> Gebser also makes it clear that his panoramic orientation is not a mere synthesis, which would only be part of the kind of systematization peculiar to the mental-rational consciousness. He speaks of his methodology as aiming at *synairesis*, which is an integral understanding, or

---

[16] Gebser, "Cultural Philosophy as Method and Venture," 78.

[17] Feuerstein, *Structures of Consciousness*, 195.

perception, of reality .... *Synairesis*, then, describes an intelligent realization of reality proceeding from the accomplished transparency of all modes of cognition.[18]

Gebser coins another term to describe his methodology, *systasis*, a term implying a process whereby partials merge or are merged into a whole:

> *Systasis* is the means whereby we are able to open up our consolidated spatial consciousness to the integrating consciousness of the whole. This integrating consciousness enables us to perceive and present the integrity or integrality of the whole.[19]

By contrast, scientific materialism, the driving operational paradigm behind contemporary science and technology, includes what is clearly a limited domain of inquiry in its definition of reality. This limitation is gradually being recognized by small segments of the scientific community, as Feurstein remarks here:

> Only a dimension that is quantifiable, measurable, analyzable, abstractable, or predictable . . . one that is flat and monochrome, and needless to say, is contradicted by the scientific evidence itself. It is for this reason that avant-garde scientists admit the need and indeed are looking for a new "paradigm" that, hopefully,

---

[18] Ibid., 194–95.

[19] Ibid., 195.

will do justice to the multidimensionality of humanness.[20]

Gebser's vision points the way to a new research methodology, an integral, multi-perspectival approach. From a wider mix of perspectives than traditionally afforded by academic analysis, the focus here is comprised of discovering a pattern, a *synairesis* emerging from multiple disciplines. From this multi-domained perspective new connections are discoverable from which new understandings may emerge. Figure 1 presents a visual diagram of the integral methodology applied specifically in this book, in which can be seen the hard problem of consciousness approached from eight perspectives.

---

[20] Ibid.

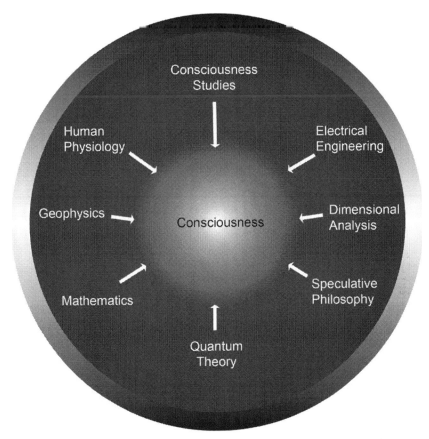

Figure 1. An integral focus on consciousness. Graphic by author.

Wilber's Integral Perspective

There is yet another perspective on integral philosophy and methodology to be found in the writing of American philosopher Ken Wilber, who expresses his own theories of an integral philosophy somewhat as a synthesis of earlier philosophers. In his essay, "A Brief History of Everything," Wilber describes the integral perspective as follows:

> If we look at the various fields of human knowledge—from physics to biology to

psychology, sociology, theology and religion—
certain broad, general themes emerge about
which there is very little disagreement. If we take
these types of largely agreed upon orienting
generalizations from the various branches of
knowledge ... and if we string these orienting
generalizations together, we will arrive at some
astonishing and often profound conclusions,
conclusions that, as extraordinary as they might
be, nonetheless embody nothing more than our
already agreed upon knowledge.[21]

Wilber integrates material from far ranging
disciplines, including psychology, Asian philosophy, and to
a lesser extent, the sciences, and he has developed a
methodology which he terms Integral Methodological
Pluralism (IMP), in which multiple perspectives are brought
together in an effort to elicit a deeper understanding of
consciousness.[22] The methodology of IMP stresses the idea
that all articulated understandings are context based,
formed within specific cultural contexts, and molded by the
unique academic, experiential, and cultural-historic
background environments from which each individual
attempts to formulate their own understanding and with
which to give their own unique expression.[23]

Wilber's methodology often works by juxtaposing
older historical paradigmatical frameworks alongside newer
paradigms. In his 1996 *A Brief History of Everything*, for
example, in developing a point he might discuss

---

[21] Wilber, *A Brief History of Everything*, 17–18.

[22] Wilber, *Integral Spirituality*, 72.

[23] Ibid., 87.

contemplative maps of consciousness developed by Indian Vedantic traditions, and then contrast these with quantum mechanical considerations from physics, and finally analyze both in terms of various transpersonal theories expressed by modern psychologists.[24]

Wilber also describes the recent emergence of an evolutionary epistemological capacity which he calls "vision-logic." Wilber's vision-logic consists of an integration of intellectual capacity with intuition in order to bring about the recognition of new relationships among seemingly radically diverse perspectives, with the objective being to discover congruencies that might bring forth new understandings of the phenomena being studied.[25]

Wilber's vision-logic, with its emphasis on the application of intuition, echoes the central methodological idea of "intuition" as developed by Henri Bergson, but Wilber's approach is also strongly influenced by the integral methodology developed by Jean Gebser.[26]

In summary, the methodology of this book, informed by the approaches of Aurobindo, Bergson, Gebser, and Wilber, is an effort to bridge the gap between the natural sciences and philosophical speculation. In this book, relevant observations from various natural sciences and humanistic disciplines are examined, compared, and coordinated to support a holoflux field theory of consciousness. Nevertheless, science, and in particular mathematics and physics, continues to be key to the

---

[24] Wilber, *A Brief History of Everything*.

[25] Wilber, *Quantum Questions*.

[26] Wilber, *Integral Spirituality*.

articulation of a workable theory of consciousness. In a recent essay, "How Consciousness Becomes the Physical Universe," Kafatos, Tanzi, and Chopra declare:

> Physics can serve a pivotal role in transitioning to this new model, because the entire biosphere operates under the same generalized principles we described from the quantum perspective, as does the universe itself. This simple unifying approach must be taken, we realize, as a basic ontological assumption, since it cannot be proven in an objective sense. We cannot extract consciousness from the physical universe, despite the fervent hope of materialists and reductionists . . . . Our approach, positing consciousness as more fundamental than anything physical, is the most reasonable alternative: trying to account for mind as arising from physical systems in the end leads (at best) to a claim that mathematics is the underlying "stuff" of the universe (or many universes, if you are of that persuasion.) . . . . In that sense, we believe the ontology of science will be undivided wholeness at every level. Rather than addressing consciousness from the outside and trying to devise a theory of everything on that basis, a successful Theory of Everything (TOE) will emerge by taking wholeness as the starting point and fitting the parts into it rather than vice versa.[27]

---

[27] Kafatos, Tanzi, and Chopra, "How Consciousness Becomes the Physical Universe," 1126–27.

Participatory Experience as Data

The consideration of *direct participatory experience* as data is one of the most important distinctions between traditional scientific and academic methodologies and the integral methodology applied within this book. In the integral, multiperspectival approach, phenomenological experience and contemplative introspection are examined in the context of the hard sciences, and are no longer banished to philosophy and psychology.[28] Evidence of experiences, particularly of a participatory, contemplative nature, are considered in the context of this book to be of major significance in the evolution of theories of consciousness put forth by Karl Pribram, David Bohm, and Pierre Teilhard de Chardin. Accordingly, their theories are presented within a biographical context, and are shown to emerge from the time line of their lives.

The inclusion of this "participatory approach" echoes the observations of Henri Bergson on the importance of *intuition*, or unmediated knowledge, as a tool with which to explore the inner nature of things.[29] Here is the opening sentence from Bergson's *Creative Evolution*, published in 1911:

> The existence of which we are most assured and which we know best is unquestionably our own, for of every other object we have notions which may be considered external and superficial,

---

[28] The hard science context in this dissertation: neurophysiology (Pribram), quantum physics (Bohm), paleontology (Teilhard de Chardin), and engineering (the author).

[29] Ferrer and Sherman, *The Participatory Turn*, 21.

whereas, of ourselves, our perception is internal and profound.[30]

Renewed interest in direct "internal perception" approaches to research are re-emerging in the twenty-first century. In the preface to *The Participatory Turn*, Ferrer and Sherman have characterized participatory knowing as having three primary elements:

1. *Participatory knowing* is knowing by presence or by identity.

2. It embraces an enactive paradigm of cognition,

3. And it is transformative.[31]

All three of these elements are examined in this here, in the context of the life experiences of each of three major thinkers: Karl Pribram, David Bohm, and Pierre Teilhard de Chardin.

Chapter Summaries

Following this Chapter 1 Introduction, the theory of sub-quantum consciousness is presented in six chapters:

- Chapter 2: The "Hard Problem": Information and Meaning

- Chapter 3: Karl Pribram's Holonomic Brain Theory

---

[30] Bergson, *Creative Evolution*, 5.

[31] Ferrer and Sherman, *The Participatory Turn*, 122.

- Chapter 4: David Bohm's Implicate Order and Holomovement

- Chapter 5: The Holoflux Field Theory of Consciousness

- Chapter 6: The Hyperphysics of Pierre Teilhard de Chardin

- Chapter 7: Summary and Conclusions

Chapter 2, "The 'Hard Problem': Information and Meaning" describes some of the problems in the field of consciousness studies, and refutes argument put forth against a field theory of consciousness in 1951 by Karl Lashley,[32] and later by Roger Sperry.[33] Also considered is a contemporary epiphenomenalist theory of consciousness put forth by Terence Deacon,[34] which though brilliantly cogent, appears to be insufficient with regard to providing any testable fundamental basis for human consciousness, lacking a clear solution to the "hard problem" proposed by David Chalmers.[35]

Chapter 3, "Karl Pribram's Holonomic Brain Theory," a thorough discussion of Karl Pribram's holonomic brain theory, lays the foundation upon which Chapter 4, "David

---

[32] Lashley, "An Examination of the Electric Field Theory."

[33] Sperry, Miner, and Myers, "Visual Pattern Perception Following Subpial Slicing."

[34] Deacon, *How Mind Emerged from Matter*.

[35] David Chalmers, "Facing Up to the Problem of Consciousness"; discussed elsewhere in this dissertation under the section "What Is Consciousness?"

Bohm's Implicate Order and Holomovement" is developed. The theories of both of these scientists establishes the base upon which the electromagnetic holoflux theory of consciousness is then developed in detail in Chapter 5, "The Holoflux Field Theory of Consciousness," and in which additional aspects of the holoflux theory are presented and explained, primarily through the use of diagrams and analogies; basic concepts are discussed, while technical jargon and mathematical notation are minimized.

Chapter 6, "The Hyperphysics of Pierre Teilhard de Chardin," consists of two sections, and begins with a historical account of the development of Teilhard de Chardin's ideas over the arc of his lifetime, and identifying his early participatory experiences of a collective consciousness during his years as a conscripted stretcher-bearer in the trenches of World War I.[36] The development of Teilhard's concepts of hyperphysics are detailed in an analysis of key essays from the collections *Human Energy*, and concludes with particular focus upon his technical essay "Centrology," in *Activation of Energy*.[37] Included in this discussion re the following terms created by Teilhard in the development of his ideas: *cosmogenesis, centro-complexification, isospheres, complexity-consciousness, tangential-energy, radial-energy, co-reflection, ultra-hominization, the Noosphere,* and *the Omega Point.* In addition to describing each of these principles in the context of hyperphysics, I discuss each of them in terms of coherency and applicability in a fuller analysis of holoflux theory.

---

[36] Teilhard, *Letters from a Soldier–Priest 1914–1919.*

[37] Teilhard, *Human Energy; Activation of Energy.*

Chapter 7, "Summary and Conclusion" summarizes the holoflux theory of consciousness, showing it to be an extension of the work of Pribram and Bohm, and highlighting the relationship of the theory to the hyperphysics of Pierre Teilhard de Chardin. In the final section are presented experimental strategies for research that may substantiate the dynamics of an infrared holoflux field of consciousness within the human body. The book concludes by discussing implications for the existence of such a field, and the possibilities for uploading elements of human consciousness as radiant information from wetware to hardware.

Throughout the book, extensive use is made of visual imagery, resulting in fifty-two figures. These images support the integral methodology by providing an additional perspective to clarify and illustrate abstract ideas as they are encountered in the text.

An Appendix has been included in which the work of Erwin László is examined in light of the holoflux theory. László's 2014 publication discusses a nonspatial, nontemporal "A-dimension," and his description of a holographic information "holofield" are shown to be in full congruence with the holoflux theory presented here.[38]

---

[38] László, *The Self-Actualizing Cosmos*.

Chapter 2: The "Hard Problem"

There is widely held agreement within the scientific community that consciousness must be an epiphenomenon, that consciousness must be considered as a recent byproduct arising from the firing of neurons within the brain. From this perspective the phenomenon of consciousness is considered to be unique to life on this planet, a serendipitous epiphenomenon of carbon-based biological forms, likely found nowhere else in the universe.[39]

Beyond Epiphenomenalism: Philosophical Zombies

Another sector of the scientific community would deny even the status of epiphenomenalism, asserting that there is no consciousness. This has led to what is called the philosophical zombie argument, a concept found in contemporary thought experiments which refute philosophies of conscious dualism, and instead assert that human behavior operates in a human body without the necessity of a dimension called consciousness.[40] Here the argument is made that without consciousness, there would still be behavior induced by the physiological activity of the material body and brain system, and yet there would be "no difference whatsoever between persons and their zombie twins."[41] Daniel Dennett goes even further, one would hope

---

[39] Flanagan, "Conscious Inessentialism and the Epiphenomenalist Suspicion," 357–58.

[40] Harnad, "Why and How We Are Not Zombies."

[41] Ibid., 41.

facetiously, by declaring that the reality of zombies precludes even epiphenomenalism:

> Are zombies possible? They're not just possible, they're actual. We're all zombies. Nobody is conscious—not in the systematically mysterious way that seems to support such a doctrine as epiphenomenalism.[42]

Whether or not consciousness is epiphenomenal, efforts are being made to interpret and to map consciousness using the tools of mainstream technology. One such approach can be found in the research of Dr. Rollin McCraty, director of HeartMath Institute in Boulder Creek, California. In an essay describing his research findings, McCraty considers the possibility of "subtle electromagnetic communication between people":

> I believe that the electromagnetic energy generated by the heart is an untapped resource within the human system awaiting further exploration and application. Acting as a synchronizing force within the body, a key carrier of emotional information, and an apparent mediator of a type of subtle electromagnetic communication between people, the cardiac bioelectromagnetic field may have much to teach us about the inner dynamics of health and disease as well as our interactions with others.[43]

McCraty thus posits a physical basis for an electromagnetic energy of consciousness, in the

---

[42] Dennett, *Consciousness Explained*, 406.

[43] McCraty, *The Energetic Heart*, 17.

electromagnetic field generated by the physiological activity of the heart and the ionic blood plasma flow.

Scientific Materialism and Contemporary Neuroscience

It has been remarked that the general consensus of scientific materialism is that the various states of consciousness can be attributed solely to the neurological structure and functioning of the brain system.[44] A professor of oncology and a physicist by training, Jack Tuszyński, for example, argues the case:

> That the brain does give rise to consciousness is a key assumption of modern neuroscience and we will take it as a given, otherwise we would be compelled to seek the answers in the realm of religion or metaphysics.[45]

Another example of such an unquestioned conviction can be seen in the assertions of neuroscientist Giulio Tononi, who holds the Distinguished Chair in Consciousness Science at the University of Wisconsin. Tononi is seen here to be unapologetic in his unequivocal belief that:

> This mind is completely based in and dependent upon the physical processes that occur in its own working, in those of other minds, and in the events involved in communication. There are no

[44] Kropf, "The Evolutionary Quest for Immortality."

[45] Tuszyński, *The Emerging Physics of Consciousness*, 37.

separate domains of matter and mind and no grounds for dualism.[46]

Such approaches have been criticized by the cognitive scientist Noam Chomsky for failing to provide any clear, consensual definition for what is truly constituted by matter. Chomsky holds that, without additional specificity, the term "materialism," itself, must be seen to be without any true definite meaning.[47]

Over a century ago Gustav Fechner, the founder of psychophysics, fought against this same assumption, which he called the "nerve issue." Fechner addresses this assumption with these amusing analogies:

> Since violins need strings to sound, then flutes also need strings; but since flutes have no strings, they cannot sound; candles and petroleum lamps need wicks in order to burn, so gas lamps also need wicks, but they have none; thus they cannot burn. Yet flutes sound without strings and gas lamps burn without wicks . . . . If fish and worms can breathe without having lungs, while mammals and birds can breathe only if they have lungs, why cannot plants without nerves experience perception, while animals can only perceive when they do have nerves?[48]

Even laboratory derived, repeatable results are not always enough to persuade skeptics, as Karen and Russell De Valois, (University of California [UC] Berkeley

---

[46] Edelman and Tononi, *A Universe of Consciousness*, 75.

[47] Chomsky, *New Horizons in the Study of Language and Mind.*

[48] Fechner, *Religion of a Scientist*, 309.

researchers and close associates of Karl Pribram) commented, in publishing their experimental results indicating that optical cognition of spatial images on the retina were routed to the cerebral cortex as their Fourier-transformed patterns (i.e., interference-patterned holographic images):

> It sometimes appears that the resistance to accepting the evidence that cortical cells are responding to the two-dimensional Fourier components of stimuli is due to a general unease about positing that a complex mathematical operation similar to Fourier analysis might take place in a biological structure like cortical cells. It is almost as if this evoked, for some, a specter of a little man sitting in a corner of the cell huddled over a calculator.[49]

Deacon's "Something That Is Not There"

A carefully articulated approach to understanding consciousness from the scientific materialist viewpoint can be seen in the work of Terrence Deacon.[50] In a concluding chapter, "Consciousness," Deacon reinforces his conviction that consciousness is an emergent property:

> The central claim of this analysis is that sentience is a typical emergent attribute of any teleodynamic system. But the distinct emergent higher-order form of sentience that is found in

---

[49] De Valois and De Valois, *Spatial Vision*, 72.

[50] Deacon, *Incomplete Nature*.

animals with brains is a form of sentience built upon sentience.[51]

Deacon also posits something not often considered by epiphenomenalists, that "sentience should be operative *in parallel* to the functioning of complex nervous systems."[52] While Deacon sees consciousness as some epiphenomenon, he also sees in it some phenomenal effect underlying information flow. In his 2012 book, *Incomplete Nature*, Deacon argues that we are "in desperate need of" a theory that establishes *the ground of consciousness* which *must underlie and inform* the information communicated:

> It is often said that we are living in the "information age." For more than half a century we have known how to measure the information conveying capacity of any given communication medium, and yet we cannot give an account of *how this relates to the content* that this signal may or may not represent . . . . That is evidence that we are both woefully ignorant of a fundamental causal principle in the universe and in desperate need of such a theory.[53]

Deacon's theory is as follows: "that which is not" should be regarded as the ground of information, not the manifesting physical phenomena in which information is encoded, modulated, and interchanged. Throughout *Incomplete Nature*, Deacon develops and supports this line

---

[51] Ibid., 508.

[52] Ibid., 509. Italics added by author.

[53] Deacon, "What is Missing from Theories of Information," 123–25.

of reasoning with numerous examples from evolutionary biology, and introduces the concept of *intentional inexistence* as *something that is not there.*[54]

> The "intentional inexistence" of the content of a thought, the imagined significance of a coincidental event, the meaning of a reading from a scientific instrument, the portent of the pattern of tea leaves, and so on, really is *something that is not there.*[55]

Deacon goes on to speculate that the difficulties of contemporary approaches to the problem of consciousness may stem from asking the wrong questions. He expresses the simple fact that answers may have been sought for in all the wrong places:

> The nearly universal tendency to attribute intentional phenomena to a disembodied realm is a reflection of this negative defining feature. . . this one, too, appears to have been a function of asking the wrong sort of questions.[56]

He implies that the current search to understand the mind–brain relationship fails precisely because of the widespread tacit assumption that mental content is all too often reduced to syntactic content:

> Talking about cognition in terms of the mind–brain—implying a metaphysically primitive

---

[54] Ibid., 140.

[55] Ibid., 141. Italics added by author.

[56] Ibid.

identity — or talking about mind as the software of the brain — implying that mental content can be reduced to syntactic relationships embodied in and mapped to neural mechanics — both miss the point. The content that constitutes mind is not *in* the brain, nor is it *embodied* in neuronal processes in bodies interacting with the outside world.[57]

Deacon recurrently returns to his concept of intentional inexistence, presenting challenging arguments, in which we are urged to seek that which is not, something which is not (obviously) there, shapes that falls between the cracks of our knowledge and understanding:

It is, in a precisely definable sense, that which determines which variations of neural signaling processes are *not* occurring, that will in a round-about and indirect way help reinforce and perpetuate the patterns of neural activity that are occurring.[58]

Although providing a clear and challenging approach to any theory of consciousness, Deacon's epiphenomenalist observations are inadequate for failing to discover a convincing linkage between physical laws and a theory of consciousness.

Ned Block's Binary Consciousness

Another approach to a binary consciousness can be found in New York University professor Ned Block's

---

[57] Ibid. Italics added by author.

[58] Ibid.

identification of two types of consciousness: *access* consciousness, and *phenomenal* consciousness. [59] Block defines access consciousness (which he refers to as "A-consciousness") as a sort of representational consciousness, a functional mode that drives reasoning and direct control of speech, action, and sensory motor systems. His definition of phenomenal consciousness ("P-consciousness") is the conscious experience of sensations: feelings, emotions, pain, or pleasure.

A New Conception of Space

Another approach is that of Colin McGinn, a British philosopher known for his theories of mind, understands consciousness by regarding it as a spatial phenomenon. This approach at first seems close to Deacon's idea of something that is not there, but is somewhat closer to the mathematical (geometric/topological) or quantum physics of David Bohm. At the end of an essay on "Consciousness and Space," McGinn states:

> I am now in a position to state the main thesis of this paper: in order to solve the mind–body problem we need, at a minimum, a new conception of space. We need a conceptual breakthrough in the way we think about the medium in which material objects exist, and hence in our conception of material objects themselves .... Things in space can generate consciousness only because those things are not, at some level, just how we conceive them to be; they harbor some hidden aspect or principle .... So it is certainly an open question whether the problem of consciousness requires

---

[59] Block, *Consciousness, Function, and Representation.*

revisions in neurophysiology alone, or whether those revisions will upset broader reaches of physical theory. [60]

Having briefly surveyed several models of consciousness as an information, electromagnetic energy, or spatial field effect, we examine the converse, the lingering impact upon consciousness studies of mid-twentieth-century opposition to any such field approaches.

Arguments Against a Field Theory of Consciousness

Until recently, any field theory approach to consciousness was largely dismissed, due to a misreading of the work of one of the founders of Gestalt psychology, Wolfgang Köhler (1887–1967).[61] An "electric field theory of consciousness" was allegedly put forward by Köhler in 1940, but in actuality, Köhler did *not* posit an electromagnetic field of consciousness, but only the observational discovery that sensory (auditory and visual) sensory stimulations caused corresponding observable changes in voltage on the brain surface, as measured between different regions on the cerebral cortex. [62] However even Köhler's theorized correlation of perception and voltage change was refuted by Karl Lashely (1950) and later by Roger Sperry (1955) in laboratory experiments that have since, themselves, been

---

[60] McGinn, "Consciousness and Space," 103–4.

[61] Rose, *Consciousness: Philosophical, Psychological and Neural Theories*.

[62] Köhler, *Dynamics in Psychology*.

seen to be questionable in light of contemporary developments in brain research.[63]

In the early 1950s, Lashley carried out a series of experiments to discover whether he could detect any evidence with which to prove or disprove Köhler's theorized electromagnetic flow of current over the surface of the brain. Lashley tested trained monkeys, then drilled holes in their skulls and inserted interconnected gold pins into multiple areas of each monkey's cerebral cortex. His assumption was that adjacent gold pins would disrupt or short-circuit any electric field activity in the cerebral cortex involved in monkey consciousness, and thus cause observable changes in future monkey test data. When no behavior impairment or differential effect of any kind was noted, Lashley concluded that he had established there to be *no electric field component* of consciousness, otherwise his pins would have disrupted the flow patterns of electricity.[64]

Though widely accepted, even now, Lashely's conclusion that consciousness cannot be an electric field phenomenon is suspect for a number of reasons: (1) Lashley only considered voltage changes between macro areas of the cerebral hemispheres, the thin, outermost region of the brain, and (2) he seems to have ignored the fact that complex three-dimensional electromagnetic fields of extremely short wavelengths, such as "thermal" infra–red, would not be affected by the presence of randomly positioned gold pins poking into the cerebral hemispheres. Though none of these experiments were definitive,

---

[63] Lashley, "In Search of the Engram"; Sperry, "Visual Pattern Perception."

[64] Lashely, "An Examination of the Electric Field Theory."

nevertheless the electric field approach to consciousness was discredited.

Information, Meaning, and Experience

As a result of difficulties in identifying a consensual strategy to exploring consciousness, the scientific community seems to have sidestepped the entire project, for it appears that, as the Australian philosopher David Chalmers observes, ". . . existing theories of consciousness either deny the phenomenon, explain something else, or elevate the problem to an eternal mystery."[65] Chalmers himself expresses a view that consciousness ought to be approached through a search for a fundamental link between information and experience, and goes so far as to conjecture that "phenomenal properties are the internal aspect of information."[66]

Information and meaning are also central to the concern of the quantum physicist David Bohm, who sees that, "Meaning is inseparably connected with information."[67] For Bohm the search for meaning is seen as an unfolding of fresh perceptions of reality, as intension is brought to focus upon a specific problem:

> When we use the term "meaning," this includes significance, purpose, intention and value. However, these are only points of departure into the exploration of the meaning of meaning. Evidently, we cannot hope to do this in a few

---

[65] Chalmers, "Facing Up to the Problem of Consciousness," 28.

[66] Ibid.

[67] Bohm, "Meaning and Information," 45.

sentences. Rather, it has to be unfolded as we go along. What is needed is a creative attitude to the whole, allowing for the constantly fresh perception of reality, which requires the unending creation of new meanings. This is especially significant, in the exploration of the meaning of meaning.[68]

For Bohm, in what he calls the "causal interpretation" or "ontological interpretation" of quantum field theory, *meaning unfolds* from out of an implicate domain, a dimension transcendent of space and time. This unfolding meaning is expressed in space–time, which Bohm calls the explicate order. Bohm's model is one that can be described by the "quantum potential" function, Q, which Bohm and Peat derived from Schrödinger's wavefunction (which describes all moving particles as wave-like functions).[69] Bohm's theories are discussed at length in Chapter 4.

Perhaps the most widely debated issue in consciousness studies can be encapsulated in the so-called "hard problem," stated by David Chalmers in 1995, in which he places emphasis squarely upon the issue of *experience*. Chalmers proposes a theory of consciousness which highlights the importance of information, while conflating it into what he calls, the "hard problem":

> The really hard problem of consciousness is the problem of *experience*. When we think and perceive, there is a whir of information processing, but there is also a subjective aspect . . . . Why should physical processing give

---

[68] Ibid., 43.

[69] Bohm and Peat, *Science, Order, and Creativity*, 80.

rise to a rich inner life at all? It seems objectively unreasonable that it should, and yet it does. If any problem qualifies as *the* problem of consciousness, it is this one.[70]

This "whir of information processing" Chalmers refers to is readily observed in the electrical information processing of the neuronal brain system in the body, like the "thinking meat" which so astounded two alien observers in a story by the science fiction writer, Terry Bisson:

> "They're meat all the way through."
> —"No brain?"
> "Oh, there is a brain all right. It's just that the brain is made out of meat!"
> —"So . . . what does the thinking?"
> "You're not understanding, are you? The brain does the thinking. The meat."
> —"Thinking meat! You're asking me to believe in thinking meat!"
> "Yes, thinking meat! Conscious meat! Loving meat. Dreaming meat. The meat is the whole deal! Are you getting the picture?"
> —"Omigod. You're serious then. They're made out of meat!"[71]

The data stored and manipulated within modern electronic technologies is a property of physical processes, and only becomes information when presented to the conscious perception of a human, at which point it becomes information. Within the computational space of the computer itself, the information is merely symbolic code,

---

[70] Chalmers, *The Character of Consciousness*, 5.

[71] Bisson, "They're Made Out of Meat," 42.

assumed physically to be unconscious. Chalmers posits a theory of consciousness that is the union of experience and the physical:

> A non-reductive theory of consciousness will consist in a number of *psychophysical principles*, principles that connect the properties of physical processes to the properties of experience.[72]

Chalmers declares that the basic principle of consciousness must involve the notion of *information*. He discusses how physically embodied *information states* must be embedded in an *information space* before it can become active and accordingly, transmittable:

> An information space is an abstract object, but following Shannon we can see information as *physically embodied* when there is a space of distinct physical states, the differences between which can be transmitted down some causal pathway. The transmittable states can be seen as themselves constituting an information space. To borrow a phrase from Bateson (1972), physical information is a *difference which makes a difference*.[73]

Information then, to Chalmers, has two basic aspects, a phenomenal aspect and a physical aspect, yet he questions whether all information has a phenomenal aspect. If there is no such constraint, he speculates, then experience might be

---

[72] Chalmers, *The Character of Consciousness,* 25.

[73] Chalmers, "Facing Up to the Problem of Consciousness," 26.

seen as being a fundamental property of the cosmos. If there is no phenomenal constraint, Chamber says,

> . . .then experience is much more widespread than we might have believed, as information is everywhere. This is counterintuitive at first, but on reflection the position gains a certain plausibility and elegance . . . . Indeed, if experience is truly a fundamental property, it would be surprising for it to arise only every now and then; most fundamental properties are more evenly spread . . . . Once a fundamental link between information and experience is on the table, the door is opened to some grander metaphysical speculation concerning the nature of the world . . . . The theory I have presented is speculative, but it is a candidate theory.[74]

Chalmers favorably compares his theory to that put forth by John Archibald Wheeler (1911–2008), the quantum physicist who coined the term "Black Hole."[75] Wheeler, who received his PhD in physics at the age of 21, suggested that information is fundamental to the physics of the universe, and regularly proclaimed that he regarded "this idea of information theory as the basis of existence.[76] Wheeler claimed that he could summarize his understanding of the cosmos with the catchphrase "It from Bit," and explains how it implies that information may be the basis of the universe:

---

[74] Ibid., 27–28.

[75] Ibid., 27.

[76] Wheeler, *Geons, Black Holes, and Quantum Foam*, 340.

It is not unreasonable to imagine that information sits at the core of physics, just as it sits at the core of a computer. Trying to wrap my brain around this idea of information theory as the basis of existence, I came up with the phrase "it from bit."[77]

Wheeler and one of his graduate students went on to calculate the information storage capacity on the spherical boundary of a black hole, and came up with an estimation of astronomical storage capacity, according to which a Bekensteinian sphere with the diameter of a typical human blood cell would have the storage capacity of 10^{60} information bits.[78]

Electromagnetic Fields: Pockett and McFadden

Several twenty-first-century researchers in the life sciences have concluded that consciousness might have a basis in electromagnetic field phenomena. In 2000, a neurophysiologist in New Zealand, Susan Pockett, published a paper hypothesizing that consciousness may very well be the electromagnetic field itself. Pockett states:

Perhaps what we have been looking for is that what has in the past been called the electromagnetic field is itself consciousness. And perhaps our individual consciousness, which unlike the field as a whole *are* bounded in space and time, are identical with particular local

---

[77] Ibid.

[78] See calculation details in section, "Isospheres," in Chapter 5.

spatiotemporal configurations of the electromagnetic field.[79]

Elsewhere, Pockett states that, "The essence of the hypothesis was that conscious experience (a.k.a. sensation) would prove to be identical with certain spatiotemporal patterns in the electromagnetic field,"[80] and indicates that perhaps researchers have been looking for consciousness in the wrong ranges of the electromagnetic frequency spectrum:

> The signals we are looking for in brain-generated electromagnetic activity might actually NOT be in the ELF (extremely low frequency) range where everyone is presently looking, but could turn out to be closer to the microwave frequency range which is of course always filtered out in present day electrophysiological recordings.[81]

It is important to note that Pockett assumes that consciousness, whatever the mechanism or bandwidth, is a recent epiphenomenon of some evolutionary process, a serendipitous emergence. This can be seen in her concluding remarks, "The present theory is quite compatible with the view that consciousness was not present in the universe before its biological evolution."[82]

---

[79] Pockett, *The Nature of Consciousness*, xvxvi.

[80] Pockett, "Difficulties with the Electromagnetic Field Theory of Consciousness," 271.

[81] Pockett, *The Nature of Consciousness*, 131–32.

[82] Pockett, *The Nature of Consciousness*, 142.

In 2002, Johnjoe McFadden, a professor of molecular genetics at the University of Surrey, put forth a conscious electromagnetic information (CEMI) field theory. [83] McFadden hypothesizes that an electromagnetic information field of the brain is the underlying basis of consciousness: "I propose that the brain's electromagnetic information field is the physical substrate of conscious awareness."[84] In 2007, McFadden identifies *information* as the agential binding element between the physical and the conscious:

> The key feature of the brain's electromagnetic field is that it is capable of integrating vast quantities of information into a single physical system and it thereby accounts for the binding of consciousness. Unlike quantum theories of consciousness, the CEMI field theory does not require any special physical states in the brains; it is perfectly compatible with brain physiology. Nevertheless, recent work has shown that classical electromagnetic waves may be used to implement quantum algorithms; therefore the brain's CEMI field may be able to perform quantum computations (but without the requirement for quantum coherent states of matter).[85]

Like Pockett, McFadden categorically links consciousness to the electromagnetic field: "I propose that

---

[83] McFadden, "The Conscious Electromagnetic Information (CEMI) Field Theory."

[84] Ibid.

[85] McFadden, "Conscious Electromagnetic Field Theory."

the brain's electromagnetic information field is the physical substrate of conscious awareness." [86] Yet whatever the degree of enthusiasm Pockett and McFadden have for the electromagnetic conjecture, their theory ends there, with no correlative suggestion for further research. The work of the neurosurgeon Karl Pribram, on the other hand, in searching for a neurophysical basis for memory, also embraced an electromagnetic field theory of consciousness, but during a lifetime of research, he was able to formulate and publish a coherent, evidence-based, holonomic brain theory based upon a mathematical Fourier-like transmission and transformation of information.[87]

---

[86] McFadden, "Evidence for an Electromagnetic Field Theory of Consciousness," 23.

[87] Pribram, *Brain and Perception*, 238.

Chapter 3: Karl Pribram's Holonomic Brain Theory

The electromagnetic holoflux theory of consciousness rests upon a series of basic concepts, and in particular the holonomic brain theory developed by the Stanford professor emeritus Karl Pribram (1919–2015). Pribram's neurosurgical and mathematical search for a reasonable solution to the so-called "hard-problem" advanced steadily during his 70-year career of experimental research. His breakthrough metaphor, reinforced through subsequent experimental-driven research, came in the form of a hologram:

> Using the mathematical holographic process as a metaphor . . . my (1991) book *Brain and Perception* provides detailed review of experimental results that support the conjecture that holography is a useful metaphor in coming to understand the brain/mind relation.[88]

Pribram, who has been called "the Magellan of the brain," published in his lifetime over 700 papers and 20 books on pattern perception, cognition, and the brain. In 1972 he put forth a "holonomic brain theory," a mathematical model of brain function in which neurodynamics aligns with quantum theory.[89] Pribram here explains the use of the term "holonomic" in his theory:

> The term for the theory, *holonomic*, was first used by Hertz to describe linear transformations

---

[88] Pribram, "Brain and Mathematics," 219.

[89] Pribram, *Brain and Perception*, 19.

when they are extended into a more encompassing domain. I have here extended its meaning to cover the spectral domain.[90]

The *spectral domain* to which Pribram here refers is also known as the *frequency domain* in quantum physics and electrical engineering. The spectral domain is a concept that has been developed in the mathematics of the Fourier transform, discussed in detail elsewhere in this book, whereby information signals in a space–time domain are transformed into a complex of frequencies in a spectral domain.[91]

Early in his career, Pribram had become fascinated by the search for the engram, the suspected location of memory recordings in the brain. [92] In the 1920s the Canadian neurosurgeon Roger Penfield, while operating on the exposed cerebral cortex of patients with severe epilepsy, discovered that electrical stimulation of small areas of the parietal lobe would cause the patients, who were always awake during such operations, to recall specific memories, often in vivid detail.[93] According to Penfield:

> It was evident at once that these were not dreams. They were electrical activations of the sequential record of consciousness, a record that had been laid down during the patient's earlier

---

[90] Ibid., xvii.

[91] Broughton and Bryan, *Discrete Fourier Analysis and Wavelets*, 72.

[92] Pribram, *Languages of the Brain*, 26.

[93] Penfield, *A Critical Study of Consciousness*.

experience. The patient "re-lived" all that he had been aware of in the earlier period of time as in a moving-picture "flashback."[94]

This discovery provided evidence to support the existence of the *engram*, a hypothesized physical storage location of memory traces, but whose mechanism and location has never been determined, in spite of decades of persistent research.[95]

Neuroanatomical Concepts

Before considering Pribram's holonomic brain theory in detail, a brief review of neuroanatomical terms and concepts here provide a context for a critical examination of Pribram's research and theories. A typical neuron cell (Fig. 2) consists of a single nucleus, a single axon, and multiple dendrites, as can be seen in the image in the left of the figure.

---

[94] Ibid., 27.

[95] Ibid., 32.

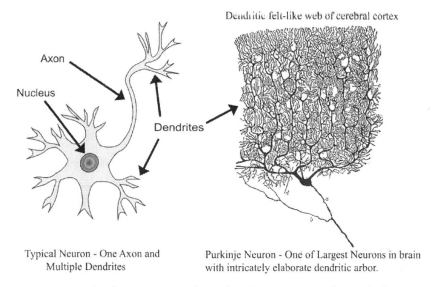

Typical Neuron - One Axon and
Multiple Dendrites

Purkinje Neuron - One of Largest Neurons in brain
with intricately elaborate dendritic arbor.

Figure 2. Typical neuron and Perkinje neuron. Above left, a multipolar neuron. Graphic by Jonathan Haas (2012). Reprinted under the terms of a Creative Commons Attribution ShareAlike 3.0 Unported license. Image retrieved from Wikimedia Commons. Above right, a Purkinje cell. Graphic by Santiago Ramon y Cajal (2006). Public domain image retrieved from Wikimedia Commons.

All cells have a nucleus, but the neuron has two types of neuronal fiber extrusions: a single, usually relatively long axon, long in comparison to the dendrite branches, which are many and complexly bifurcated.[96] The longest axons in the body belong to the sciatica nerves that run from the brain down through the spine and ending in the big toe. Axons are also known as "nerve fibers" and most neurological research focuses on these fibers as they carry the relatively large "nerve impulse" electrical spikes that are easily measured. The numerous dendrites, on the other

[96] Romanes, *Cunningham's Textbook of Anatomy*, 556.

hand, resemble finely bifurcating tree-like branches that gather in highly complex felt-like regions.

The thick-layered dendritic region of Perkinje neurons can also be seen to the right in Fig. 3 where a typical section of the cerebral cortex is depicted. Surprisingly thin, the entire cortex, at its thickest, is only 2 millimeters in depth, about the thickness of four human hairs placed side-by-side.[97]

Three aspects of a 2mm-thick cerebral cortex slice can be seen in Fig. 3: in the left area, a single sensory nerve fiber is shown; in the center of the drawing is revealed an interlinked systems of fibers, grouped into four cell-type layers as labeled on the left axis; finally, the right-most region of the figure indicates fiber bundle types.[98]

_____

[97] Netter, *Anatomy of the Nervous System.*

[98] Ibid.

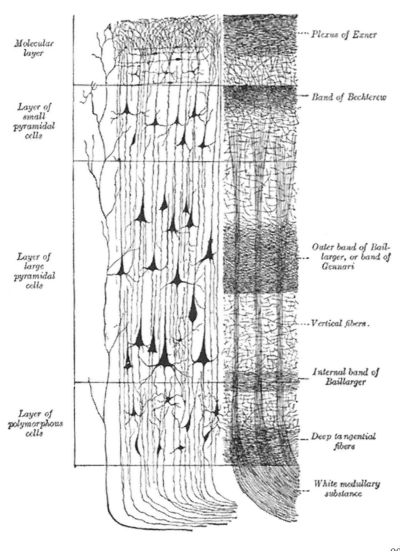

Molecular
layer

Layer of
small
pyramidal
cells

Layer of
large
pyramidal
cells

Layer of
polymorphous
cells

Plexus of Exner

Band of Bechterew

Outer band of Bail-
larger, or band of
Gennari

Vertical fibers.

Internal band of
Baillarger

Deep tangential
fibers

White medullary
substance

Figure 3. Cerebral cortex. Graphic by Henry Gray (1918).[99]
Public domain image retrieved from Wikimedia Commons.

---

[99] To the left, the groups of cells; to the right, the systems of
fibers. Quite to the left of the figure a sensory nerve fiber is
shown. Cell body layers are labeled on the left, and fiber layers
are labeled on the right.

Due to an extremely intricate folding and refolding, the cortex alone occupies fully 88% of the human brain mass.[100] Within this cortex region can be found three distinct types of cells: neurons, glial cells, and blood capillary cells.

The major focus of scientific research is upon the 86 billion neuron cells in the human brain; glial cells and capillary cells are dismissed as having no role in cognition or consciousness. Glial cells, since their discovery in 1856, have been tacitly dismissed in the widespread agreement that they have evolved primarily for mechanical purposes, acting in supportive, structural roles (the word *glia* in Greek γλοία means "glue"). Glial cells do not conduct electrical impulses, as do neurons (even though glial cells wrap around neuron axons to form myelin sheaths and thus are capable of modulating the speed and strength in the neural conduction of electrical impulses passing through these glial "wraps"). Likewise, any possible function of the blood capillary cell system in consciousness has also been dismissed; it is assumed that the function of the circulatory system is fully understood, and not involved in thought or conscious sensation.[101]

Memory: The Search for the Engram

After graduating with an MD in neurosurgery from the University of Chicago at the age of 21, Pribram began work with the renowned zoologist Karl Spencer Lashley, head of the Yerkes Laboratory of Primate Biology, a joint effort of Harvard and Yale, where the newly graduated neurosurgeon

---

[100] Herculano-Houzel, "The Human Brain in Numbers," 1.

[101] Fields, *The Other Brain*.

became Lashley's assistant, conducting research on memory in the brains of primates.[102]

Lashley had been searching for the elusive engram for over 30 years, but during his work with Pribram, reached the surprising conclusion that the engram did *not* exist in the cortex at all; he based his conclusion on the fact that no matter how much of a rat's cerebral cortex was removed, the rat would continue to remember its route through a maze that had been learned over a period of several weeks, prior to removal of massive sections of its cortex.[103] Lashley stated his conundrum as follows:

> Here is the dilemma. Nerve impulses are transmitted over definite, restricted paths in the sensory and motor nerves and in the central nervous system from cell to cell, through definite intercellular connections. Yet all behavior seems to be determined by masses of excitation, by the form or relations or proportions of excitation within general fields of activity, without regard to particular nerve cells. It is the pattern and not the element that counts. What sort of nervous organization might be capable of responding to a pattern of excitation without limited, specialized paths of conduction? The problem is almost universal in the activities of the nervous system and some hypothesis is needed to direct further research.[104]

---

[102] Squire, *The History of Neuroscience*, 314.

[103] Talbot, *The Holographic Universe*, 13.

[104] Lashley as quoted in Pribram; Pribram, *The Form Within*, 22.

The search for such a hypothesis fired Pribram's research interest, and, working with Lashley, Pribram discovered areas of the brain surface that, when stimulated or removed, significantly affected the processing of sensory information, even though no direct sensory links existed between neurons in the sensory organs and the areas in question; Pribram called these areas of the cerebral cortex "intrinsic," having no direct connection to the sensory organs, and contrasted these with "extrinsic" areas of the cerebral cortex in which could be traced identifiable, direct neuronal connections to sensory organs.[105]

In 1948, Pribram left Florida for New England to accept an offer to join the faculty at Yale, where Pribram had found the Gestalt theorist Wolfgang Köhler's pioneering dissertation in the field of psychoacoustics to be of great interest.[106] Köhler was famous at Yale for having emigrated from Nazi Germany in 1935, after refusing to acquiesce, as a full professor, to giving the Nazi salute at the beginning of each class. But Pribram was attracted to Köhler's approach to research, which had been formed by the Gestalt paradigm "that the whole is *different* from the sum of the parts."[107]

Pribram soon began working on an auditory cognition project at a laboratory in Massachusetts run by Köhler, whose ideas reinforced Pribram's own; if the whole is discovered to be something much more than simply the sum of the parts of which it is comprised, then perception and cognition, in this case the psychoacoustic perception that

---

[105] Pribram, *The Form Within*, 24.

[106] Ibid.

[107] Köhler, *The Task of Gestalt Psychology*, 10.

interested Köhler, might indeed be something categorically different from that of the functioning of sensory neurons capturing light and sound.[108]

Pribram did not share Köhler's view of perception, a view commonly held among brain researchers at the time, that somewhere on the cerebral cortex would be found direct current electrical analogues, two dimensional voltage images perhaps, having the same physical shape as the objects perceived; such a view, held in common by the Gestalt psychologists, is often termed "geometric isomorphism," (*iso* = same, *morph* = shape).[109] Pribram doubted Köhler's supposition that direct current fields would eventually be found to support the theory of geometric isomorphism, but agreed that electromagnetic fields were somehow involved in visual, auditory, and cognitive perception, and in particular, something Pribram termed "minding." As Pribram understood the term, "Minding is attending, looking out and ahead, grounded on looking back and within."[110]

For over two years Köhler and Pribram made extensive measurements, both of ape and human subject brains, trying to detect voltage changes between locations on the cerebral cortex surface which would correspond to changes in sensory stimulation.[111] Pribram's procedure was fairly simple, though it required access to the surface of the

---

[108] Pribram, *The Form Within*, 35.

[109] Ibid.

[110] Ibid., 356.

[111] Ibid., 36.

cerebral cortex, accessible immediately beneath the cranial bones.[112]

During the eight years Pribram worked with Köhler, a typical series of experimental procedures might involve holding up alternately white and then black cards while measuring any detectable and repeatable voltages changes between two adjacent surface areas of the cerebrum; to support his theory, Köhler sought to locate patterns of voltage gradient on the cerebral cortex itself that would be a mirror of the optical visual pattern falling upon the optic field receptor neurons of the eye.[113]

Köhler's Theory of Geometric Isomorphism

After several years of research in Köhler's laboratory, Pribram (never having himself believed in geometric isomorphism) designed a successful experiment that provided a refutation of the assumption, after which, in an amusing exchange, Köhler asked Pribram, "Now that you have disproved not only my theory of cortical function in perception, but everyone else's as well, what are you going to do?" to which Pribram replied, "I'll keep my mouth shut."[114]

In the mid-1950s Pribram's research led him to focus upon the neuro-electric activity associated with the fine-fibered webs formed by dendrites, rather than the more obvious electrical impulses which are seen to run along the much thicker axon trunks:

---

[112] Netter, *Anatomy of the Nervous System.*

[113] Köhler and Henle. *The Selected Papers of Wolfgang Köhler.*

[114] Pribram, *The Form Within*, 37.

At about the same time, in the 1950s, that Hodgkin had begun his work on the retina, I shared a panel at a conference held in 1954 at MIT with Stephen Kuffler of the Johns Hopkins University . . . . Kuffler focused my thinking on the type of processing going on in the fine-fibered webs of the nervous system, a type of processing that has been largely ignored by neuro-scientists, psychologists and philosophers.[115]

Based upon his half century of research as a neurosurgeon, Pribram described how, it seemed to him, the thick, richly intertwining fine-fibered dendrite branch regions are where focused islands of complex frequency activity are to be found:

The fine fibers composing the web—the branches or dendrites of nerve cells—cannot sustain nerve impulse conduction the way axons can. The electrical activity of dendrites rarely "sparks" but oscillates between excitation and inhibition; thus, dendritic activity occurs locally, forming patches or nodes of synchronized oscillating activity . . . . When the formative processing web provided by the dendrites has to be accessed by the rest of the brain, axons relay the results of these interactions to other parts of the brain or to receptors and effectors in the body.[116]

The "form of the fine-fibered distributed web of the brain" became Pribram's passion and eventually led to his

---

[115] Pribram, *The Form Within*, 50.

[116] Ibid., 54.

conclusion that the form of the ultra deep structure of thinking is a holographic-like distributed process:

> According to the reasoning proposed ... the potential of the ultra-deep structure of thinking is realized when the holographic distributed process becomes transformed by way of the memory-motive and memory-emotive processes into cortically engendered complex verbal and nonverbal language and language-like cultural forms.[117]

In 1958, after 10 years at Yale, Pribram accepted an offer from Stanford to continue his research in California as Director of the Center for Advanced Studies. Over the next 30 years, Pribram published over two hundred papers mapping innumerable features of neuroanatomy and brain function. [118] The general consensus among neurophysiologists assumes that perception is a one-way street, that neuronal receptors in the external sense organs transmit information to the brain via neuronal impulses, however during his years at Stanford, Pribram began to find evidence that the process is more of a "two-way" cybernetic transform, with information flowing both ways, simultaneously:

> Critical to understanding is the acceptance of evidence that brain perceptual systems operate as top-down as well as bottom-up processors. It is this evidence that my colleagues and I have spent almost a half-century in amassing. Some 1,500 nonhuman primates, 50 graduate students,

---

[117] Pribram, *The Form Within*, 458.

[118] Ibid.

and an equal number of postdoctoral fellows have participated. The results of these researches have cast doubt on viewing brain perceptual processing as elementaristic, bottom-up, reflex-arc, stimulus-response—views that still characterize many texts in neurophysiology, psychology, and perception.[119]

Pribram would later put forth the critique that it is this very "neglect of a science based on pattern that has resulted in a science based on matter, an overarching materialism."[120]

During the course of his research, Pribram gathered sufficient evidence to convince him that not only visual reception of neurons seemed to exhibit top-down patterns of activity, but also auditory, and motor systems in the brain exhibited similar distributed field patterns of activity and response. As early as 1962, in a paper published on the work of Sigmund Freud, Pribram began to express his interest in focusing on the *pattern* of brain activity, rather than tracing specific neuroanatomical circuit connections:

> For Freud, a neuron may "fill"—i.e., become *cathected*—with excitation even though no transmitted activity results.... This emphasis on cathexis is one of those strokes of luck or genius which in retrospect appears uncanny, for only in the past decade have neurophysiologists recognized the importance of the graded non impulsive activities of neural tissue—graded mechanisms such as those of dendritic networks whose functions are considerably different from

---

[119] Pribram, *Brain and Perception*, xvi.

[120] Pribram, *The Form Within*, 16.

those of the transmitted impulsive activity of axons.[121]

The Holographic Paradigm

In 1965 Pribram was introduced to the holographic use of the Fourier transform through the widely reported implementation of three-dimensional holographic imagery, both in the United States and in the Soviet Union.[122] In 1962 engineers, independently in the Soviet Union and the United States, had created the first three-dimensional holographic images, a feat that required use of a split beams of coherent radiation, coherent laser radiation, a capability that itself had only been discovered two years earlier.

The mathematics of the hologram had been pioneered almost 20 years earlier by Dennis Gabor, a physicist and electrical engineer who used the mathematics of the Fourier transform to develop a novel optical approach for improving the resolution of the electron microscope. Gabor had earned his PhD in Berlin by analyzing the properties of high voltage transmission lines through the use of the cathode-ray oscillographs, leading to his interest in electron optics. In 1933 he left Nazi Germany for London, recruited by Thomson-Houston Electric Company (the British subsidiary of General Electric). There, in 1947, Gabor developed the mathematical basis of his holographic method, for which he was awarded the Nobel Prize in 1971. In referring to his predicted phenomenon, Gabor invented the name

---

[121] Pribram, "The Neuropsychology of Sigmund Freud," 445.

[122] Johnston, *Holographic Visions: A History of New Science.*

holography (from Greek *holos*, meaning "entire" or "whole," and *grafe*, "writing").[123]

However, Gabor did not produce an actual hologram. This had to await the invention of a perfectly coherent lights source, the laser; instead, using a highly filtered mercury arc light, Gabor was able to apply his holographic method to marginally improve the resolution power of electron micrographs. Unfortunately, Gabor's actual implementation of his holographic idea was not widely embraced; his technique was considered to be a somewhat awkward, if theoretically intriguing variant of microscopy, which did not achieve financial success due to the time consuming method required to produce an image.[124]

> Instead of the immediacy of seeing an image on a fluorescent screen (as some electron microscopes then produced), the reconstructed image was to be obtained more painstakingly via a half-hour exposure, followed by conventional photographic processing, unintuitive optical transformation, and observation through a conventional microscope eyepiece . . . Gabor blamed lack of enthusiasm from his industrial collaborators and microscope manufacturers, and microscopists dismissed what they saw as a hybrid and unfamiliar technique.[125]

In 1958, Yuri Denisyuk, a Russian engineer, working at the Vavilov State Optical Institute in Leningrad,

---

[123] Gabor, "Theory of Communication."

[124] Wasson and Brieger, *Nobel Prize Winners*, 358.

[125] Johnston, *Holographic Visions: A History of New Science*, 3.

developed a holographic imaging system similar to Gabor's, also using filtered mercury arc lighting. However, as Gabor had experienced in Britain, Denisyuk found little subsequent support in the Soviet Union for his holographic process. [126] In 1962, however, Emmett Leith and Juris Upatnieks, working in a highly classified laboratory near the campus at the University of Michigan where they were trying to develop a new form of side-looking optical radar, were able to run an experiment using the coherent source of light from a laser (a technology itself developed only in 1960). [127] Through use of laser light they were able to create a three-dimensional holographic image that could be viewed directly, without the requirement of peering through a microscope. Their significant discovery, as well as the almost identical, simultaneous discovery of the holographic method in the Soviet Union, remained classified for almost two years before the news was revealed to the public. [128]

The creation of a hologram requires two fixed sources of radiation of the same frequency, often created in practice by splitting one original beam of electromagnetic radiation into two separate paths. The two resulting beams of energy (often infrared) are then aimed, from different angles of incidence, to fall upon a three-dimensional object, resulting in complex phase interference fringe shadows upon a two-dimensional film plane where the patterns are recorded. These shadows form what are termed "holographic interference patterns." The information, captured in the

---

[126] Ibid.

[127] Leith and Upatnicks, "Reconstructed Wavefronts and Communication Theory."

[128] Johnston, *Holographic Visions: A History of New Science*, 4.

recorded holographic image, can be subsequently reproduced by reversing the process.[129]

The full sequence of transformation is as follows: the three-dimensional information is first transformed into two-dimensional interference patterns of waves in space–time. The three-dimensional information has been transformed *out of* the space domain *into* a frequency-phase data which can be stored on a flat two-dimensional film. From film, it can be transformed back again into the space domain through the focus of light energy of a single frequency through the complex fringe patterns imprinted on the film. This results in the formation of interference of light waves in space on the other side of the film from the source, phase interferences in the light create a virtual three-dimensional image, identical to the one existing during the original recording. It is this resulting transmitted image that is termed a *hologram*.[130]

A major breakthrough in his search for a nonlinear frequency-based model occurred in 1965 when Pribram learned of the holographic method of memory storage in an article by a *Scientific American* article written by the researchers Leith and Upatnieks.[131] What most impressed Pribram was that the article "described how the recording of interference patterns on photographic film had tremendously enhanced the storage capacity and retrieval of images." [132] The potential for rich data storage in

---

[129] Ibid., 7.

[130] Ibid.

[131] Leith and Upatniecks, "Photography by Laser."

[132] Pribram, *The Form Within*, 42.

holographic image technology intrigued Pribram, as it seemed to hold up new possibilities for visual processing and a new mechanism for memory storage.[133]

In 1971, Gabor was awarded the Nobel Prize for his invention of the hologram, and in his Nobel Lecture acceptance speech, likely much to Pribram's delight, he described the possible relationship of the hologram to human memory:

> In a hologram the information is spread over the entire hologram area.... The appearance of such a "diffused" hologram is extraordinary; it looks like noise.... A diffuse hologram is therefore a distributed memory, and this has evoked much speculation whether human memory is not perhaps, as it were, holographic, because it is well known that a good part of the brain can be destroyed without wiping out every trace of a memory.[134]

That same year, 1971, Pribram published *Languages of the Brain*, summarizing the results of six years of experimental work at Stanford, and supporting a new theory proposing cognitive holographic patterns in the brain. He proposed that while memories might not be localized in any

---

[133] Author's note: A hologram may not necessarily be limited to visual information. Each holographic imprinting might be a complete snapshot of all current physiological, sensory, and cognitive activity at a particular moment of perception. These "snapshot holograms" of multidimensional information might be stored and chained sequentially, perhaps in layers, or filaments, or as overlapping shells as in the rings of a tree. Such holographic memory engrams would then be available for future retrieval and playback, triggered perhaps by neuronal activity, in the selective recall of strings of specific memory sequences

[134] Lundqvist, *Nobel Lectures, Physics 1971–1980.*

specific brain cell, laboratory data indicates that memories are found to be spread, holographically, throughout wide regions of the fine-fibered web of the brain's dendritic synapses, like complex nets or networks.[135] Pribram's new hypothesis integrates the mathematical paradigm of optical holography with his observations that the processing of parallel information intercepted by sensory receptors is transformed orthogonally into horizontally interacting cortical fiber-mesh areas:

> I propose that interactions among the patterns of excitation which fall on receptor surfaces become, after transmission over pathways organized in a parallel fashion, encoded by virtue of horizontally interacting processes . . . . The hypothesis is based on the premise that neural representations of input are not photographic but are composed not only by an initial set of feature filters but by a special class of transformations which have considerable formal resemblance to an optical image reconstruction process devised by mathematicians and engineers. This optical process, called holography, uses interference patterns. It has many fascinating properties, among which the facility for distributing and storing large amounts of information is paramount.[136]

In contrast to the prevalent neurosurgical research paradigm that focused upon tracing the activity and wiring diagrams of single neurons to tease out the answer to the memory problem in the brain, Pribram had chosen, instead,

---

[135] Pribram, *Languages of the Brain*.

[136] Pribram, *The Form Within*, 140–41.

to search for evidence of some field or wavelike propagation in the junction of multiple neurons in the fine-fibered synaptic junction regions where complex dynamic electromagnetic fields could provide the vehicle for information patterning, processing, and storage.[137]

> The arrival of impulses at synaptic junctions is never a solitary event. Axonal terminations are usually multiple—i.e., axons branch at their ends. As many as 1,000 synapses may characterize the junctional possibilities between a pair of neurons. Dendrites are tree-like almost by definition, displaying many fine fibered branches which crisscross, making multiple contacts among neurons to form a pattern .... Inferences about the nature of such a pattern can be made from the known fine structure of the brain and the electrical activity recorded from it. Several such inferences suggest that these patterns make up wave fronts ... an advancing wave may sweep over 100,000 neurons in a single second. Such a wave has rich potentiality, and the hypothesis that the mechanism of the junctional microstructure of slow potentials provides this organization.[138]

Pribram was also encouraged in 1964 when results of several independent research projects proved that the general consensus that there must be a single location for a memory engram was false. [139] Computer systems had

---

[137] Pribram, *Languages of the Brain*, 19.

[138] Ibid., 19–23.

[139] Borsellino and Poggio, "Holographic Aspects of Temporal Memory."

detected three-dimensional patterns over clusters of cerebral neurons, revealing the possibility of distributed, parallel processing, rather than simply the previously assumed linear neuron-to-neuron processing. Pribram immediately related these patterns to the distributed geometric patterns he had observed in holograms, and he began referring to them as "holoscape contours."[140]

Pribram devised an experiment in which, through use of small spinning, notched gears, he measured the electrical response of a rat's buccal (lip) neuron to mechanical frequency stimulation of the rat's whiskers. The outcome revealed specific yet distinct complex three-dimensional contour patterns in response to different frequencies of whisker vibration.[141]

Such results strengthened Pribram's suspicion that perceptual processing would be found in patterns described by groups of neurons processing information in a spectral, frequency domain, rather than neuron-to-neuron impulse transmission:

> In my experience, each cortical neuron encodes several features of our visual environment, each neuron is like a person with many attributes, and thus our ability to recognize features had to depend on patterns displayed by groups of neurons for further processing.[142]

Pribram believed that he had found evidence that vision was undergoing two-way mathematical Fourier

---

[140] Pribram, *Brain and Perception*, 28–29.

[141] Pribram, *The Form Within*, 84.

[142] Ibid., 69.

transforms in the processing of sight signals from photons striking eye cells to images perceived inside the brain. He relates a story of a conversation he had at the time, while climbing with colleagues on a hike in Colorado just prior to attending a neuroscience conference in Boulder:

> We had climbed high into the Rocky Mountains. Coming to rest on a desolate crag, a long meditative silence was suddenly broken by a query from Campbell: "Karl, do you really believe it's a Fourier?" I hesitated, and then replied, "No Fergus, that would be too easy, don't you agree?" Campbell sat silently awhile, then said, "You are right, it's probably not that easy. So what are you going to say tomorrow down there?" I replied, this time without hesitation, "That the transform is a Fourier, of course." Campbell smiled and chortled, "Good for you! So am I."[143]

Yet even in light of published, repeatable evidence, this Fourier transform based theory met with substantial resistance within the mainstream research community. Neurophysiologists were reluctant to consider this mathematical, frequency field approach to perception and cognition, when they were already invested deeply in biochemical and physiological approaches. This led to what Pribram here describes, rather amusingly, as the formation of two camps among researchers, those captivated by "feature creatures" vs. the "frequency freaks":

> Within the research community the contrast between these two views of perception was wittily joked about as pitting "feature creatures" against "frequency freaks." Feature creatures were those

---

[143] Pribram, *Brain and Perception*, xvii.

who focused on "detectors" within our sensory systems, of features in our external environment—a purely "bottom-up" procedure that processes particulars into wholes. Frequency freaks, by contrast, focused on similarities between processes in the visual mode and those in the auditory (and incidentally the somatosensory) mode. For the frequency freaks, the central idea was that our visual system responds to the spectral, frequency dimensions of stimulation very much as the auditory system responds to the oscillations that determine the pitch and duration of sound. The approach of the frequency freaks, therefore, is "top-down"— wholes to particulars. Within the neuroscience community, the feature creatures still hold the fortress of established opinion, but frequency freaks are gaining ascendance with every passing year.[144]

In 1988, at age 70, Pribram retired from his Stanford position as professor emeritus of psychophysiology, and relocated to Virginia to head the new Center for Brain Research and Informational Sciences (BRAINS) at Radford University, where he also began lecturing on cognitive neuroscience and computational neuroscience.[145]

In the 1990s his theories continued to mature with the discovery of the Gabor function, in Paris, over a dinner with Dennis Gabor (1900–1979). Gabor had been awarded the Nobel Prize in Physics in 1971 for his early work in the mathematics of communications, which eventually led to the invention of the hologram. What intrigued Pribram was

---

[144] Ibid., 60.

[145] Squire, *The History of Neuroscience*, 322.

not simply that Gabor found the Fourier transform so important in the mathematics of communication, but that Gabor had pioneered an entirely new way of encoding and transmitting information using what came to be known widely as the "Gabor elementary function."[146]

When he discovered the Fourier holographic procedure, Gabor had been working on the problem of maximizing telecommunication across the newly laid trans-Atlantic cable.[147] He wanted to establish the *maximum* amount a message could be compressed without losing its intelligibility. To do this, Gabor developed the mathematics to model the two-way translations (movements) of Fourier flux (packets of information) through both space and time (in Gabor's application, a proposed undersea cable).[148]

This may be understood as the movement of the results of a Fourier transform, the transportation of a "packet" of frequency information, which normally has no time component, through time and space. Gabor designed a procedure to maximize information flow across the trans-Atlantic cable by first performing a Fourier transform on incoming frequency spectrum packets (typically milliseconds of audio conversation or music), and then transmitting the Fourier transformed information as electronic snapshot packets across the trans-Atlantic cable, where they could be received and de-encoded through application of a reverse Fourier transform.

---

[146] Pribram, *Brain and Perception*, 70.

[147] Pribram, "What Is Mind that the Brain May Order It?," 323.

[148] Pribram, *The Form Within*, 103.

A true mathematical Fourier transform requires an infinite range of frequencies, and in 1946 it was Gabor's challenge to determine the minimum number of frequencies that could be included in the transform to maintain intelligibility, while maximizing the amount of data being sent simultaneously across the cable.[149]

Over dinner, Gabor explained to Pribram how he solved the problem, using music as an example. While the pitch of a tone is dependent on the frequency of vibration, and there may be many harmonics accompanying that tone in the frequency spectrum, the duration of the tone complex is not measured in any of those frequencies but is instead measured on a completely different time axis. Accordingly the function Gabor was seeking must include coordinates describing both a "windowed-packet" of tone information and *also* a set of space–time coordinates to map the packet flow.[150]

Gabor solved his problem through application of a "Hilbert space," a vector mathematical method capable of mapping an arbitrary number of dimensions, beyond the usual four dimensions of space (x_d, y_d, z_d) and time (t). The Hilbert space is named after the German mathematician David Hilbert (1942–1943), who in 1926 described a way to extend the methods of algebra and calculus to any number of dimensions. Since 1926, quantum theorists had been able to use Hilbert's approach to represent classical concepts within the new quantum framework, and use of the Hilbert space also offers a computable framework for the Fourier

---

[149] Gabor, "Theory of Communication."

[150] Pribram, *The Form Within*, 104.

expansions required by quantum mechanics.[151] Hilbert, a close friend and associate of Albert Einstein, was reputed to have an acerbic sense of humor, and once, upon hearing that one of his students had dropped out of mathematics to study poetry, Hilbert was heard to reply, "Good, he did not have enough imagination to become a mathematician."[152]

The concept of a Hilbert space is essentially the consideration of a "space" having more than three dimensions, allowing the exploration of mathematical relationships involving an infinite number of dimensions (the subject is sometimes referred to as "infinite dimensional function spaces").[153] A simplified example of a Hilbert space is shown in Fig. 4 where the superposition of the two orthogonal dimensions found in the top half of the figure result in a Hilbert space of six dimensions shown at the bottom center.

[151] Crease, *The Great Equations*, 263.

[152] Darling, *The Universal Book of Mathematics*, 151.

[153] Alabiso and Weiss, *A Primer on Hilbert Space Theory*.

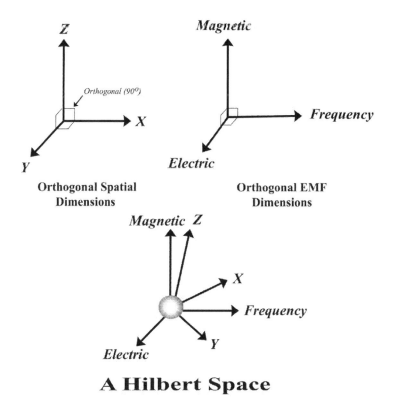

A Hilbert Space

Figure 4. A Hilbert space of six orthogonal dimensions. Graphic by author.

At the bottom is the "Hilbert space," a "space" where all six dimensions now intersect at a common point, the "origin." Understanding this superposition became key for Pribram in expressing his holonomic theory, which he refers to as "deep processing," and states that the "the holonomic theory uses vectors in Hilbert phase space to express covariance."[154]

Though six dimensions do appear around the same origin in the Hilbert space in Fig. 4, (X, Y, Z, Electric,

---

[154] Pribram, "Brain and Mathematics," 221.

Magnetic, Frequency), the dimension of *time* is missing. In 1946 Gabor published a new mathematical approach which solved the problem of applying the Fourier transform to a Hilbert space, by translating information from Hilbert dimensions into slices of time-based data; Gabor originally called his method, the "windowed Fourier transform," but soon after publication it became known as the "Gabor function." Gabor had successfully devised a way to encode multiple "packets" of electromagnetic data and transmit them down the trans-Atlantic cable, simultaneous in both directions, to maximize transference rates and frequency content.[155]

Pribram was delighted; from the Paris dinner with Gabor had emerged a feasible mechanism with which to model the two-way flow of memory imprinting and retrieval in the brain, Gabor's "windowed Fourier Transform." Pribram related the process to that of the operation of a barcode system:

> Based on descriptions of the maps of receptive fields of cortical cells, I have proposed that the deep structure of our memory, as it is encoded in fine fibers in the brain, is much like a windowed Fourier transformation. The surface structure of memory, our retrieval and updating procedure, resembles what goes on at a checkout counter. It is only a step to conceive of a name as a barcode trigger identifying a purchase.[156]

---

[155] Gabor, "Theory of Communication," 415.

[156] Pribram, *The Form Within*, 364–65.

Holoflux and the Frequency Domain

In evaluating the evidence he had collected from hundreds of experiments in over 40 years of neurosurgical research at Yale, Harvard, and Stanford, Pribram observed that both visual sensory processing and audio sensory processing displayed holographic-like contour patternings among neuronal dendrites in the cerebral cortex. "In fact," he speculates, "the receptor mechanisms of the ear, the skin and probably even the nose and tongue work in a similar fashion." [157] With his new understanding of the Fourier transform and a working example functional holography, Pribram pushed the envelope of his theory forward, though always supported by data:

> For me, theory is data-based and, I have, whenever possible, obtained in my own laboratory at first-hand the data critical to theory. [158]

In contrast with the lack of success others were having in their efforts to establish the mechanism and location of memory engrams, Pribram put forth a theory that the brain mechanics of vision might be seen as holographic processes, projections onto the cortical surface from a frequency domain through the mechanism of frequency superposition and electromagnetic wave interference. [159] Pribram called

---

[157] Ibid., 516.

[158] Ibid., 338.

[159] Ibid., 142.

this "the holonomic brain theory," and postulated the importance of the *frequency domain*:

> Essentially, the theory reads that the brain at one stage of processing performs its analyses in the *frequency domain* ... a solid body of evidence has accumulated that the auditory, somatosensory, motor, and visual systems of the brain do in fact process, at one or several stages, input from the senses in the *frequency domain*.[160]

Pribram's theory holds that the mathematics of the Fourier transform operates within the brain, modulating electromagnetic fields of flux to create, store, replay, and process holograms within some as yet unidentified physiological context or substrate, but one that Pribram conjectures may be found within the fine-fibered dendritic webs of cerebral cortex regions.[161]

Pribram clearly distinguishes between observations made in the frequency domain and those made in space and time. While the ontological realization of flux in space–time can be conceptualized in the gyrations of three-dimensional electromagnetic waves, Pribram defines the ontological substrate of spectra in the frequency domain to be pure spectra or holoflux:

> The spectral domain is characteristically a *flux*, composed of oscillations, fluctuations, whereas interference patterns among waves intersect to

---

[160] Pribram, "What the Fuss Is All About," 29.

[161] Pribram, "Prolegomenon for a Holonomic Brain Theory."

reinforce or cancel. Holograms are examples of spectra, that is, of a *holoflux*.[162]

This holoflux is essentially the same concept as David Bohm's *holomovement*, though in "Brain and Mathematics," Pribram takes exception to Bohm's use of the words "flow" or "movement," holding that such words cannot be used to characterize dynamism in a dimension devoid of space or time axes:

> David Bohm (1973) had a concept similar to flux in mind, which he called holomovement. He felt that my use of the term "flux" had connotations for him that he did not want to buy into. I, on the other hand, felt holomovement to be vague in the sense of asking, "what is moving?"[163]

Perhaps the flow issue can be resolved in the model of a Hilbert space; this can be accomplished by the superposition of the orthogonal dimensions of space (XYZ) and the electromagnetic frequency field (electromagnetic) in the movement of holoflux packets along the dimension of time (Fig. 5, "Flux packets moving through space–time").

Within the frequency domain itself, the holoflux can be seen neither static nor dynamic in the spatial and temporal sense, because the energy in the flux domain is understood (by definition) to be "outside of time" and "outside of space."

---

[162] Pribram, *The Form Within*, 495.

[163] Pribram, "Brain and Mathematics," 232.

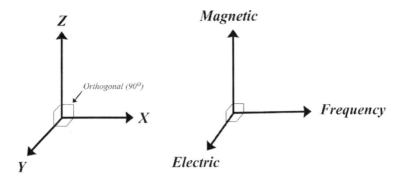

Spatial Field Dimensions   **EMF Field Dimensions**

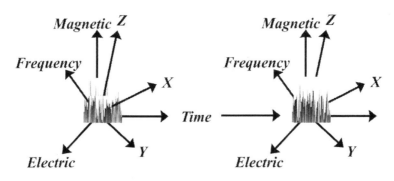

Holoflux Packets in A Hilbert Space

Figure 5. Flux packets moving through space–time. Graphic by author.

These conditions of the frequency domain correlate with David Bohm's concept of the "implicate order," the enfolded, sub–quantum dimension of his ontological quantum theory.[164] While Bohm's theory is examined in detail in Chapter 5, here a parallel concept can be visualized in Pribram's flow of holoflux energy from out of a frequency domain into actualized phenomena in space and time:

---

[164] Bohm, *Wholeness and the Implicate Order.*

Only through their manifestations in space and time do we get to know of the existence of potentials such as those of energy, of momentum, and of holographic processes. We can know the potential domain only by way of realization in space and time.[165]

Pribram regarded frequency as the direct mathematical link between a space–time electromagnetic domain and a transcendent flux domain, the mathematics of frequency bridging the two through a Fourier transform process, and he goes so far as to say, "The frequency approach . . . is essentially Pythagorean." [166] At a San Francisco Zen Center physics and consciousness conference Pribram came across a conceptual diagram of the Fourier transform process (Fig. 6), which perfectly encapsulated what he saw to be the function of the Fourier Transform, linking a spectral (frequency) domain to a space–time domain via the mathematics of the Fourier transform.[167]

---

[165] Pribram, *The Form Within,* 496.

[166] Ibid., 87.

[167] Pribram, "Brain and Mathematics," 230

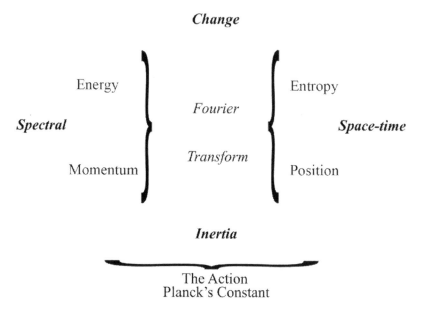

Figure 6. Pribram's Fourier Transform diagram. Image from Pribram, Brain and Being, page 230, figure 1; reprinted with permission.

Pribram first encountered this diagram during a presentation given by the physicist Geoffrey F. Chew, a Berkeley theoretical particle physicist, who told Pribram that he himself had received it from his colleague at Berkeley, Henry Stapp, who himself said he had been given it directly from Dirac. Whatever the origin of the figure, Pribram chose to include the diagram in several future papers: in "Consciousness Reassessed," Pribram's caption to the figure reads, "The Fourier transform as the mediator between spectral and spacetime descriptions."[168] In *Brain and Being* Pribram captions the figure, "The wave/particle dichotomy is orthogonal to the above distinction."

---

[168] Pribram, "Consciousness Reassessed," 8.

In the diagram, the spectral domain is to the left and space–time to the right. The diagram can be seen as a key to Pribram's model, and also posits that the Fourier transform process operates at a boundary dimension of Planck's constant, termed in the diagram, "The Action: Planck's Constant." While Pribram himself never discusses what "The Action: Planck's Constant" might imply for the diagram and his theory, the concept is perfectly congruent with David Bohm's discussion of the Planck length as boundary between the implicate domain and the explicate domain (discussed in Chapter 4). This Fourier diagram, according to Pribram, implies the following:

> Matter can be seen as an "ex-formation," an externalized (extruded, palpable, compacted) form of flux. By contrast, thinking and its communication (minding) are the consequence of an internalized (neg-entropic) forming of flux, its "in-formation." My claim is that the basis function from which both matter and mind are "formed" is flux (measured as spectral density).[169]

An enhanced depiction of the spectral domain and the space–time domain is presented in Fig. 7 where electromagnetic fields and matter can be seen in the space–time domain to the right, and holoflux fields and frequency flux can be seen to the left, separated by the bi–directional Fourier transform.

---

[169] Ibid., 13.

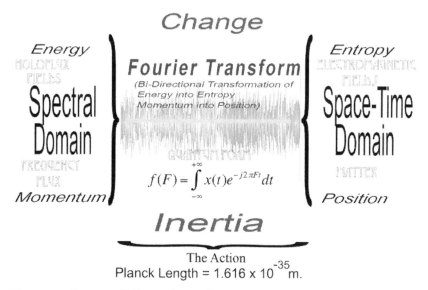

Figure 7. Spectral domain and space–time domain. Graphic by author.

Here it is suggested that this transformation occurs at the Planck length of 1.616×10^{-35} m, also called "The Action." Bohm comments on holograms and the spectral domain:

> Spectra are composed of interference patterns where fluctuations intersect to reinforce or cancel. Holograms are examples of the spectral domain. I have called this pre-spacetime domain a potential reality because we navigate the actual experienced reality in spacetime.[170]

How then might we model the dynamics of the process behind the transformation (or collapse) of holoflux packets from the spectral domain (Bohm's enfolded cosmos) into the space–time brain structure? In a 1997

---

[170] Ibid.

paper published in the *Proceedings of Symposia in Applied Mathematics*, Pribram suggests the following answer:

> An answer to the questions as to how mind becomes organized by brain rests on our understanding of the lessons of quantum mechanics and especially of that aspect which encodes the spectral domain, the implicate order. Although engineers daily use the spectral domain in radar, crystallography and tomography— wherever image processing is important— cognitive neuroscientists are, as yet, only barely acquainted with the pervasive nature of this order. It is now necessary to make accessible, both by experiment and by theory, the rules for "tuning in" on the implicate domain so that this domain can become more generally understood and scientifically validated.[171]

Another model of the spectral-space-time domains can be seen in Fig. 8, which suggest that it is the Gabor function, operating in parallel with the Fourier transform, that describes mathematically the flow of holoflux packets moving back and forth simultaneously between the spectral frequency domain and the space–time domain.

An interesting theory, a proposal that provides a digital "clock" to describe the timing of this process, the movement between space–time and the spectral domain, can be seen in the "theory of laminated space–time," proposed by Dewey in 1985.[172]

---

[171] Pribram, "What Is Mind that the Brain May Order It?," 322.

[172] Dewey, *The Theory of Laminated Spacetime*.

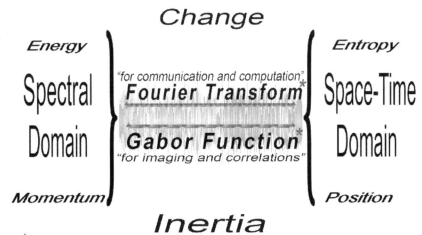

Figure 8. Gabor and Fourier transform processes. Graphic by author.

This theory proposes that energy vibrates digitally between two domains at a sub-quantum dimensional level, alternating between cyclical transformations, like the ticks of a clock, sequentially, between the spectral (frequency) domain and the space–time domain. The timing of such "ticks" as measured in the space–time domain, can be calculated, and corresponds to the Wien calculated frequency derived from this smallest possible wavelength, the Planck distance itself, or 1.616199×10^{-35} m. The frequency corresponding to such a wavelength would be at the limit of the frequency domain's extrusion into space–time, in other words, it must be the highest frequency (smallest wavelength) within the space–time domain. Dewey's theory visualizes the process of this flux extruding into space–time as a series of shells moving out at the speed of light, each shell a brane separated from the next by a spatial gap equal to the Planck length, as described here:

I believe the universe to be composed of *nothing but* shells of electromagnetic particles which the theory of Laminated Spacetime describes as laminae of spacetime.[173]

In order to generate a hologram, laser-based holographic technology greatly simplifies the generation of a hologram by: (1) using a laser generated beam of photon energy (a *single frequency*), and (2) illuminating the object from two distinct fixed points in space (a *single, fixed phase-angle*). An interference pattern is created from the spherical waves of radiation incoming from the two fixed points in space, rippling at exactly the same frequency in space–time.

In nature, however, the situation is vastly richer in complexity: one can imagine radiant holoflux interactions processing in the space–time domain as a highly complex interaction of dynamic shells of every space–time radiation frequency conceivable, impinging from an infinity of phase angles, like inwardly–directed radii directed toward a central point. As contrasted with the human generated holograms of a single frequency of electromagnetic flux and a single vantage point (phase angle), each point in space–time actually experiences an *entire frequency flux spectrum* impinging on a particular point in space–time. In nature, all frequencies of the spectrum and all incoming angles of approach must be considered in the process configuration of the holoflux considered by Pribram and Bohm.

That such a process would involve quantum-scale phenomena as well as super–conductivity has been strongly

---

[173] Ibid., 95.

suggested, not only by Karl Pribram, but by two of his colleagues:

> Mari Jibu and Kunio Yasui, an anesthesiologist and a physicist from Notre Dame Seishen University in Okayama, Japan, and I have suggested that the membranes of the fine fibers, the media in which the receptive fields are mapped, may have quantum-scale properties. The membranes are made up of phospholipids, oscillating molecules that are arranged in parallel, like rows of gently waving poplar trees. The lipid, fatty water-repellent part makes up the middle, the trunks of the "trees," and the phosphorus water-seeking parts make up the inside and outside of the membrane. These characteristics suggest that water molecules become trapped and aligned in the phosphorus part of the membrane. Aligned water molecules can show super-liquidity and are thus super-conductive; that is, they act as if they had quantum-scale properties.[174]

In 1979, Karl Pribram, at that time a Stanford professor, met David Bohm, Fritjof Capra, and Brian Josephson at a conference in Cordoba, Spain, where the four presented papers.[175] At the time, Bohm was Professor of Theoretical Physics at London University, Capra, a theoretical physicist, was conducting research at the Lawrence Berkeley Laboratory, and Josephson a theoretical professor from Oxford who had been presented the Nobel

---

[174] Pribram, *The Form Within*, 106–7.

[175] Cazenave, *Science and Consciousness: Two Views of the Universe.*

Prize in 1973 for his work on quantum tunneling and superconductivity (and who had become a serious student of transcendental meditation in 1971).[176]

During the conference, Pribram discovered that David Bohm's model of the implicate order and its projection, or extrusion, into space–time corresponded surprisingly well with his own holonomic theories, in particular where Bohm describes how the implicate unfolds into the explicate and then the explicate enfolds into the implicate in a two-way process:

> The implicate order can be thought of as a ground beyond time, a totality, out of which each moment is projected into the explicate order. For every moment that is projected out into the explicate there would be another movement in which that moment would be injected or "introjected" back into the implicate order. If you have a large number of repetitions of this process, you'll start to build up a fairly constant component to this series of projection and injection. That is, a fixed disposition would become established. The point is that, via this process, past forms would tend to be repeated or replicated in the present, and that is very similar to what Sheldrake calls a morphogenetic field and morphic resonance. Moreover, such a field would not be located anywhere. When it projects back into the totality (the implicate order), since no space and time are relevant there, all things of a similar nature might get connected together or resonate in totality. When the explicate order enfolds into the implicate order, which does not have any space, all places and all times are, we

[176] Oates, *Celebrating the Dawn: Maharishi Mahesh Yogi and the TM Technique.*

81

might say, merged, so that what happens in one place will interpenetrate what happens in another place.[177]

In 1984 Pribram and a colleague obtained laboratory proof that cells respond to specific bandwidths of frequencies, further support for his holonomic theories:

Together with an engineering student, Amand Sharafat (Pribram et al., 1984),[178] I performed an experiment in which we investigated whether neurons in the cat motor cortex were tuned to certain bandwidths of frequencies of passive movements of their forelimbs. Here, for once, we were testing a specific hypothesis, and the hypothesis was supported by our results. Certain cells in the motor cortex are responsive to the frequency.[179]

In a 1997 paper presented at a symposia for applied mathematics, Pribram offers a view even more congruent with Bohm's theories, hypothesizing that the mind–brain ontology is monistic, that a duality between mind and matter only *appears* to manifest because information that can be measured is unfolded into observable space–time coordinates from an enfolded potential.[180]

---

[177] Bohm and Weber, "Nature as Creativity," 35–36.

[178] Pribram, Sharafat, and Beekman, "Frequency Encoding in Motor Systems."

[179] Squire, *The History of Neuroscience*, 337.

[180] Pribram, "What Is Mind that the Brain May Order It?," 320.

According to this view, another class of orders lies behind the level of organization we ordinarily perceive. The ordinary order of appearances can be described in space–time coordinates. The other class of orders is constituted of fine-grain distributed organizations, which can be described as potential in the Aristotelian sense because only after "radical" transformation is their palpability in spatiotemporal terms realized. When the potential is actualized, information (the form within) becomes unfolded into its ordinary space–time manifestation; in the other direction, the transformation enfolds and distributes the information much as this is done by the holographic process .... Thus, on the one hand, there are enfolded potential orders; on the other, there are unfolded orders manifested in space–time.[181]

But the model of mind/brain as a quantum mechanical process poses a new question. In 2002 Pribram presented a paper in Torino, Italy, in which he discusses the application of the Fourier basis of the holographic principle as a useful metaphor in describing the brain/mind relation with regard to perception.[182] In this paper he poses the following question:

Does this application indicate that the formalism of quantum physics applies more generally to other scales of inquiry? Alternatively, for brain function, at what scale do actual quantum physical processing take place? At what anatomical scale(s) do we find quantum

---

[181] Ibid.

[182] Pribram, "Brain and Mathematics."

coherence and at what scale does decoherence occur?[183]

Pribram himself discounted the possibility that electrical brain waves recorded by electrodes placed on the scalp might be significant carriers of cognitive information:

> There is some considerable doubt whether "brain waves" as presently recorded form the substrate of any meaningful interference pattern organization for information processing, although they may indicate that such process is taking place. The wavelengths recorded are, of course, considerably longer than those of light waves and can therefore only be carriers of small amounts of information—though in the form of spatially interfering holographic patterns.[184]

While Pribram never proposed an answer to his question as to what scale the holonomic process occurs in human physiology, it is my thesis that the anatomical scale required for Fourier holography lies in the infrared wavelength region, perhaps not coincidentally within which the human mammalian body operates, a wavelength that perfectly fits the average inner diameter of blood capillaries, which range from 8 to 10 microns, found throughout the brain.[185] Infrared waves in space–time have a wavelength of approximately 10 microns, but the spectral frequency associated with these waves, according to Pribram, lie in a non space–time spectral domain:

---

[183] Ibid., 219.

[184] Ibid., 151.

[185] Romanes, *Cunningham's Textbook of Anatomy*, 840.

Waves occur in space–time. Spectra do not. Spectra result from the interference among waves—and, by Fourier's insightful technique, the locus of interference can be specified as a number that indicates the "height" of the wave at that point. The number is represented by a Gabor function (or other wavelet.) Frequency in space–time has been converted to spectral density in the transform domain.[186]

Ontological Reality of the Frequency Domain

But is this frequency domain "real" in the same sense that science (and most philosophers) regards the dimensions of space and time, (the so-called "space–time" dimensions); is the enfolded spectral domain, in which quantum mechanical mathematics works so well, a "real" domain, or is it simply a mathematical abstraction?

This question has been at the heart of quantum physics since Erwin Schrödinger, often referred to as "the father of quantum mechanics," first described the wavefunction (ψ) in January 1926.[187] Prior to the discovery of the wavefunction, physicists were trying to understand the strange situation of experimental data that returned both wave-like and particle-like behavior.

Schrödinger was happy to dispense with particles altogether. He viewed the wavefunction as the very real manifestation of a completely undulatory material world. In his description, particle-like behaviour was an illusion created by

---

[186] Pribram, *The Form Within*, 109.

[187] Baggott, *The Quantum Story*, 64.

the overlapping and reinforcing of collections of "matter waves."[188]

However, the mathematician turned physicist Max Born soon radically re-interpreted the success of Schrödinger's wavefunction. In July 1926, just six months after Schrödinger's discovery, Born wrote a paper stating that:

> the wavefunction represents the *probabilities* that the electron wave will be scattered in certain directions . . . . A more precise consideration shows that the probability is proportional to the square of the wavefunction.[189]

Though Born's mathematically statistical calculations worked in quantum mechanical experimental predictions at the time, Einstein himself was not very happy with this probabilistic, statistical approach, and in a letter to Born later that year (December 3, 1926), Einstein remarked:

> Quantum mechanics is certainly imposing. But an inner voice tells me that it is not yet the real thing. The theory says a lot, but does not really bring us any closer to the secret of the "old one." I, at any rate, am convinced that *He* is not playing at dice.[190]

Much later in the century, David Bohm, a young colleague and neighbor of Einstein's at Princeton, also

---

[188] Ibid., 71.

[189] Ibid., 74.

[190] Born, *The Born–Einstein Letters*, 91.

adopted the realist view, that the wavefunction directly describes a reality, not a set of probabilities. In developing his own quantum potential wavefunction (Q) in the 1980s, Bohm's primary assumption was that the wavefunction must be assumed to be real:

> The wavefunction is assumed to represent an objectively real field and not just a mathematical symbol . . . we suppose that there is, beside the field, a particle represented mathematically by a set of coordinates . . . . We suppose that the particle is acted on not only by the classical potential but also by an additional "quantum potential."[191]

The debate between the two approaches to the wavefunction has continued into the 21st century, with the realist side supporting what has come to be called the $\psi-$ *ontic* model (holding that it is the "real state of affairs") vs. the ψ *-epistemic* model group, which holds that the wavefunction should be regarded as a mathematical device only, a probability distribution).[192]

The debate has recently taken a turn in favor of the Bohmian realist approach; in early 2015, experimental proof supporting the ontological reality of the wavefunction was published in *Nature*, indicating that the quantum wave function may, indeed, be ontologically "real." [193] Experiments carried out at the University of Queensland

---

[191] Bohm, *Wholeness and the Implicate Order*, 76.

[192] Wiseman et al., "Experimental Proof of Nonlocal Wavefunction."

[193] Ibid., 1.

consisted of repeatable measurements of a nonlocal wave function collapsing into a particle in space–time, yet the results failed to be predicted by probability distribution calculations. Single photons were manipulated in both horizontal and vertical polarizations, and their paths were controlled by an interferometer, while, according to the team, "every optical element in the experimental setup was carefully calibrated and characterized." [194] The paper, published in the January edition of *Nature,* is summarized as follows:

> Our results conclusively rule out the most compelling ψ –*epistemic* models . . . . This suggests that, if we want to hold on to objective reality, we should adopt the ψ–*ontic* viewpoint— which assigns objective reality to the wavefunction, but also has some intriguing implications such as non–locality or many worlds . . . . The only alternative is to adopt more unorthodox concepts such as backwards-in-time causation, or to completely abandon any notion of objective reality. [195]

Brain Operation in Space–time Domain

Modern brain research in general has consistently approached study of the brain as if it were a machine operating only in space–time domains. In some sense this approach exhibits disinterest in actual consciousness or cognition per se, but rather finds it of greater urgency to explore how information might be stored, retrieved, and

---

[194] Ibid., 3.

[195] Ibid., 5.

processed by the component parts of the brain acting as a computing machine.[196]

An example of this assumption can be seen in the Preface to a textbook on neuroelectrodynamics, published in 2010, where the authors criticize the conventional neuronal spike pattern approach, and champion an electrodynamic field approach, yet continue to focus primarily on the paradigms of information processing of the brain as a computer:

> The brain is an incredibly powerful computing machine shaped by an evolutionary process that has developed over millions of years. The essence of brain function consists in how information is processed, transferred and stored. Understanding how our brain computes can explain why our abilities of seeing and moving in space are substantially more powerful as compared to any artificially built system . . . .
>
> However, from a neurophysiological point of view, current doctrine remains focused within a spike timing paradigm. This paradigm has limited capability for advancing the understanding of how the brain works . . . . Neuroelectrodynamics is a completely different model where the intrinsic computational processes are described by the dynamics and interaction of charges . . . . Spike timing including spike patterns can be regarded as an epiphenomenon or a result of these hidden processes.[197]

---

[196] Pribram, *The Form Within*, 408–10.

[197] Aur and Jog, *Neuroelectrodynamics: Understanding the Brain Language*, v–viii.

Pribram's Participatory Experiences as Data

Among the more than 700 papers and books published by Pribram during his lifetime, there is almost no reference to any personal knowledge or opinion regarding religion, meditative exercises, or psychotropic drug experience.[198] However, late in his career he did discuss such topics, and from these comments we may infer his own experience; such evidence can be found in interviews or panel discussion, but almost never in formal publication.

In a 1984 publication Pribram states that *consciousness* has now become central to the mind–brain problem due to "drugs, meditation, and a variety of other techniques."[199] It is certainly possible here that Pribram is alluding factually to his own first-hand participatory experience of such explorations, particularly as he sees them as "designed to promote psychological growth":

> Currently, the study of *consciousness* as central to the mind–brain problem has emerged from the explorations of altered and alternative states produced by drugs, meditation, and a variety of other techniques designed to promote psychological growth.[200]

---

[198] Karl Pribram authored more than 700 papers and other publications; see Pribram, "Karl Pribram: Bibliography."

[199] Pribram, "Mind, Brain, and Consciousness," 129.

[200] Ibid.

An even stronger indication of first-hand participatory knowledge may be found in a remarkable paragraph, written at age 94, in which Pribram describes an experience of "holoflux." Here, his use of the phrases "we experience" and "we can experience" strongly implies direct knowledge of such states:

> Boundaries determine what is "without" and what is "within." This raises the issue as to whether the skin can really be considered a boundary between our self and the outside world .... Meditative exercises, drugs and dreams go further in dissolving these boundaries. First, we experience patterns rather than shapes and, if taken to the extreme, we can experience the loss of patterns as well: only a holoflux, "the white light" remains.[201]

There is also evidence of Pribram's association with the Transcendental Meditation movement; in 1977 a Stanford newspaper published an announcement of an upcoming presentations to be given by Karl Pribram and his Stanford colleague, William Tiller, at an event sponsored by local Transcendental Meditation organizations.[202] One of the primary teachings of the Transcendental Meditation organization, under the guidance of Maharishi Mahesh Yogi, is the practice of mantra, and it is possible that Pribram studied and practiced mantra himself.[203] Pribram specifically mentions the use of mantra in a 1991

---

[201] Pribram, *The Form Within*, 535–36.

[202] *The Stanford Daily*, Monday, September 26, 1977: 8.

[203] Dawson, *Comprehending Cults*, 54

publication, at the close of his book, in which he describes experiences of an enfolded, spectral dimension, in a somewhat cryptic final sentence:

> Perceptual experiences may on occasion however, reflect the spectral energy/momentum potential more than they reflect space–time configurations ... *stimuli provided by a mantra,* for example. When the spectral dimension dominates the production of a perception, space and time become enfolded in the experienced episode. Time evolution ceases and spatial boundaries disappear .... The boundary between mind and matter, as all other boundaries, becomes dissolved. More on this at a future occasion.[204]

It is easy to argue that Pribram is talking about his own participatory experience of the contemplative practice of mantra, when he states "The boundary between mind and matter, as all other boundaries, becomes dissolved."[205] Pribram explains the experience of mantra stimulation in words that, as we shall see in Chapter 4, are virtually identical to David Bohm's description of quantum dynamics ("space and time become enfolded"). Pribram describes "perceptual experiences" as moving between "space–time configurations" and "spectral energy," though fails to say anything beyond this about his altered perceptual experiences. Nor does he follow up on his promise of "More on this at a future occasion," and the rest of the book

---

[204] Pribram, *Brain and Perception,* 272–73.

[205] Ibid., 173.

consists of a 55-page technical appendix written by Kunio Yasue and Mari Jibu.[206]

Pribram on Spirits as Small-Fibered Electrical Fields

More than 20 years after describing his experience of mantra in *Brain and Perception*, Pribram, in *The Form Within*, discusses his understanding of "spirit" in the context of his life's work:

> Spirit is ordinarily defined as being immaterial. And thermodynamics is a scientific endeavor that is based on the utilization of forms of energy, not matter. Also, descriptions of holoflux, (the quantum potential, zero-point energy) and quantum holography are devoid of any space–time structure. These endeavors are scientific and the patterns they investigate describe the patterns ordinarily probed under the rubric "spirit." There was a time when brain processes were described as mediated by "breath"— that is, spirit. Now we affirm that these "spirits" are electrical, and in the small-fibered web, they form electrical fields. And as we continue to explore the effects of magnetism and "soft photons," that is of heat, there is likely a great deal more we will discover about brain processing that affirms our spiritual nature. We know that Homo sapiens has experienced the spiritual aspect of "being" since the dawn of our species. Science is a quest and, as I have tried to show, there is no reason scientists should

---

[206] Pribram, *Brain and Perception*, 275–330.

continue to restrict that quest to be confined merely to the composition of matter.[207]

But a more complete example of Pribram's interest in both Yoga and Zen, specifically in regard to his understanding of neurophysiology, can be found in a panel discussion held during a conference in Cordoba in 1979, Science and Consciousness, at which Pribram gave a presentation.[208] Table 1 shows that Pribram and Bohm presented at the conference, along with several other important thinkers in the field of physics and consciousness. It is possible that the Conference provided Pribram and Bohm their first chance to meet and exchange ideas, as Bohm was living near London at the time, and Pribram in California.

Table 1
Cordoba Conference Panel, 1979

Participant	Title of presentation
Fritjof Capra	"The Tao of Physics"
Karl H. Pribram	"Mind, Brain, and Consciousness"
David Bohm	"Imagination and the Implicate Order"
Brian Josephson	"Conscious Experience and Its Place in Physics"

Note. Data adapted from Cazenave, *Science and Consciousness*, 16. Author's table.

---

[207] Pribram, *The Form Within*, 533.

[208] Cazenave, *Science and Consciousness*.

During a panel discussion held at the Conference, Pribram provides a fascinating description of the difference between Zen and Yoga as mirrored in his own experience seen through the lens of his research in brain neurophysiology:

BRIAN JOSEPHSON: I would like to make a few comments on this question, especially with regard to the results of meditation . . . . Meditation can help those who practice it to find improved states of being. That said, meditation is not merely a technique, it also of necessity implies a spiritual dimensions and I do not think that we can ever measure spiritual values.

KARL PRIBRAM: You are right on that point. The experiences of meditation are definitely of a spiritual nature, there is no doubt about that.

Actually there are, roughly speaking, two types of procedure used in the East, Zen and Yoga, and we are going to see how they show up in neurophysiology . . . . What we have done in our laboratory is to study the observation of recuperative cycles in primary sensory systems. In carrying out this research, we have realized that it was in fact possible to manipulate the recuperative time of the system by stimulating either the frontal or posterior part of the brain.

When the frontal part is stimulated, a much more rapid recovery is obtained—the channel acting as a synchronizer—and everything operates simultaneously.

If, on the other hand, we stimulate the posterior part, we reduce the speed of the recovery of the system, but the channel is then of multiple type and carries much more information.

I wonder, therefore, whether it is not this difference between the frontal and posterior parts of the brain that is operating in the various methods of meditation. That is, various techniques designed to induce modified states of consciousness, Zen appealing to the frontal part, and Yoga to the posterior.[209]

In an interview for *Psychology Today*, Pribram expands on his belief that, approached with the understanding that a holographic system of consciousness is operating in the universe, certain otherwise-unexplainable phenomena such as synchronicity, nonlocality, and paranormal phenomena can be explained:

> It isn't that the world of appearances is wrong; it isn't that there *aren't* objects out there, at one level of reality. It's that if you penetrate through and look at the universe with a holographic system, you arrive at a different view, a different reality. And that other reality can explain things that have hitherto remained inexplicable scientifically: paranormal phenomena and synchronicities, the apparently meaningful coincidence of events.[210]

In his autobiography published in 1998, Pribram discusses his affirmation that there lie other "classes of order" behind the conceptually-ordering map of our world given to us by Euclidean Cartesian space–time coordinates and Newton's laws; here can be seen, certainly in the phrases "enfolded potential orders" and "unfolded orders manifested in space–time," the influence and adoption of

---

[209] Cazenave, *Science and Consciousness: Two Views of the Universe*, 129–30.

[210] As quoted in Talbot, *The Holographic Universe*, 10.

the ontological ideas of his friend and colleague, the quantum theorist David Bohm:

> This other class of orders constitutes distributed organizations described as potential because of their impalpability until radical changes in appearance are realized in the transformational process. When a potential is realized, information (the form within) becomes unfolded into its ordinary space–time appearance; in the other direction, the transformation enfolds and distributes the information, as this is done by the holographic process. Because work is involved in transforming, descriptions in terms of energy are suitable, and as the form of information is what is transformed, descriptions in terms of entropy (and negentropy) are also suitable. Thus, on the one hand, there are enfolded potential orders; on the other, there are unfolded orders manifested in space–time.[211]

And on the closing page of his final work, published in his 92nd year, Pribram ends with the following affirmation on the future scientific investigation of consciousness as it manifests in the domains of what is commonly called spirituality:

> Much of the research that I have reported here has dealt with forms, with patterns, that are, in themselves, not matter per se. These patterns can be considered the spiritual complements of matter. In this sense, spirit and spirituality now

---

[211] As quoted in Squire, *History of Neuroscience*, 342.

have status as topics ripe for scientific investigation.[212]

Pribram has developed extensive laboratory data to support his paradigm that neuronal systems in the cerebral cortex and in the sensory systems of vision, hearing, and smell, operate on holographic principles. His contention is that such activity is not primarily in and among the neurons themselves, but that the process manifests within an extended electromagnetic field among the fine-meshed dendritic fibers of the cerebral cortex. He has found evidence to support his contention in the outer reaches of the cerebral hemisphere, where he has mapped detectable holographic transformations which has led him to the conclusion that there exists an on-going "language" of transformation between space–time information and frequency-based information in the brain.[213]

In view of the serious nature of his discoveries during a lifelong search to understand the dynamic of memory and consciousness in the brain, it is refreshing to read Pribram's published answer to his own question of "what all this research is good for," expressed here at the age of 94:

> There are more than 37,000 neuroscientists currently performing experiments that address the topics that have formed my scientific life and the chapters in this book. From them we can expect a torrent of research results that bear on the health of our bodies and our brains. But there is more we need to know. I am often asked what all this research is good for? My answer is the

---

[212] Pribram, *The Form Within*, 538.

[213] Pribram, *Languages of the Brain*.

one Faraday gave when asked this question regarding his discoveries of the properties of electricity: "Someday you'll be able to tax it."[214]

While Pribram and his associates in California were trying to understand a holonomic Fourier transform paradigm of brain processing (from direct experimental evidence and first-hand observation), a complementary paradigm was emerging in London, in the work of the theoretical physicist David Bohm, who began using concepts from quantum field theory and the Fourier transform to develop and support the cosmology of what he called the "implicate order."[215]

---

[214] Pribram, *The Form Within*, 531.

[215] Bohm, *Quantum Theory*, 1.

Chapter 4: David Bohm's Implicate Order

Strong support for Karl Pribram's holonomic theories relating brain and consciousness can be found in the quantum physics of the American physicist David Joseph Bohm (1917–1992), a Professor Emeritus of Theoretical Physics at Birkbeck College, University of London. Bohm's early research career began at the University of California in Berkeley, where he completed his dissertation in plasma physics in 1944 under Robert Oppenheimer at the Lawrence Radiation Laboratory in Berkeley.[216]

Much as Pribram's was a search for a mind/brain process that was missing in mainstream research approaches, Bohm's search was a focus on something that was missing in quantum theory, the relationship between matter and consciousness. Bohm derided physicists who seemed to show no interest in the *meaning* of the quantum world, those who used quantum mechanics merely as a mathematical tool for effectively predicting results in nuclear physics experiments. At the same time, Bohm perceives that reality lies beyond appearances, that it is the creative process of a whole, beyond theorizing, even given the repeatable appearances of scientific measurement:

> The quantum jump or quantum leap is a creative process . . . . I called it the implicate order because its the order of enfoldment that counts not the movement in a line. It manifests in the explicate. What we thought was the essence is now the appearance . . . . Namely, that the particle which was thought to explain the reality is now seen as an appearance. The essence of the

---

[216] Peat, *Infinite Potential.*

true being is unknown. Even the implicate order is merely a concept, so even that should turn out to be an appearance. But we say be bringing in deeper more penetrating appearances we understand better, but we are never going to grasp the whole. Even a unified theory will only be an appearance.[217]

In his approach, Bohm stresses that the distinction between information and meaning is an important one, as did Karl Pribram (particularly in his *Languages of the Brain*, 1972). Unlike many physicists, whom he criticized for being information intoxicated, Bohm felt it of the utmost importance to search for meaning behind the information, and not to regard quantum mechanics simply as some exotic branch of calculation methodology. Understanding the underlying ontology behind quantum mechanics, Bohm felt, was a key to understanding the relationship between matter and consciousness, and here Bohm criticizes Bohr, the founder of quantum mechanics, who had won the Nobel Prize in 1913 for his quantum theory in modeling the hydrogen atom:

> Bohr's approach is to say nothing can be said about quantum mechanics at all other than to use it is a calculator, but my approach is to give it another appearance, more meaning. In the mechanical order it is hard to get much meaning.[218]

------

[217] Bohm, *Beyond Limits*, 8:00.

[218] Bohm, *Beyond Limits*, 12:55.

In the middle of his career as a theoretical physicist, Bohm's search for the underlying meanings to quantum theory was enriched through an introduction to a contemplative approach to the mind and consciousness expressed in the ideas of Jidu Krishnamurti. In 1961, while a professor of physics at Bristol University, Bohm attended a conference in London to hear a series of Krishnamurti lectures on perception, a topic that, as a quantum physicist, greatly interested Bohm. During the prior year, Bohm had become interested in theories of consciousness and perception expressed in the writings of philosophers and mystics, and had begun reading books on Yoga, Buddhism, and the work of the mathematician P. D. Ouspensky, a follower of the mystic G. I. Gurdjieff.[219] Public knowledge of his new interest resulted in further loss of credibility among Bohm's critics in the United States, as recounted here by his colleague and biographer, the physicist F. David Peat:

> When his former colleagues in the United States learned of this change of interest, it caused them considerable distress. In the years that followed, some lamented that Bohm had gone "off the rails," that a great mind had been sidetracked, and the work of an exceptional physicist was being lost to science.[220]

Bohm, however, was completely serious in his search for an understanding of quantum theory, even though the quest had led him into these areas of philosophy, psychology, and mysticism. Bohm's driving interest can be

---

[219] Peat, *Infinite Potential*, 193–94.

[220] Peat, *Infinite Potential*, 194–95

seen in the first paragraph of *The Undivided Universe: An Ontological Interpretation of Quantum Theory*, completed in 1992, only weeks before he suffered a fatal heart attack; here he expresses his passion to understand the mysteries that continue to lie behind quantum theory, rather than regarding the theory simply as something "which we know how to use":

> The formalism of the quantum theory leads to results that agree with experiment with great accuracy and covers an extremely wide range of phenomena. As yet there are no experimental indications of any domain in which it might break down. Nevertheless, there still remain a number of basic questions concerning its fundamental significance which are obscure and confused. Thus for example one of the leading physicists of our time, M. Gell-Mann, has said "Quantum mechanics, that mysterious, confusing discipline, which none of us really understands but which we know how to use."[221]

To understand Bohm's approach to quantum theory it is useful to examine their development in the context of the complexity of his life. Born in Pennsylvania in 1917, Bohm took an early interest in science, having become an avid reader of science fiction by the age of seven. After graduating in physics and receiving the school's Mathematics Prize from the University of Pennsylvania, he accepted a fellowship to enter graduate studies at Cal Tech. Within a year he found himself dissatisfied with the seemingly exclusive focus on problem solving at Cal Tech, a focus which seemed to discount Bohm's passion for seeking

---

[221] Bohm and Hiley, *The Undivided Universe*, 1.

an understanding of what must be underlying ontological realities, favoring instead the development of mathematical models and their manipulation.[222] In 1941 Bohm met with J. Robert Oppenheimer at the University of California, Berkeley, having heard that in addition to being a brilliant theoretical physicist, the thirty-seven year old Oppenheimer encouraged wide ranging intellectual discussion among his grad students and postdoctoral researchers. Bohm soon after accepted a fellowship offer from Oppenheimer to study at Berkeley, and in 1941 Bohm moved from Los Angeles to begin graduate work in plasma research at Berkeley.[223]

After a year of intense collaboration with other physicists at the laboratory, often working more than sixty hours a week, Bohm gave his first presentation of the ideas he had thus far developed to model the complex nature of plasma, but early in the presentation, as he began to try to convey his new ideas to Oppenheimer and the rest of his committee, something unexpected occurred:

> A naturally shy person, as he began to speak he nonetheless felt that everything was going extremely well. Soon he had the sensation that he was going beyond physics into something almost mystical, to the point where he felt himself in direct contact with everyone in the room. He was convinced that each individual consciousness had been transcended so that his audience was also sharing this experience. [224]

---

[222] Ibid., 31.

[223] Peat, *Infinite Potential*, 46.

[224] Ibid.

This intense feeling was overwhelming, leading immediately to a deep depression, and Bohm took a leave of absence, during which he was unable to work or study for almost an entire year.[225]

Even more problematical for Bohm during the first year of work on his dissertation under Oppenheimer was his growing interest in several activist antiwar groups, including the Committee for Peace Mobilization, the Campus Committee to Fight Conscription, and the Young Communist League, and "it was noted that Bohm had been involved in organizing activities for the Communist party and had distributed copies of Earl Browder's *Victory—and After*."[226] These associations and activities were later to haunt him.[227]

The Communist party in the United States had peaked at about 30,000 members in 1941, having grown steadily during the Great Depression due in part to the rapid growth of labor unions, but also because Communism was seen as a clear enemy of Fascism.[228] In November 1942, Bohm joined the Communist party in Berkeley, but membership was not particularly exciting or eventful, as Bohm later described to the historian Martin Sherwin during an interview: "The meetings were interminable, discussing all these boring attempts to stir up things on the campus which didn't amount to much."[229]

---

[225] Ibid., 47.

[226] Ibid., 62.

[227] Hiley and Peat, *Quantum Implications*.

[228] Peat, *Infinite Potential*, 57–58.

[229] Ibid., 58.

Back at Berkeley in 1943, Bohm completed his doctoral research project, an effort to develop a mathematical theory with which to model the dynamics of plasmas, a poorly understood phenomenon that greatly intrigued Bohm:

> As he studied the plasmas he became struck by their extraordinary nature. They began to take on, for him, the qualities of living beings. When physicists studied a plasma by introducing an electrical probe, it would generate a charged sheath around the probe and neutralize its effects. It was as if the plasma were protecting itself and preserving its internal status.[230]

Bohm completed his project, and the results were considered by Oppenheimer to be spectacular; the calculations that Bohm developed in his thesis were able to model accurately the behavior of uranium fluoride plasma in an electric arc, and led directly to an elegant technique for separating U^{235} from U^{238}, a critical step in the Oppenheimer's effort toward building a nuclear bomb.[231]

Unfortunately, shortly before the publication of his dissertation, Bohm's previous political activities caught up with him. It was suddenly apparent that his affiliation with Communism made it impossible for him to obtain a security clearance, while paradoxically the importance of his own dissertation for the war effort led to it being considered highly classified:

---

[230] Ibid., 66.

[231] Ibid., 65.

The scattering calculations (of collisions of protons and deuterons) that he had completed proved useful to the Manhattan Project and were immediately classified. But without security clearance, Bohm was denied access to his own work; not only would he be barred from defending his thesis, he was not even allowed to publish his own thesis.[232]

Oppenheimer was accordingly forced to petition the University of California Regents to rule on an exception to academic policy in order to approve Bohm's doctoral dissertation without allowing it to be published. The Regents assented and Bohm was awarded his doctorate and permitted to remain working at the Lawrence Laboratory, where he continued to focus his intense intellect upon the behavior of plasma flow and the mathematics of flux movement.[233] Here in an interview, Bohm describes his early interests and work with Oppenheimer during the period 1943–1946:

> When I worked at the Lawrence Laboratory, after taking my PhD, I became very interested in the electron plasma. This is a dense gas of electrons that exhibits radically different behavior from the other, normal states of matter and it was a key to much of the work the laboratory was doing at the time. My insights sprang from the perception that the plasma is a highly organized system, which behaves as a whole. Indeed, in some

---

[232] Ibid., 64.

[233] Plasmas constitute over ninety-nine percent of the matter of the universe—most stars and interstellar gases exist in this fourth state of matter (Peat, *Infinite Potential*, 65).

respects, it's almost like a living being. I was fascinated with the question of how such organized collective behavior could go along with the almost complete freedom of movement of individual electrons. [234]

Unfortunately, Bohm's early flirtation with Communism made the suppression of his dissertation only the first of what would eventually be a series of challenges to his academic career. Nevertheless, in 1947 the young physicist was hired as an assistant professor by Princeton University. During the relocation to New Jersey, he found a room near campus, and soon met his neighbor, another Princeton professor, the 57-year-old Albert Einstein, who, like Bohm, objected to quantum mechanics for its "lack of an objective description."[235] Bohm's clarity on this topic was no doubt helped by the many discussions he had with Einstein in his days at Princeton.[236]

During his time at Princeton, Bohm also continued his research on the mathematics of plasma dynamics, while giving classes and public lectures on quantum mechanics, but he refused to accept the majority view which was, "and still is," in the words of his colleague, B. J. Hiley,

> that the precise nature of the conceptual changes is not important . . . . All that is needed is to work with the self-consistent mathematical formalism, which, in some mysterious way, correctly predicts the numerical results of actual

---

[234] Bohm and Peat, *Science, Order, and Creativity*, xiii.

[235] Peat, *Infinite Potential*, 88.

[236] Bohm, *The Special Theory of Relativity*, vi.

experiments. After lecturing on the subject for three years, Bohm thought that this was not a satisfactory position to adopt so he decided to try to get a better understanding of the subject by writing a definitive textbook in which the physical aspects of the mathematics would be emphasized.[237]

Bohm worked furiously in his spare time on this major textbook that was to be a full interpretation of quantum theory, grounded both in mathematics and conceptual clarifications, which he hoped would resolve major unanswered problems within the quantum theory.[238] He also began working on a reinterpretation of quantum theory in a paper of his own, which he called the "hidden variable theory." His textbook was published in 1951, and the paper in 1952, but in October 1951 Bohm fled the United States for Brazil, his reputation having been seriously affected by the politics of McCarthyism, and under the fear of being jailed for Contempt of Congress.[239]

In late 1949, while working on the final chapters of his book, Bohm had been served with a summons, a subpoena ordering him to appear before Senator Joseph McCarthy at the House Un-American Activities Committee. At the hearing, Bohm was asked to identify which of his previous numerous colleagues at Berkeley had been interested in Communism. Not wishing to incriminate his friends and colleagues, Bohm repeatedly had his attorney plead his

---

[237] Hiley and Peat, "The Development of David Bohm's Ideas," 4.

[238] Bohm, *Quantum Theory*.

[239] Peat, *Infinite Potential*, 120.

"right to silence" under the Fifth Amendment to the United States Constitution. Notwithstanding, on December 4, 1950, Bohm was arrested at his home for Contempt of Congress, and though he made bail and was released, the administration at Princeton University peremptorily suspended him from "all teaching and other duties" for the duration of the trial.[240]

The publicity associated with the McCarthy hearings soon led to Bohm's dismissal from his position at Princeton, and subsequent inability to find employment in the United States. With letters of reference from Einstein and Oppenheimer, Bohm was offered a position in the physics department of the University of São Paulo, the largest university in Brazil, then in the throes of development and expansion, during which had been seeking to attract a prominent quantum physicist from a mainstream American university.[241] Bohm decided to accept the position and prepared to make a hasty departure for Brazil, a day described here by his biographer:

> On the October day in 1951 when Bohm left the United States, thunderstorms and hurricane-force winds swept across New Jersey and New York. The flooded streets made it difficult for him to reach the airport . . . . On board the aircraft while taxiing to takeoff, he heard an announcement that the plane would return to the terminal because of an irregularity in the passport of one of the passengers. Already highly nervous, Bohm wondered if he was going to be arrested. The problem, however, concerned

---

[240] Peat, *Infinite Potential*, 98–99.

[241] Baggott, *The Quantum Story*, 305.

another passenger, who was removed from the flight.[242]

In December 1951, two months after his arrival in Brazil, the US consulate in São Paulo confiscated Bohm's passport, effectively stripping him of his US citizenship, and making it impossible for him to leave Brazil other than to return to the United States.[243]

Undeterred, with his passion for learning undiminished, Bohm continued to work, and he was soon fluent in self-taught Portuguese, sufficiently fluent to lecture at the University of São Paulo. [244] He was especially encouraged by favorable peer reviews of his recent US publication of *Quantum Theory*, a 628-page textbook interpreting quantum theory, and which begins in the first paragraph to emphasize the importance of familiarity with Fourier analysis:

> Modern quantum theory is unusual in two respects. First, it embodies a set of physical ideas that differ completely with much of our everyday experience, and also with most experiments in physics on a macroscopic scale. Second, the mathematical apparatus needed to apply this theory to even the simplest example is much less familiar . . . . It seems impossible, however, to develop quantum concepts extensively without *Fourier analysis*. It is, therefore, presupposed

---

[242] Peat, *Infinite Potential*, 120.

[243] Ibid., 124.

[244] Ibid., 126.

that the reader is moderately familiar with Fourier analysis.[245]

Theory of Hidden Variables

But perhaps the greatest significance of *Quantum Theory* lies in the fact that Bohm presents, once again, but this time in a major text book, his theory of hidden variables: "Perhaps there are hidden variables that really control the exact time and place of a transfer of a quantum, and we simply haven't found them yet."[246] Einstein's major objection to the quantum theory was its almost complete lack of an objective description, and it was this that Bohm addressed in his new interpretation.[247]

At Princeton, Bohm and Einstein had agreed that there must be underlying processes yet to be discovered. Quantum mechanical calculations, while they work in the prediction of experimental evidence, treat particle actions collectively; in a similar way as taking temperature measurements are used to predict the motion of billions of gas molecules. In neither case can actual particle motion be mapped or predicted at the real dimensions being examined. Einstein and Bohm felt there must be principles that affect motion at a lower scale than that addressed by the collective mathematics of quantum mechanics (or temperature measurements).

---

[245] Bohm, *Quantum Theory*, 1. Italics added.

[246] Ibid., 29.

[247] Peat, *Infinite Potential*, 86.

This assumption has been the object of severe criticisms, notably on the part of Einstein, who has always believed that, even at the quantum level, there must exist precisely definable elements or dynamical variables determining (as in classical physics) the actual behavior of each individual system, and not merely its probable behavior . . . . The suggested interpretation provides a broader conceptual frame-work than the usual interpretation, because it makes possible a precise and continuous description of all process, even at the quantum level. This broader conceptual framework allows more general mathematical formulations of the theory than those allowed by the usual interpretation. Now, the usual mathematical formulation seems to lead to insoluble difficulties when it is extrapolated into the domain of distances of the order of 10^{-33} cm or less. It is therefore entirely possible that the interpretation suggested here may be needed for the resolution of these difficulties.[248]

In his paper on hidden variables can be seen Bohm's early fascination with the physics of the greatest depths of scale, far below the normal range at which even quantum mechanics is applied, down at distances of the Planck length (approximately 10^{-33} cm), a scale at which "classical notions such as causality or distance between events cannot be expected to be applicable."[249] The Planck constant is discussed in detail in Chapter 5.

---

[248] Bohm, "Interpretation of the Quantum Theory in Terms of 'Hidden Variables,'" 166.

[249] Garay, "Quantum Gravity and Minimum Length," 145.

Motion of "Particles" in Space–Time

Bohm explains apparent linear motion with an ontology derived from quantum theory when he speculates that, rather than manifesting as a solid, continuous particle in space–time, "the proton takes the form of a wave that collapses inward from all space," like a whirlpool in water.[250]

Similarly, in a conclusion that is contrary to the conventional assumption that electrons and protons are well-defined particles, Bohm describes the apparent motion of protons and electrons as:

> a continuous process of inward collapse and outward expansion. Therefore, every elementary particle collapses inward from the whole of space. In fact, each elementary particle is a manifestation of the whole universe.[251]

While his textbook on *Quantum Theory* was generally well received, and subsequently used in undergraduate courses on quantum mechanics worldwide for its clarity of language, analogy, and supporting calculus, the concept of *hidden variables*, described in the book and in his 1952 paper published exclusively on the "hidden variables" was pounced upon almost universally by quantum physicists, as being incompatible with the prevailing "Copenhagen interpretation."[252] In Copenhagen, during 1925 and 1927,

---

[250] Peat, *Infinite Potential*, 48.

[251] Peat, *Infinite Potential*, 48–49.

[252] Bohm, "Interpretation of the Quantum Theory in Terms of 'Hidden Variables.'"

Niels Bohr and two of his young students, Heisenberg and Pauli, at a series of meetings and conferences, both formal and informal, had developed what was later to be called the Copenhagen Interpretation of quantum mechanics, a conjectural descriptive explanation of what the working mathematical equations seemed to imply. [253] To most physicists, having worked under general agreement for over 20 years under the Copenhagen interpretation, Bohm's hidden variable theory was seen as being almost heretical, a direct challenge to the Copenhagen interpretation; yet from Bohm's point of view, it was the Copenhagen approach, with its heavy reliance on mathematical probability theory, that was random. [254] In this, Albert Einstein, Bohm's former neighbor, friend, and mentor at Princeton, can be seen in full agreement; Einstein is quoted here in a 1926 letter to Max Born, where he comments on the recently published Copenhagen interpretation, and expresses special concern regarding the deep reliance of probability theory in quantum mechanics:

> Quantum mechanics is certainly imposing. But an inner voice tells me that it is not yet the real thing. The theory says a lot, but does not really bring us any closer to the secret of the "old one." I, at any rate, am convinced that He does not throw dice.[255]

The prevailing consensus, in accord with the Copenhagen interpretation, holds that quantum events are

---

[253] Peat, *Infinite Potential*, 51.

[254] Ibid., 52.

[255] Born, *The Born–Einstein Letters*, 91.

indeterminate and discontinuous, and therefore the physics of process is not linearly predictable at quantum scales of matter, and that only probability mathematics works in predicting outcomes. Bohm opposed this axiom with his conviction that the process of the universe cannot be attributed to purely random statistical activity, but that there is an underlying order and comprehensive connectivity, a unity to the cosmos, a wholeness not predicted by mere probability theory.[256]

In his hidden variable theory, however, Bohm assumes the universe to be coherent and predictable, and considers the apparent randomness to be misleading, proposing instead that there must exist hidden variables operating at sub-quantum levels, hidden forces and processes operating at lower levels, below the currently assumed lower limit of matter, and not yet accessible with current instrumentation. Understandably, Bohm's new theory of hidden variables was immediately rejected by the community of physicists, in part for political reasons (Bohm's earlier communist affiliations), but primarily due to the firm attachment to the consensual acceptance of the Copenhagen interpretation and the predictable results proven by use of quantum mechanical calculations.[257]

At best, Bohm's new theory was ignored, but some went so far as to accuse him of being a Trotskyite and a traitor; one physicist termed Bohm's work "juvenile deviation," and another called Bohm "a public nuisance."[258]

---

[256] Peat, *Infinite Potential*, 108.

[257] Ibid., 148.

[258] Ibid., 133.

This strong reaction against Bohm's *hidden variable* hypothesis even led his own one-time supervisor, mentor, and hero, Robert Oppenheimer, to gather a meeting of physicists at Berkeley in 1953 with the objective of disproving Bohm's theory; the meeting closed with Oppenheimer being heard to say, "If we cannot disprove Bohm, we must continue to ignore him."[259]

In 1955, Bohm left Brazil to accept a position as a physics professor at the Israel Institute of Technology in Haifa, where he meets his future wife, Saral, an artist. In 1957 Bohm and Saral left Israel where Bohm accepted a position at Bristol University in England. In London, that same year, Bohm presented his mature version of the hidden variable concepts, which he had first begun to develop in 1952 in *Quantum Theory*. In his London paper Bohm introduced the idea of processes occurring at sub-quantum levels, operating at considerably smaller dimensions than those at which quantum mechanical calculations modeled the activity of atomic particles. This was the beginning of Bohm's conceptualization of the implicate order, through considering the possible ontological reality of dimensions far below the quantum dimensions being explored by quantum mechanics.

During his second year in England, Bohm presented a series of lectures at London University detailing his hidden variable theory; the lecture was attended by a young doctoral student in physics, John Bell, who had become interested in mathematical approaches to the nonlocality problem in quantum mechanics. Bell, encouraged by Bohm's theories, went on to develop a mathematical proof of nonlocality, a phenomenon that has since been verified

---

[259] Ibid.

several times in rigorous experiment.[260] It is of interest to note that Bell said, of Bohm's theory, "No one can understand this theory until he is willing to see psi as a real objective field rather than just a probability amplitude."[261]

Bohm did not limit his intellectual pursuit exclusively to physics. During his three years at Bristol University he began to read widely in areas of speculative philosophy and soon became acquainted with the process philosophy of Alfred North Whitehead, the Cambridge mathematician turned Harvard philosopher. One evening, according to Bohm, while reading *Process and Reality*, he experienced what seemed to be an epiphany, a visualization of infinity in the image of a large number of silvered spherical mirrors, each one reflecting all of the others, a cosmos composed of an infinity of reflections, and of reflections of reflections: "Every atom was reflecting in this way, and the infinity of these reflections was reflected in each thing; each was an infinite reflection of the whole." [262] The influence of this image can be found 20 years later in Bohm's understanding of what he had by then come to call, "the Implicate Order." The image of mirrors reflecting the whole is echoed in *Wholeness and the Implicate Order* in the following passage, which describes Bohm's concept of the holomovement:

> In certain ways this notion is similar to Leibniz's idea of monads, each of which "mirrors" the

[260] Ibid., 168.

[261] J. T. Bell, *The Speakable and Unspeakable in Quantum Mechanics*, 128.

[262] Peat, *Infinite Potential*, 186.

whole in its own way, some in great detail and others rather vaguely. The difference is that Leibniz's monads had a permanent existence, whereas our basic elements are only moments and are thus not permanent.[263]

At Bristol in the early 1960s, during his wide-ranging reading in philosophy and Eastern metaphysics, Bohm was introduced to the writings of the Russian mathematician P. D. Ouspensky, who had written several books on the metaphysics of the mystic G. I. Gurdjieff.[264] In 1962 Bohm managed to meet in London with J. G. Bennet, himself a mathematician as well as an authority on Gurdjieff; the two corresponded over the next several years, but "their connection was broken," as Bohm's biographer says, in a footnote:

> Bohm became increasingly critical of Gurdjieff's emphasis upon the essential separation of an observing consciousness. For Bohm there was a "total awareness" that lies beyond consciousness and is the field in which creativity operates.[265]

Krishnamurti and Meditation

It was also while at Bristol University that Bohm first became acquainted with the philosopher Jidu Krishnamurti. In the Bristol public library, Bohm's wife, Saral, discovered a book in the philosophy section discussing the topics of perception and thought, and brought it home as of possible

---

[263] Bohm, *Wholeness and the Implicate Order*, 207.

[264] Ouspensky, *In Search of the Miraculous*.

[265] Peat, *Infinite Potential*, 213.

interest. Bohm was immediately fascinated by what Krishnamurti had to say:

> My first acquaintance with Krishnamurti's work was in 1959 when I read his book *First and Last Freedom*. What particularly aroused my interest was deep insight into the question of the observer and the observed ... I felt that it was urgent for me to talk with Krishnamurti directly and personally as soon as possible. And when I first met him on one of his visits to London, I was struck by the great ease of communication with him, which was made possible by the intense energy with which he listened and by the freedom from self-protective reservations and barriers with which he responded to what I had to say ... it was in essence of the same quality as that which I had met in contacts with other scientists with whom there had been a very close meeting of minds. And here, I think especially of Einstein who showed a similar intensity and absence of barrier in a number of discussions that took place between him and me. After this, I began to meet Krishnamurti regularly and to discuss with him whenever he came to London.[266]

In 1961, Bohm left Bristol University to accept the offer of Chair of Theoretical Physics, offered to him by J. D. Bernal, the head of the physics department (and a dedicated Marxist) at Birkbeck College, University of London. In that same year Bohm, for the first time, arranged a private conversation with Krishnamurti in London. The two continued their dialogues, at first privately, and then

---

[266] Bohm and Krishnamurti, *The Limits of Thought,* vii.

eventually in public venues, before audiences in London, Switzerland, and later in Ojai, California.[267]

In Switzerland in 1965, the first public recordings were made of a series of dialogues between Krishnamurti and Bohm. Undoubtedly Bohm's previous reading experience of Whitehead, Hegel, Ouspensky, and Indian philosophy had prepared him well for these flowing dialogues with Krishnamurti, and likely influenced his own conceptualizations. In addition to published books containing transcripts of many of these dialogues, numerous video and audio recordings have been released; a recent YouTube search on "Krishnamurti" and "Bohm" pulls up 32,000 results.[268]

It was in 1967, during the "Summer of Love," that Bohm and his wife, at the urging of Krishnamurti, both became vegetarians and took up the daily practice of meditation. Bohm was particularly interested in Krishnamurti's teaching on the process of "dying to thought" in which the physical brain no longer gives energy to the movement of thought process in the brain. [269] According to Krishnamurti, it is this incessant conditioned mental thought process that masks and conceals the silence within which the less conditioned consciousness process might be perceived, and within which new modes of "non-verbal thought" might operate. Bohm here describes his own understanding of Krishnamurti's teaching on the process of meditation:

---

[267] Peat, *Infinite Potential*, 213.

[268] Bohm and Krishnamurti, *The Ending of Time*; and Bohm and Krishnamurti, *The Limits of Thought*.

[269] Peat, *Infinite Potential*, 227–28.

Krishnamurti has observed that the very act of meditation will, in itself, bring order to the activity of thought without the intervention of will, choice, decision, or any other action of the "thinker." As such order comes, the noise and chaos which are the usual background of our consciousness die out, and the mind becomes generally silent . . . . In this silence, Krishnamurti says that something new and creative happens, something that cannot be conveyed in words, but that is of extraordinary significance for the whole of life. So he does not attempt to communicate this verbally, but rather, he asks of those who are interested that they explore the question of meditation directly for themselves.[270]

It is easy to imagine how Bohm's exceptional, trained capability (as a theoretical physicist) for focus on abstractions served to reinforce his growing capabilities in the practice of formless meditation. Bohm soon established a daily period in the early morning during which he would walk slowly in the park or countryside while watching the movement of this thoughts, not allowing himself to become distracted or "caught up" in their content; this practice continued throughout his life.[271]

The Implicate Order

It is of interest to note that within two years of beginning his daily meditation walk, Bohm conceptualized a significantly new idea, the "implicate order," which ontologically strengthened his hidden variables theory. By

---

[270] Bohm and Krishnamurti, *The Limits of Thought,* vii.

[271] Peat, *Infinite Potential,* 229.

1969 the subjects of topology, nonlocality, and pre space had come to the forefront of discussion within the physics department at the University of London, and as his colleague, the physicist B. J. Hiley recalls, Bohm had a breakthrough in his understanding: "Suddenly, a new idea emerged from Bohm, apparently entirely out of the blue . . . Bohm called it the *implicate order*."[272]

Bohm identified this implicate order as being the source of the hidden, sub-quantum variables which he hypothesized were providing the causality underlying the operation of quantum mechanics, and he began an effort to model the effect of the implicate order mathematically.[273] In 1925, Werner Heisenberg had taken a similar view:

> Heisenberg, who at age twenty-four, was young even by physics standards, tried to save classical mechanics by abandoning it at Nature's bottom rung. Inside the atom, he declared, not only do particles and electron orbits have no meaning, but neither do even such basic classical properties as position, momentum, velocity, and space and time. And because our imaginations require a space–time container, this atomic world cannot be easily pictured.[274]

But Heisenberg's approach fell by the wayside when the Copenhagen approach proved so successful in predictive calculations of nuclear particle trajectories using probabilities. Decades later, Bohm pursued alone a similar

---

[272] Peat, *Infinite Potential*, 256.

[273] Ibid.

[274] Crease, *The Great Equations*, 220.

idea, and in 1980 published *Wholeness and the Implicate Order*, in which is revealed both the mathematics and a mature conceptual model for his proposed implicate order, a model based not on "things" considered as objects, nor restricted solely to phenomena in a Cartesian space–time order, but rather modeling a lens-like flowing of simultaneous enfolding and unfolding dimensions between two orders, an implicate order and an explicate order, as Bohm explained:

> There is the germ of a new notion of order here. This order is not to be understood solely in terms of a regular arrangement of *objects* . . . . Rather, a *total order* is contained, in some *implicit* sense, in each region of space and time. Now, the word "implicit" is based on the verb "to implicate." This means, "to fold inward." So we may be led to explore the notion that in some sense each region contains a total structure "enfolded" within it.[275]

Bohm went so far as to describe the implicate order as the ground within which the entire universe is enfolded at each and every "point" in space–time, as the Finnish philosopher Paavo Pylkkänen, a former student and friend of Bohm's, explains clearly:

> Just think of all the atoms and particles that constitute your body. We are used to thinking about them as tiny little things that just passively sit there. But quantum field theory, as interpreted by Bohm, suggests otherwise. There is a sense in which each particle in your body enfolds information about the whole universe . . . . There is also a sense in which

---

[275] Bohm, *Wholeness and the Implicate Order*, 149.

information about each particle in your body is enfolded throughout the universe.[276]

However, Bohm's focus of interest clearly ranged beyond the conventional boundaries of physics, into theories of mind, thought, and consciousness. It is easy to conclude that Bohm's dialog with Krishnamurti influenced the expansion of this focus, bringing to the forefront for Bohm issues of thinking and mind. But with his deep understanding of quantum theory, Bohm was able to see a direct connection between thought, consciousness, and the implicate order, as can be discerned in his description of the thinking process, recorded in a 1990 interview:

> And that's how the thinking process goes, it's enfolded in your consciousness, it unfolds to a certain thought, folds back, and then the next thought appears, different; a series of thoughts not too different seems to be continuous.[277]

In imagining this process as an "enfoldment," we are led to the obvious next question, "Enfoldment into what?" And Bohm's non-Cartesian answer then, is enfoldment *into something within*, enfoldment into the implicate order. How then might this be conceptualized? Imagine the universe at the lowest possible spatial range. Moving to ever-smaller dimensions, to the very bottom of the dimensional scale, we encounter the end of space, according to accepted quantum theory, at a limiting length, below

---

[276] Pylkkänen, *Mind, Matter, and the Implicate Order*, 21.

[277] Bohm, *Beyond Limits*, 8:00.

which length has no meaning.[278] Thus this implicate order, located at the center, everywhere, can be seen as the ground, base, or center out of which dynamically springs the space–time continuum itself, the explicate order.

The Sub-Quantum Order and the Sub-Relativistic Level

Bohm applied the term "sub-quantum order" to that order of physics which he viewed as expressing the underlying causal reality *from which* quantum mechanics operates, calling this approach "going beyond the quantum theory."[279] While quantum mechanical theory works well for predicting the path of nuclear particles in dimensional ranges around 10^{-15} meters, the theory places a heavy insistence on pure probability considerations, and this randomness had always bothered Bohm. As early as 1952, in his textbook, *Quantum Theory,* Bohm states:

> We have come to the point of view that the wavefunction is an abstraction, providing a mathematical reflection of certain aspects of reality, but not a one-to-one mapping.[280]

He further argues that the ontological cause is to be discovered at lower levels, below quantum mechanical dimensions, and that "quantum theory is inconsistent with the assumption of hidden causal variables" governing

---

[278] As discussed shortly, this is the Planck length of 10^{-33} cm.

[279] Bohm and Hiley, *The Undivided Universe,* 9.

[280] Bohm, *Quantum Theory,* 622

processes at the lowest, sub quantum levels.[281] At the end of the Introduction to his 1993 book, Bohm predicts the failure of the "current laws of physics" at the Planck length:

> The idea is that there will be a stochastic sub-quantum and sub-relativistic level in which the current laws of physics will fail. This will probably first be encountered near the Planck length of 10^{-33} cm .... This idea is connected with our ontological interpretation by means of a model of a particle as a sequence of incoming and outgoing waves, with successive waves very close to each other .... One of the main new ideas implied by this approach is that the geometry and the dynamics have to be in the same framework, i.e. that of the implicate order.[282]

This leads us to the observation that there exist three sets of framework-dependent mathematical models, applicable in three ranges: (1) Newtonian mechanics, operating at human dimensions, in the 10^0 meter range, (2) quantum mechanics, operating at nuclear particle dimensions, in the 10^{-15} meter range, and (3) Bohm's "hidden variables," operating at the boundary of space–time, in the 10^{-35} meter range. Here Bohm reiterates an observation he had previously made regarding the important significance of the dimension 1.616×10^{-33} cm, the Planck length, and designated with the symbol ℓ_P in

---

[281] Ibid.

[282] Bohm and Hiley, *The Undivided Universe*, 9–10.

quantum theoretical calculations.[283] Over a decade earlier, in a 1980 publication, *Wholeness and the Implicate Order*, Bohm, in discussing the calculation of what is called "the zero-point energy" for point in space, provides another explanation for the significance of this 10^{-33} cm distance:

> We come to a certain length at which the measurement of space and time becomes totally indefinable. Beyond this, the whole notion of space and time as we know it would fade out, into something that is at present unspecifiable .... When this length is estimated it turns out to be about 10^{-33} cm. This is much shorter than anything thus far probed in physical experiments (which have gone down to about 10^{-17} cm or so). If one computes the amount of energy that would be in one cubic centimeter of space, with this shortest possible wavelength, it turns out to be very far beyond the total energy of all the matter in the known universe.[284]

It is here then, in the region of the Planck length at 10^{-33} cm, that Bohm predicts that there will be found *a boundary* separating an outer, *explicate order* from an inner, *implicate order*. There will also be seen gaps of, at minimum, 10^{-33} cm between each and every concentric shell

---

[283] See also Chapter 5, "The Planck Constant"; the Planck length of 10^{-33} cm. was first discussed by the German physicist Max Planck, the 1918 Nobel Prize winning originator of quantum mechanics, and is derived from three values: (1) the speed of light in a vacuum, (2) the gravitational constant, and (3) the Planck constant, h, which is required to calculate quantum changes of wavelength as a function of temperature (Bruskiewich, *Max Planck and Black-Body Radiation*).

[284] Bohm, *Wholeness and the Implicate Order*, 190–91.

that might be surrounding the central area, a spherical locus of Planck length diameter ℓ_P. This is in accord with the founding quantum theory of Max Planck, first published in 1900, in which he proposed that a photon could have only distinct, fixed energy states, separated by integers, which he termed "quanta."[285] Bohm uses such quantum theoretical considerations to point out a fallacy still held by many, the classical Cartesian assumption that space is continuous:

> What of the order between two points in space? The Cartesian order holds that space is continuous. Between any two points, no matter how close they lie, occur an infinite of other points. Between any two neighboring points in this infinity lies another infinity and so on. This notion of continuity is not compatible with the order of quantum theory . . . . Thus the physicist John Wheeler has suggested that, at very short distances, continuous space begins to break up into a foam-like structure. Thus the "order between" two points moves from the order of continuity to an order of a discontinuous foam.[286]

According to Bohm, at the ultimate bottom level of these subdivided infinities, between two points in space, like an end-of-stop bumper terminating a railroad track, will be found a cosmologically fixed boundary at the Planck length of 10^{-33} cm, beyond which no further subdivision is meaningfully possible. It is here, at this smallest of possible spatial coordinates, that we encounter the origin of the

---

[285] Bohm, *Quantum Theory*, 18.

[286] Bohm and Peat, *Science, Order, and Creativity*, 311–12.

dimension of space that finds its maximum in the diameter of the currently expanding universe (the bandwidth continually increases, at the speed of light).

Viewed another way, to use the depths of the ocean as an analog or metaphor, Bohm's sub-quantum mechanics can be viewed as being at the bottom of a dimensional ocean with a floor significantly below the depths of the region mapped and explored by the mathematics of quantum mechanics. The image in Fig. 9 plots three ranges of dimensional scale along a vertical axis. On the same vertical axis can be seen dimensional ranges within which operate (1) classical Newtonian physics, (2) Quantum physics, and (3) Bohmian physics, each operating within distinct ranges, separated by over 10^{15} orders of magnitude. In a real sense, Bohm was plumbing this depth of dimensional physics, far below the level at which conventional quantum theory is applied, at depths of scale considerably below those of the dimensions of a Monarch butterfly wingspan, a uranium atom nucleus, a proton, or a calculated electron (photon) diameter. Bohm comments on the depths of this range:

> It is interesting to note that between the shortest distance now measurable in physics (10^{-16} cm) and the shortest distance in which current notions of space–time probably have meaning (10^{-33} cm), there is a vast range of scale in which an immense amount of yet undiscovered structure could be contained. Indeed this range is roughly equal to that which exists between our own size and that of the elementary particles.[287]

---

[287] Ibid., 86.

130

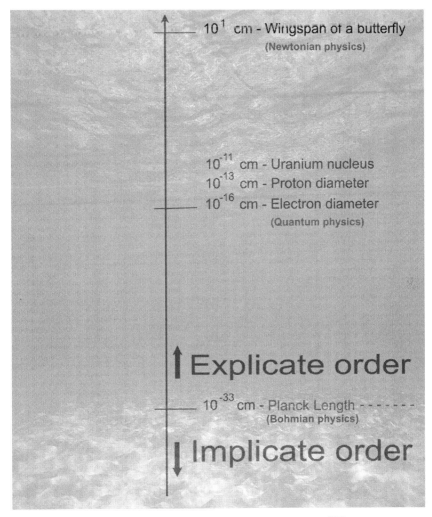

Figure 9. Sub-quantum ocean floor metaphor.[288] Graphic by author.

Note that quantum mechanics is applicable in a range only halfway down between the scale of the human biosphere and the depths of space–time at the Planck

---

[288] Data from Benenson, Harris, Stocker, and Holger, *Handbook of Physics.*

length. The mathematical models (and operational physics) that work in one range (for example, Newtonian mechanics as it operates within the human body parts) are in general not applicable within the other ranges (such as the operational physics of quantum mechanics working in electron and proton ranges).

At the absolute bottom of the figure's ocean floor lies the Planck length of 10^{-33} cm., above which the explicate order manifests in increasingly larger ranges of scale until the dimensional length of a butterfly (about 1 cm) is reached, floating on the surface of the explicate order's ocean depth of scale. Of course, a more inclusive scale would expand upwards to include the size of the universe, with a diameter of 10^{26} meters, and the human dimensional range would then be seen to lie approximately half way between these two limits, the size of the universe (10^{26} m) and the Planck length (10^{-35} m).[289] Such a complete scale range, spanning the entire cosmos, is depicted in Fig. 10.

---

[289] Gott et al., "A Map of the Universe."

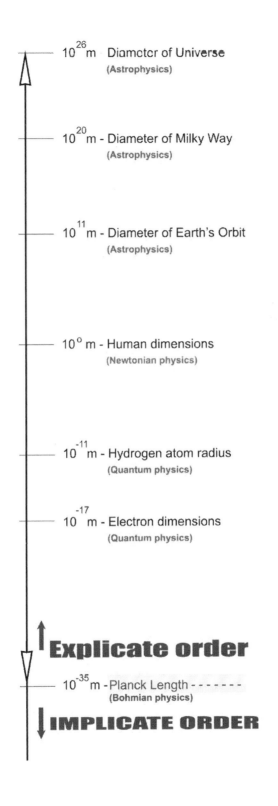

Figure 10. Spectral domain and space–time domain. Graphic by author.

Another foundation upon which Bohm's model of the universe grew can be seen in his vision of an endless infinity of ordered fields, as he describes here:

> We may suppose that the universe, which includes the whole of existence, contains not only all the fields that are now known, but also an indefinitely large set of further fields that are unknown and indeed may never be known in their totality. Recalling that the essential qualities of fields exist only in their movement we propose to call this ground the *holomovement*. It follows that ultimately everything in the explicate order of common experience arises from the holomovement. Whatever persists with a constant form is sustained as the unfoldment of a recurrent and stable pattern, which is constantly being renewed by enfoldment, and constantly being dissolved by unfoldment. When the renewal ceases the form vanishes.[290]

Fields need not exist only within space–time. Einstein's theory of general relativity posits ten fields to describe the movement of gravity in four dimensions.[291] As early as 1919 a German mathematician, Theodor Kaluza, sent Einstein a paper proposing an extremely small fifth dimension in which additional frequency and phase fields could provide a solution to resolve Einstein's struggle to

---

[290] Bohm and Hiley, *The Undivided Universe*, 357.

[291] Yau and Nadis, *The Shape of Inner Space*, 10.

resolve the connection between gravity and electromagnetism.[292] In 1926 the Swedish physicist Oskar Klein "drawing on quantum mechanics, calculated the size of this compact dimension, arriving at a number that was tiny indeed—around 10^{-30} cm in circumference."[293] The theory became known as the Kaluza-Klein theory, offering the potential of extra fields in an additional dimension as a promising approach to resolving Einstein's search to connect gravity and electromagnetism. Einstein wrote to Kaluza, saying he liked the idea "enormously" and in fact continued working with the theory for the next 20 years; ultimately, however, the Kaluza-Klein theory was discarded because of its prediction of a particle so small that it could not be proven to exist using any foreseeable technology.[294]

But by the same token it has also been impossible to *disprove* a cosmological reality existing at such small dimensions, and it is here, at the limiting space–time scale of 10^{-33} cm, that Bohm hypothesizes an implicate order.[295] In Fig. 11, Pribram's diagrammatic concept of the Fourier transform is depicted with Bohm's implicate order to the left, in the spectral domain, and Bohm's explicate order to the right, in the space–time domain.

---

[292] Ibid., 10–11.

[293] Ibid., 12.

[294] Ibid., 13.

[295] Bohm, *Wholeness and the Implicate Order*, 190.

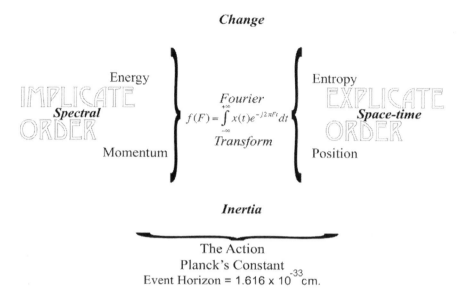

Figure 11. The implicate/explicate order transform. Graphic by author.

In the diagram, the process linking the two orders is shown as the Fourier transform function, implementing a reciprocal flow of spectral information between the implicate order into the explicate order, a two-way process, operating at an event horizon of the Planck limit of 10^{-33} cm, a process which Bohm terms the "holomovement," and which, he tells us, is grounded in the implicate order:

> The implicate order has its ground in the holomovement which is vast, rich, and in a state of unending flux of enfoldment and unfoldment, with laws most of which are only vaguely known, and which may even be ultimately unknowable in their totality.... Nevertheless, the overall law (holonomy) may be assumed to be such that in a certain sub-order, within the whole set of the implicate order, there is a totality of forms that have an approximate kind of recurrence, stability, and separability. Evidently these forms

are capable of appearing as the relatively solid, tangible, and stable elements that make up our "manifest world."[296]

Holomovement and Holoflux

In 1978 Bohm discusses these concepts with remarkable clarity during a Harvard conference on "Science and Mysticism: Exploring the New Realities." After his presentation, which he called, "The Implicate Order: The Holodynamic Model of the Universe," Bohm was interviewed by Renée Weber for *ReVision* magazine, and here he expresses the difference between holography and the holomovement, and introduces the term "holoflux":

> **Weber**: Could we begin by clarifying the difference between the holomovement, the holograph and the implicate order?
>
> **Bohm**: Holomovement is a combination of a Greek and Latin word and a similar word would be holokinesis or, still better, *holoflux*, because "movement" implies motion from place to place, whereas flux does not. So the *holoflux* includes the ultimately flowing nature of what is, and of that which forms therein. The holograph, on the other hand, is merely a static recording of movement, like a photograph: an abstraction from the holomovement. We therefore cannot regard the holograph as anything very basic, since it is merely a way of displaying the holomovement, which latter is, however, the ground of everything, of all that is. The implicate order is the one in which the holomovement takes place, an order that both enfolds and

---

[296] Ibid., 186.

unfolds. Things are unfolded in the implicate order, and that order cannot be entirely expressed in an explicate fashion. Therefore, in this approach, we are not able to go beyond the holomovement or the *holoflux* (the Greek word might be holorhesis, I suppose) although that does not imply that this is the end of the matter.[297]

In a theory congruent with Pribram's, Bohm hypothesizes that consciousness must operate dynamically in a holonomic fashion, driven by a quantum potential wave, and that the information guiding motion in space–time must originate from an *other order*, the implicate order, which lies outside of the commonly perceived explicate order of the space–time domain.[298] From early in his career, Bohm had tried to visualize the motion of quantum "particles," not moving in linear sequential tracks as viewed in a cloud chamber, but as oscillating in and out of space–time.[299]

Bohm, here in a 1990 interview recorded for Dutch television, not only describes this movement or "holomovement" as superseding the so-called "particle" phenomena of quantum mechanics, but in doing so, Bohm emphasizes the reality of the whole, the continuum of mind and matter, and discusses the general implications of this for perception:

---

[297] Weber, "The Physicist and the Mystic," 187. Italics added.

[298] Hiley and Peat, eds. *Quantum Implications: Essays in Honour of David Bohm.*

[299] Ibid.

Bohm: Now, I saw that you could understand the quantum mechanics in terms of that process. That instead of saying an electron, for example, is a particle just moving along, you could think that there is a wave coming in, enfolding, or it's really unfolding at a point, it's enfolded in the whole universe. Then it folds back. Then another wave comes in, at a slightly different point. You get a series of points that are very close together so we imagine they're a particle, right? But, because of that wave nature, from which it comes, you understand, the wave/particle nature, that is, it's a wave.[300]

Support for this view is found in an interpretation of holodynamics put forth by a consciousness researcher at UC Irvine, Gordon Globus, who describes Bohm's holodynamic process as follows:

There are two primary phases of this holodynamics according to Bohm: *implication* and *explication* .... Implication is the "enfolding" of world to the whole and explication is the cotemporaneous "unfolding" of world from the whole. Each moment of unfolding/enfolding has a brief duration .... The world is explicate order continually unfolded from implicate order, rather than explicate order persisting.[301]

And what then might be the temporal rate of such an oscillation or "brief duration" of unfolding of the world in

---

[300] Bohm, *Beyond Limits*. The source is an interview with Bill Angelos; the quoted dialogue begins 32:23 into the interview. The interview runs 1:08:13 total.

[301] Globus, *The Transparent Becoming of World*, 50.

space–time? Here again it is the Planck constant that sets the limiting boundary condition. The Planck second, or "Planck time," calculated to be 5.44×10^{-44} seconds, is the smallest conceivable time interval consistent with quantum theory, and below this interval time has no meaning. If indeed time is granulated at such a limit, then the cosmos may be created, destroyed, and recreated a staggering number of times per "human second." In the limiting case, space–time reality can be seen to emerge from an implicate order into an explicate order, from flux into space–time, at a recurring clock cycle every 5.44×10^{-44} seconds, only to collapse out space-time and back into the implicate order in alternate intervals between each of these sub-quantum clock cycles. Such a cyclic pattern of unfolding potential accords well with Bohm's description of the holomovement here, in a 1990 paper:

> All things found in the unfolded, explicate order emerge from the holomovement in which they are enfolded as *potentialities*, and ultimately they fall back into it. They endure only for some time, and while they last, their existence is sustained in a constant process of unfoldment and re-enfoldment, which gives rise to their relatively stable and independent forms in the explicate order.[302]

Meaning, Form, and Information

In developing an appreciation of the ontological and cosmological implications of quantum theory, Bohm placed

---

[302] Bohm, "A New Theory of the Relationship of Mind and Matter," 51.

great importance in maintaining a clear distinction regarding three terms: meaning, form, and information.

He describes the essential significance of form as being the conveyor and shipping container of embedded meaning:

> What is essential for a form to constitute information is that it shall have a meaning . . . . The form in the radio wave thus literally "informs" the energy in the received . . . this form is then *transformed* ("form carried across") into related forms of sound and light.[303]

How then is the meaning unpacked from the shipping container? How is information related to meaning? Bohm says that for information to become meaning requires, specifically, what Bohm terms "active information."[304]

> The basic idea of active information is that a *form*, having very little energy, enters into and directs a much greater energy. This notion of an original energy form acting to "inform," or put form into, a much larger energy has significant applications in many areas beyond quantum theory.[305]

For Bohm, active information is the state in which a receiving energy is informed by the *form* of a transmitted energy, the receiving energy is "in-formed." Here he gives as

---

[303] Bohm, "Meaning and Information," 45.

[304] Bohm and Peat, *Science, Order, and Creativity*, 84.

[305] Ibid.

an example a radio wave of electromagnetic energy being "in-formed"

> In the radio wave, the form is initially inactive, but as the form enters into the electrical energy of the receiver, we may say, that the information becomes active. In general, this information is only potentially active in the radio wave, but it becomes actually active only when and where there is a receiver which can respond to it with its "own energy."[306]

Bohm goes on to say that the operation of active information can be detected in nature outside of the human context, and can be seen, for example in the action of RNA as it decodes information locked in the form of DNA:

> it is assumed that the DNA molecule constitutes a code (i.e. a language), and that the RNA molecules "read" this code, and are thus in effect "informed" as to what kind of proteins they are to make.[307]

Finally, Bohm identifies the *activity* of the energy in the receiving entity as the *meaning*, (i.e., the active information flow *is* the meaning):

> I would like to suggest then that the activity, virtual or actual, in the energy and in the soma *is* the meaning of the information, rather than to say that the information affects an entity called

---

[306] Bohm, "Meaning and Information," 45.

[307] Ibid., 2.

the mind, which in turn operates somehow on the matter of the body.[308]

What Bohm is implying here is that perhaps there is, in actuality, no "thing" that can be called mind, that there is no "entity called the mind," but that, rather, it is the *active information* itself, sourced in the implicate domain, that is in-forming the region of the explicit domain, directly. Bohm concludes:

> The thinking process unfolds certain explicate thoughts, then folds back into the implicate, and then the next thought appears, the entire process forming a series of thoughts, which, seeming not too different, appear to be flowing in a continuous stream.[309]

Active Information and the Quantum Potential

To better understand "active information," imagine that from each Planck length diameter "point" or "holosphere" in the universe (but outside of space–time) radiating waves of information encoded energy emerge from the implicate domain at the center, radiating outward into space–time in expanding shells. Active information, like conceptual thought, does not need to be of great magnitude to be the effective cause of relatively large orders of magnitude of effect in the explicate domain. An example given by Bohm is the action of a tiny electrical signal that guides the flight of a large ship, airplane, or missile in flight. Here he provides a common example of how, even in the

---

[308] Ibid.

[309] Bohm, *Beyond Limits*, 5:30.

explicate world, a source of active information, comprising relatively minute quantities of energy, can effectively influence a receiver operating at considerably higher energy levels:

> As an example, let us take a radio wave, whose form carries information representing either sound or pictures. The radio wave itself has very little energy. The receiver, however, has a much greater energy (e.g. from the power source). The structure of the radio is such that the form carried by the radio wave is imposed on the much greater energy of the receiver.[310]

Here Bohm claims that it is not the magnitude of energy that is important for active information to be effective, but *only the form itself*, guiding larger sources of energy in the explicate system. Bohm developed his mathematics of active information by deriving a potential function directly from the Schrödinger equation in quantum mechanics, and designating it as Q, the "quantum potential":[311]

> As time went on, Bohm emphasized the role played by the quantum potential. The quantum potential—whose influence depends on its overall form and not on its strength—is totally unlike anything previously postulated in physics.[312]

---

[310] Ibid., 1.

[311] Globus, *The Transparent Becoming of the World*, 55.

[312] Peat, *Infinite Potential*, 220.

In order to prove that there is *real* causation acting in quantum mechanics, rather than accepting the commonly held theory that it is all probability and stochastic process, Bohm proposed that a quantum potential (Q) also acts upon quantum particles such as electrons and protons and states that this Q function

> expresses the activity of a new kind of implicate order. This implicate order is immensely more subtle than that of the original field, as well as more inclusive, in the sense that not only is the actual activity of the whole field enfolded in it, but also all its potentialities, along with the principles determining which of these shall become actual.[313]

Bohm derives the quantum potential mathematically by taking derivatives of quantum mechanical Hamiltonian models of particle motion to give the following equation for the quantum potential.[314]

$$Q = \frac{-h^2 \, \nabla^2 \, |\psi|^2}{2m \, |\psi|^2}$$

Equation 1. Equation of the Quantum Potential.[315]

In Bohm's equation of the quantum potential (Q) of active information, the function ψ is the quantum field or "wavefunction" derived from Schrödinger's equation, h is Planck's constant, and m is the mass of the electron or

---

[313] Bohm, "Hidden Variables and the Implicate Order," 43.

[314] Bohm and Peat, *Science, Order, and Creativity*, 81.

[315] Ibid.

"particle."[316] The symbol ∇ is called a "curl," and this symbol indicates an infinitesimal rotation of multidimensional coordinates (usually three or more) around a common origin, in order to obtain the differential motion of the wave in space–time. Bohm here points out what appears to be of special importance:

> What is mathematically significant in the above equation is that the wavefunction is found in both the numerator and the denominator.... The fact that ψ is contained both in the numerator and the denominator for Q means that Q is unchanged when ψ is multiplied by an arbitrary constant. In other words, the quantum potential Q is *independent of the strength, or intensity,* of the quantum field but *depends only on its form.* This is a particularly surprising result.[317]

Of great significance for Bohm is that fact that Q, the quantum potential, is seen to be independent of strength, or signal energy magnitude. This provides support for his insistence on causality, by implying that there is a formal cause, independent of magnitude, below the postulated randomness that is otherwise implied by the probabilistic calculations of quantum mechanics, and here Bohm concludes:

> "In the causal interpretation, the electron moves under its own energy, but the information in the

---

[316] Ibid.

[317] Ibid., 82. Italics added.

146

form of the quantum wave directs the energy of the electron."[318]

This can be visualized in the figure below, (Fig. 12, "Active Information and the Quantum Wave"), in which the function *Q*, sourced in the implicate order, molds or informs the quantum wave ψ in the explicate order. Here the metaphor of waves influencing the course of a ship is applicable.

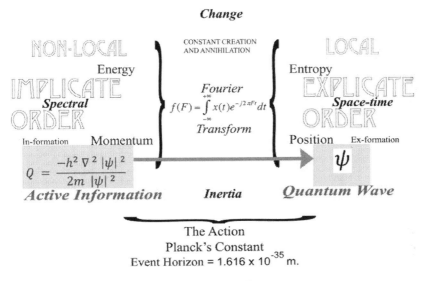

Figure 12. Active Information and the Quantum Wave. Graphic by author.

In fact, a "pilot wave theory" similar to Bohm's active information model was proposed by de Broglie in 1927, though his idea was immediately criticized by the skeptical Wolfgang Pauli for being untestable.[319] In consequence, de

---

[318] Ibid.

[319] Bohm and Hiley, *The Undivided Universe*, 38–39.

Broglie abandoned his suggestion in favor of probability theory, but some years later Bohm brought up the idea again when he published, in 1952, "A Suggested Interpretation of the Quantum Theory in Terms of 'Hidden Variables.'"[320]

In the figure, the Active Information function can be seen to be guiding the Quantum Wavefunction. Bohm here provides another example of *form* as active information in everyday human experience:

> It is clear, of course, that the notion of active information also applies directly to human experience. For example, when the form of a road sign is apprehended in the brain and nervous system, the form is immediately active as meaning.[321]

But not all information is active, and Bohm refers to information which is not active as *virtual information*, "the activity of meaning may be only virtual, rather than actual. Virtual activity is more than a mere potentiality . . . it is a kind of suspended action."[322] And until it is made explicate as active information, this virtual information exists only in the implicate domain.

Indeed, Bohm's logic leads him to the conclusion that consciousness, at least of the nonactive kind, ("non-minding" as Karl Pribram might have said) is of, or resides "within," the implicate order (though, of course, the word "within" has no clear meaning for the spaceless, timeless

---

[320] Ibid., 399.

[321] Bohm, "Meaning and Information," 45.

[322] Ibid., 46.

implicate order.) And while he speaks of the actual "substance" of consciousness as residing primarily in the implicate order, he sees the ranges of "human experience" of consciousness residing in reality as a whole, in a continuum of the implicate/explicate orders:

> In some sense, consciousness (which we take to include thought, feeling, desire, will, etc.) is to be comprehended in terms of the implicate order, along with reality as a whole ... the actual "substance" of consciousness can be understood in terms of the notion that the implicate order is also its primary and immediate actuality.[323]

Bohm goes on to point out that some forms of information *from within* the implicate order are perceived, or can be perceived, by modes of consciousness in the explicate order: "Evidently this order is *active* in the sense that it continually flows into emotional, physical, and other responses." And here he provides as an example, music: "In listening to music, *one is therefore directly perceiving an implicate order.*"[324] But it is not only in listening to music that consciousness resonates in the implicate order, but also in ordinary, everyday experience, as Bohm says, perhaps even further:

> A great deal of our difficulty comes from the fact that we accept the idea that not only matter, but all of our experience as well, is in the explicate order, and then suddenly we want to connect this up with consciousness, which is of a totally different order ... we should consider the nature

[323] Bohm, *Wholeness and the Implicate Order*, 196–97.

[324] Ibid., 200.

149

of ordinary, everyday experience. I say that it is totally misunderstood, that it is actually part of the implicate order . . . in that order everything contacts everything else and thus there is no intrinsic reason why the paranormal should be impossible.[325]

In a 1978 interview at the Krishnamurti center in Ojai, by which time Bohm had been practicing meditation for over a decade, Bohm comments on distinctions between different modes of consciousness, and how it may be possible to experience the implicate order as a mode of consciousness which is timeless:

> **Question**: When mystics use the visualization of light they don't use it only as a metaphor, to them it seems to be a reality. Have they tapped into matter and energy at a level where time is absent?
>
> **Bohm**: It may well be. That's one way of looking at it. As I've suggested the mind has two-dimensional and three-dimensional modes of operation. It may be able to operate directly in the depths of the implicate order where this timeless state is the primary actuality. Then we could see the ordinary actuality as a secondary structure that emerges as an overtone on the primary structure . . . . The ordinary consciousness is one kind of music, and the other kind of consciousness is the other kind of music.[326]

---

[325] Bohm, "The Physicist and the Mystic," 196.

[326] Bohm, "The Implicate Order and the Super-Implicate Order," 45–46.

The Sense of "I" and the Implicate Order

Bohm argues that none of this indicates that consciousness and the world of matter are absolutely separate, as assumed by Cartesian dualists. Consciousness and matter form a continuum, a whole, as Bohm says here in the final words of his last book, *The Undivided Universe*, and he uses the metaphor of a mirror:

> At no stage is there a break in this process.... There is no need, therefore, to regard the observer as basically separate from what he sees, nor to reduce him to an epiphenomenon of the objective process. Indeed, the notion of separateness is an abstraction and an approximation valid for only certain limited purposes. More broadly one could say that through the human being, *the universe is making a mirror to observe itself*.... All proposals are points of departure for exploration. Eventually some of them may be developed so far that we may take them as working hypotheses.[327]

Here it may be useful to examine the conception of dualism versus monism. In Fig. 13, "Dualism vs. Monism," Cartesian dualism, denoted to the left, contrasts with three positions of Monism; Bohm's "neutral monism" can be seen in the lower right on the diagram, where matter and mind are both shown as derivative (both are in Bohm's explicate order of space–time), while the fundamental "3rd substance" would be Bohm's implicate order.

---

[327] Bohm, *The Undivided Universe*, 389–90. Italics added.

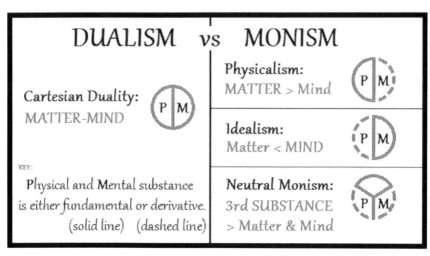

DUALISM vs MONISM

Cartesian Duality: MATTER-MIND

Physicalism: MATTER > Mind

Idealism: Matter < MIND

KEY: Physical and Mental substance is either *fundamental* or *derivative*. (solid line) (dashed line)

Neutral Monism: 3rd SUBSTANCE > Matter & Mind

Figure 13. Dualism vs. monism. Graphic by Dewynne (2012). Reprinted under the terms of a Creative Commons CC0 1.0 Universal Public Domain Dedication. Image retrieved from Wikimedia Commons.

In an interview videotaped in Amsterdam in September of 1990, by the Dutch Public Television Network, Bohm discusses the phenomenon of the sense of Self, that sense that individuals have of being "I," and in his interview he states clearly that this sense of self is a *product* of thought, and not the real situation. Rather, he points to the implicate order as being the source of deeper reality, as being the true "I," "the Me" which we all assume to be so very unique:

> **Bohm**: Remember, thought is conditioned reflex at a very high subtle level. It just goes by itself, but it has in it the thought that thought is being produced by a center, which it calls "Me." And all the feelings, which should belong to that center, are thrown onto Consciousness as if from "Me," right?

> **Interviewer**: And our society reinforces that.

Bohm: Everybody says the same thing, like everybody sees the same rainbow, everybody sees the same "Self," whether it's there or not.

In fact, it becomes all-important, the concept is regarded as central and supremely important. All sorts of powerful feelings will arise if it's questioned. You see, now, it all goes on by itself...and, you see... ...there's a deeper being, I say, which can...which is...that being which may be able to reveal itself anew...rather than being a fixed being...it's deep in the Implicate Order...in the Infinite.

Interviewer: So, thought creates "the Me," rather than "Me" creating the thought?

Bohm: Yes. If you don't see that happening, you will treat that as real and give it apparent reality. The whole being will take actions on that basis which seems to be coming from the center.[328]

Bohm's Quantum Theories and Consciousness

Bohm's interest, like Pribram's, also lay in trying to understand and map consciousness and its role in cosmology, an area outside of the normal range of inquiry in both their respective professional careers. Bohm was forthright in his inclusion of consciousness as an important aspect of his quantum cosmology. According to Bohm there is a two-phase reciprocal movement or holomovement at the boundary of (between) the implicate order and the explicate order, [329] and in a 1978 interview, he states

---

[328] Bohm, *Beyond Limits*, 5:30.

[329] Peat, *Infinite Potential: The Life and Times of David Bohm.*

153

unequivocally, "Let me propose that consciousness is basically in the implicate order."[330]

In the closing words of his final published work, Bohm reifies his proposal that consciousness and quantum mechanics are connected, that "they have the implicate order in common."[331]

> Several physicists have already suggested that quantum mechanics and consciousness are closely related and that the understanding of the quantum formalism requires that ultimately we bring in consciousness in some role or other ... the intuition that consciousness and quantum theory are in some sense related seems to be a good one .... Our proposal in this regard is that the basic relationship of quantum theory and consciousness is that they have the implicate order in common.[332]

Bohm's Waves Coming into and Going Out of a Point

David Bohm saw a similar process underlying what proponents of quantum mechanics theorized to be simply "quantum jump" of energy, and here in an interview, he describes the reality as waves coming in to a point and waves coming out of a point, for all points in the holoplenum:

---

[330] Bohm, "The Enfolding-Unfolding Universe," 62.

[331] Bohm and Hiley, *The Undivided Universe*, 381.

[332] Ibid., 381–82.

Angelos: Could we... Again, the term "quantum" itself has its base in?

Bohm: Well, the "quantum"... That's one of the features of "quantum"... The quantum has its base in the fact that energy is transferred in discrete jumps or "quanta" rather than continuously...

Angelos: I see.

Bohm: Now, you can see that some sort of quantum appears here... the wave comes to a point, then there is a jump to another point. See one thing—according to quantum theory—was that the electron could go from one state to another without passing in between. Now you said: That is an utter mystery, right? But you see, if the wave comes in to this point... then it spreads out... it could come in to another point. So, therefore, it needn't look so mysterious.[333]

To more fully grasp the relationship of consciousness to the implicate order and the explicate order, two visual metaphors are now considered: the metaphor of the micro black hole, and the metaphor of the Yin/Yang symbol.

Metaphor of the Quantum Black Hole

It is appropriate here to use the image of a quantum black hole as a visual metaphor for realizing the topology of the implicate order.

Micro black holes, which have also been called quantum mechanical black holes, quantum black holes, or mini black holes, are hypothetical tiny

---

[333] Bohm, *Beyond Limits*, 7:20.

black holes . . . . It is possible that such quantum primordial black holes were created in the high-density environment of the early Universe (or Big Bang). [334]

Visualizing the implicate order as a micro black hole, we can perhaps view its boundary as a spherical event-horizon shell, marking the limits of an "external," explicate order and the outer limits of an "internal," implicate order. Below the surface of such a sphere, of diameter equal to the Planck length, lies a transcendental implicate order, while outside the quantum black hole begins a universe of the explicate order, replete with time and space.

With this image in mind, it is appropriate here to review the topological understanding of a "point," in preparation for an examination of Teilhard de Chardin's concept of the "Omega Point" as discussed in Chapter 6.[335] The conventional definition of a point is a mathematical one, that it has no diameter at all, or that it is a sort of sphere with an infinitely small diameter. But a cosmological understanding of the point, considering that below the Planck length there is no space as we know it, the closest approximation to a point in space–time would seem to be a micro black hole of Planck length diameter.

Metaphor of the Yin/Yang Symbol

Bohm's cotemporaneous enfolding/unfolding process can be visually captured in the Yin/Yang symbol (Fig. 14),

---

[334] Carr and Giddings, "Quantum Black Holes."

[335] Teilhard, "The Nature of Point Omega."

attributcd historically to Chinese Taoist sages of the third century BCE.[336]

Figure 14. Implicate/explicate as yin/yang.[337] Graphic by Alkari (2013). Public domain image under the terms of Title 17, Chapter 1, Section 105 of the US Code Image retrieved from Wikimedia Commons.

In the Yin/Yang symbol, one side can be taken to represent a timeless, spaceless implicate order, and the other side can be seen as the expressed space–time explicate order. And yet each one is also at the heart of the other (designated by the dots in the two regions of the symbol).

It is of interest to note that the physicist Niels Bohr, famous for his visionary conception of electrons moving in fixed orbits around the nucleus of an atom, selected this Taoist symbol for his personal seal to adorn his "coat of

---

[336] Wong, *The Shambhala Guide to Taoism*, 124–31.

[337] This is the Taoist yin-yang symbol, with black representing yin and white representing yang. It is a symbol that reflects the inescapably intertwined duality of all things in nature, a common theme in Taoism.

arms" on the occasion of receiving the Royal Danish Award for Physics (Fig. 15).[338]

Figure 15. Niels Bohr and his coat of arms. Above left: Graphic by Bain (2012). Public domain image under the terms of Title 17, Chapter 1, Section 105 of the US Code; above right: Graphic by Fulvio314 (2013). Reprinted under the terms of a Creative Commons Attribution ShareAlike 3.0 Unported license. Image retrieved from Wikimedia Commons.

That an ancient Taoist symbol might capture so well the essence of a cosmological process that theoretical quantum physicists have only arrived at in the twentieth century speaks well for the efficacy of human consciousness in previous ages and cultures for perceiving the mechanics of the cosmos via shamanic, contemplative experience.

---

[338] Globus, *Quantum Closures and Disclosures*, 175.

Chapter 5: The Holoflux Field Theory of Consciousness

"Words   strain,
Crack and sometimes break, under the burden,
Under   the   tension,   slip,   slide,   perish,
Decay with imprecision, will not stay in place,
Will not stay still."[339]

–T. S. Eliot, "Burnt Norton," (1935)

T. S. Eliot's warning here is appropriate for introducing this chapter, in which an effort is made to use words to describe a topology of an abstraction in which we attempt to integrate the theories of Bohm and Pribram. However, in *The Holographic Universe*, the writer Michael Talbot succinctly integrates the two holonomic principles:

> Considered together, Bohm and Pribram's theories provide a profound new way of looking at the world: Our brains mathematically construct objective reality by interpreting frequencies that are ultimately projections from another dimension, a deeper order of existence that is beyond both space and time: The brain is a hologram enfolded in a holographic universe.[340]

That David Bohm and Karl Pribram influenced one another and became both professional and personal friends has been noted. In Fig. 16 can be seen the two enjoying

---

[339] Eliot, *Collected Poems 1909–1962*, 176.

[340] Talbot, *The Holographic Universe*, 54.

themselves in Prague, with Bohm's wife, Saral, just four months before Bohm's death in October 1992.

In this chapter the ontological platform begun with the Pribram/Bohm holonomic theories is extended through integration with properties of the electromagnetic field implicated by Pribram's approach to holonomic brain theory.

Figure 16. David Bohm and Karl Pribram in Prague, June 1992.[341] Photo by Katherine Neville. Reprinted with permission.

The holoflux field theory of consciousness is described here as a process of an energy of awareness transforming in and out of two domains: the explicate and the implicate.

The theory is supported by a set of concepts from physics, electrical engineering, and mathematics. These concepts (bulleted below) are developed in this chapter through use of verbal description, analogy, and topological

---

[341] Neville, "Saral and David Bohm," picture 8.

diagrams, with minimal recourse to equations or mathematical notation. In each case, focus is upon the ontological meaning of each concept:

- the Planck constant

- the holoplenum

- Wheeler's "Self-observing U"

- frequencies

- wavelengths

- Wien's law

- information

- superposition

- resonance

- dimensional analysis

The Planck Constant ($\hbar$)

Bohm makes frequent reference to a fundamental numerical value, the Planck length of 10^{-33} cm, widely used in quantum mechanical calculations, and derived from "the Planck constant" (denoted in calculations as $\hbar$). In speaking on the implicate order, Bohm states:

> It must be remembered that even this vast sea of cosmic energy takes into account only what happens on a scale larger than the critical length of 10^{-33} cm .... But this length is only a certain kind of limit

on the applicability of ordinary notions of space and time. To suppose that there is nothing beyond this limit at all would indeed be quite arbitrary. Rather, it is very probable that beyond it lies a further domain.[342]

In 1900 the Berlin physicist Max Planck (Fig. 17), like Bohm decades later, found himself dissatisfied with what he saw as a problem with the tendency toward over-reliance on mathematical statistics, rather than the attempt to discern some mechanism which would explain more clearly the underlying reality of the phenomenon of energy and thermodynamics.

---

[342] Bohm, *Wholeness and the Implicate Order*, 193.

Figure 17. Portrait of Max Planck, 1878. Graphic by Jbarta (2014). This work is in the public domain under the terms of Title 17, Chapter 1, Section 105 of the US Code.

In his 1879 doctoral thesis, Planck discussed two major approaches to the second law of thermodynamics that were at the forefront of the physics of his day: one theory stressed the use of mathematically continuous equations to model unbroken flows of radiant field energy, while the other theory, the "atomist" theory, held that since matter is not continuous, it is preferable to apply statistics to calculate the mechanical motions of atoms and molecules in thermodynamics processes.[343] Planck felt that the atomist approach, relying as it did on statistical calculations, was masking the underlying realities. Over the next 20 years his research focused on the search for a nonstatistical mathematical model to reflect the ontological realities that linked radiation and the phenomenon of "heat."

On December 14, 1900, a date "widely acknowledged to be the date on which the quantum revolution began," Planck presented his derivation of a new radiation equation to a meeting of the German Physical Society, and in his presentation stated, "We therefore regard—and this is the most essential point of the entire calculation—energy to be composed of a very definite number of equal finite packages."[344] He went on to describe the constant in the equation which he had derived (later to be called the "Planck constant"), and stated that, "since it has the dimensions of a product of energy and time, I called it the elementary quantum of action." Planck postulated that

[343] Baggott, *The Quantum Story*, 7–8.

[344] Ibid., 15.

electromagnetic energy both absorbed and emitted only in these elementary quanta of actions, or discrete packets of energy, which he also referred to as "energy elements." Planck's new theory, and his constant, published a month later in a 1901 issue of the journal *Annalen der Physik*, soon became a cornerstone of quantum mechanics.[345]

Earlier, in 1893, William Wien had discovered a mathematical relationship that allowed him to calculate the peak frequency of electromagnetic radiation for a given temperature, but his equations were only accurate for extremely high temperatures. Planck's paper solved the problem by assuming that any measurable electromagnetic fluctuation for a given temperature must consist of a unique spectrum of discrete frequencies, an integral set of separately calculable single frequency oscillators, each one making its own radiant contribution to the whole. Using his derived constant, Planck was able to calculate precisely the energy, E, radiating in all directions from a theoretical "point" for a given macro "temperature."[346] The accepted value of this constant, as determined by Planck, is $\hbar$ = 6.62606957 x 10^{-34} Joule-seconds.[347]

The Planck constant was derived specifically from other fundamentally agreed upon physical constants, including gravity and the speed of light. In presenting his constant, Planck expressed the importance of this constant in rather mystical terms, claiming that the discovery paved the way for, as he described:

---

[345] Ibid., 15.

[346] Planck, "On the Law of Distribution of Energy in the Normal Spectrum."

[347] Ibid.

The possibility of establishing units of length, mass, time and temperature which are independent of specific bodies or materials and which necessarily maintain their meaning for all time and for all civilizations, even those which are extraterrestrial and nonhuman, constants which therefore can be called with surety, "the fundamental physical units of measurement."[348]

In his 1901 paper, Planck presented a simple equation to describe the energy output of a single "energy element" or "quantum." The equation is:

$$\varepsilon = h\nu$$

In this equation the first term, ε, the energy element, is equal to the product of the constant (Planck's constant, **h**) times the frequency, ν. The use of the constant **h** to unify, or normalize, the basic cosmological constants in physical calculations was immediately found to be so useful to simplify previously complex calculations, that the number was soon referred to as "Planck's constant," although in reality his discovery involved a set of constants, several of which are listed here in Table 2.[349]

---

[348] Baggott, *The Quantum Story*, 11.

[349] Benenson, Harris, Stocker, and Holger, *Handbook of Physics*.

Table 2
Several Plank Constants

Constant	Value
Length	1.616199×10^{-35} meter
Time	5.39106×10^{-44} seconds
Area	2.6121×10^{-70} square meter
Power	3.62831×10^{52} watts

Note. Data adapted from Benenson et al. (2006), *Handbook of Physics*, 47. Author's table.

In the spring of 1905, a 26-year-old named Albert Einstein published four papers, soon to become famous in the world of physics. His first paper extended Planck's theory to include light, by asserting that Planck's radiation law only made sense if radiant energy of all wavelengths consists of discrete packets of energy, which Einstein called "light-quanta," or "photons."[350]

To obtain a better feel for the magnitude and use of these constants, let us calculate the velocity of one photon as it travels the distance of one Planck length in one Planck second. The equation for velocity is: velocity = length / time. If we substitute the Planck values for length and time (values found in Table 2), the velocity of a photon at the Planck level can be calculated as follows:

---

[350] Baggott, *The Quantum Story*, 21.

The equation: *Velocity* = Planck Length/Planck Time

The values used: Planck Length = 1.616199×10^{-35} meter
                   Planck Time = 5.391060×10^{-44} seconds

Substituting: ***Velocity*** = 1.616199×10^{-35} meter /
                   5.39106×10^{-44} seconds

Results in the following velocity of the photon:

Velocity = 2.99792×10^{8} meters / second

This happens to be the exact speed of light in a vacuum.

If we try to move faster by decreasing the time it takes to move the same distance, the denominator in the velocity equation would have to be a smaller value, and a smaller value in the denominator would make the equation produce a higher velocity, violating the ceiling to the speed of light in a vacuum. Conversely, if we keep the same time interval and try to increase the distance travelled to something greater than the Planck length, we would again be increasing the velocity, exceeding the speed of light. Accordingly, there can exist no measurable (or conceivable) space smaller than that of the Planck length, and there can be no time interval smaller than that of the Planck second.

The Planck "second," then, at roughly 10^{-44} human "seconds," is the smallest possible time measurement, according to quantum mechanics, and is understood as a time period below which time has no meaning.[351] According to contemporary models of cosmological origin, this number

---

[351] Wheeler, *A Journey into Gravity and Spacetime.*

also happens to be the time marked as the very beginning of our universe, at which time expansion into space began:

> The early inflationary universe is proposed to have had an accelerated expansion, the duration of which depends on the particular inflationary model. In any case, inflation is believed to have lasted an extremely short time: in the range of 10^{-33}–10^{-35} sec. In particular, in the chaotic inflationary model, inflation starts at the Planck time, $t_p = 10^{-44}$ sec.[352]

Similarly, the Planck length (at 10^{-35} meters, or its equivalent, 10^{-33} cm) is the smallest measurable length in physically defined space, below which space as we know it has no meaning. Below the Planck length one cannot say "smaller," because there is no spatial dimension definable below 10^{-35} meters. It is worth considering the contrast, between the Planck length of at 10^{-35} meters, and the diameter of a proton at 10^{-15} meters. The proton is enormous at an order of 20 magnitudes larger than a sphere of Planck length diameter.

It is also of interest to examine the last entry in the list of Planck constants shown in Table 2, the "Power" value, which indicates that a photon vibrating at the dimensional frequency corresponding to one Planck wavelength contains unimaginable power. The raw power flowing out from all of the stars in the known universe has been estimated to be 2×10^{49} watts.[353] The Planck Power, by contrast, has been calculated to be an incredible 10^{52} watts, three orders of

---

[352] Zizzi, "Consciousness and Logic in a Quantum Computing Universe," 459–60.

[353] Ledrew, "The Real Starry Sky."

magnitude *greater* than the luminosity of all of the stars in the visible universe combined.[354]

While quantum physics indicates that below the limiting Planck length there can be no space–time as we know it, Bohm predicts that it is precisely there, below the inner space–time boundary, that manifests a nonspatial, nontemporal domain which he identifies as "the implicate order."[355] The relationship of explicate order to implicate order should not necessarily be understood as a one-to-one relationship. On the contrary, as Bohm conjectures here, in a 1987 paper, there may in fact be *multiple explicate orders* (supporting the widely held "multiverse hypothesis"), suborders of a single, omni-connected implicate order:

> The principles of organization of such an implicate order can even define a unique explicate order, as a particular and distinguished sub-order, in which all the elements are relatively independent and externally related. To put it differently, the explicate order itself may be obtainable from the implicate order as a special and determinate sub-order that is contained within it.[356]

The Sub-Quantum Holosphere

We have seen that Bohm proposes two orders, an explicate (space–time) order and what he terms "an implicate order beyond the critical limit of 10^{-33} cm," a sub-

---

[354] Benenson, Harris, Stocker, and Holger, *Handbook of Physics*.

[355] Bohm, *Wholeness and the Implicate Order*, 190.

[356] Bohm, "Hidden Variables and the Implicate Order," 44.

quantum (below space–time) order.[357] Having established the relative location of these two domains, it is useful to further identify the structural relationship of the implicate order to the explicate order by considering another image. The previous metaphor (Fig. 9) was presented in the image of an "ocean depth," visualized in a vertical "up/down" geometry, having a "sub-quantum bottom" at the Planck depth of 10^{-33} cm. This ocean depth metaphor can be improved with a new metaphor based upon cosmology, that of a three-dimensional "outer/inner" shell of spherical geometry.

In the following diagram (Fig. 18, "A Sub-Quantum Holosphere"), the implicate order is seen as having its origin at the center of space, beginning at a spherical shell with a Planck length diameter of 10^{-33} cm, manifesting a spherical region that the physicist Paola Zizzi calls a "fuzzy quantum black hole."[358] According to Zizzi, "its event horizon is a fuzzy sphere."[359] Here, within the deepest "inside" possible in a space–time universe and located at the geometric center of every point in the space–time universe, lies the implicate order. In the figure, the sub-quantum holosphere or implicate order is depicted at the center of a spherical explicate region of the space–time universe, at the boundary separating time from the nontemporal. The holosphere is fixed and does not move, while around it move waves of space–time energy. The previous scale from Fig. 9 is shown

---

[357] Ibid., 100.

[358] Zizzi, "Consciousness and Logic in a Quantum Computing Universe," 469.

[359] Ibid., 468.

here as a radius extending outward from the implicate order within the central sub-quantum holosphere.

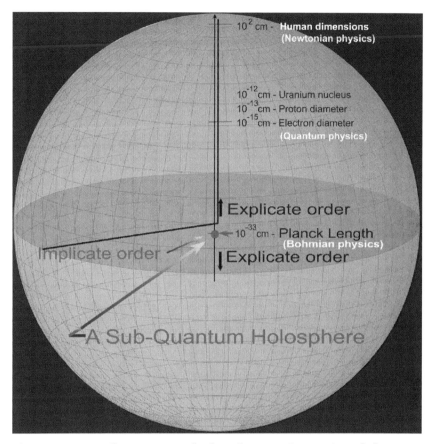

Figure 18. A sub-quantum holosphere. Dimensional data from Benenson et al. (2006), Handbook of Physics. Graphic by author.

Again, the words of the poet T. S. Eliot may here be appropriate:

> And do not call it fixity,
> Where past and future are gathered. Neither
> movement from nor towards,
> Neither ascent nor decline. Except for the point,
> the still point,

There would be no dance, and there is only the dance.[360]

The Sub-Quantum Holoplenum

This concept of a sub-quantum holosphere is mirrored both in Bohm's conceptualization of the implicate order as well as in contemporary theories of quantum computing, where quantum black holes are seen to carry and store information in the event horizon, described here by P. Zizzi, a physicist at the University of Pavia, Italy:

> The event horizon of such a quantum black hole is the surface of a fuzzy sphere.... Fuzzy quantum black holes and quantum human minds can be viewed as subroutines of the whole quantum-computing universe.... This cosmic network exploits quantum communication complexity, and, thanks to entanglement, allows its parts to accomplish a distributed task without the need of any kind of communication. This is possible because all its parts share a common quantum space–time background, which is nonlocal.[361]

The physicist John Wheeler (1911–2008) has hypothesized that a considerable amount of information is storable on the surface boundary of a spherical black hole. His theory is discussed in detail elsewhere in this chapter, but here it is worth mentioning that his calculations indicate that the surface boundary of a one-centimeter diameter

---

[360] Eliot, *Four Quartets*, 16.

[361] Zizzi, "Consciousness and Logic in a Quantum Computing Universe," 468–69.

spherical black hole is capable of storing 10^{64} bits of information.[362] Compared even to the total number of stars in the universe, which has been estimated to be 10^{24}, this is a great deal of potentially storable information.[363]

Assuming the existence of a sub-quantum holosphere, the next question to ask would be how many might there be, underlying our universe? Perhaps to coincide with Big Bang theory there was only one, out of which the universe of space–time emerged. An alternate approach would be to imagine the universe as consisting of an infinity of quantum black holes, each one having a diameter of the Planck length. In such a model, the implicate order would be distributed evenly, to be found at the center, everywhere, throughout the space–time cosmos. Bohm describes such a model, arguing here for a cosmological bedrock of actuality, which he calls "the plenum."[364]

> It is being suggested here, then, that what we perceive through the senses as empty space is actually the plenum, which is the ground for the existence of everything, including ourselves. The things that appear to our senses are derivative forms and their true meaning can be seen only when we consider the plenum, in which they are generated and sustained, and into which they must ultimately vanish.[365]

---

[362] Wheeler, *A Journey into Gravity and Spacetime*, 222.

[363] Van Dokkum and Conroy, "A Substantial Population of Low-Mass Stars."

[364] Ibid.

[365] Bohm, *Wholeness and the Implicate Order*, 191–92.

Bohm points out that in early Greece, the philosophers Parmenides and Zeno also held that "space is a plenum." [366] Here, located in a communion of Planck holosphere, we find a plausible explanation for the peculiar observed phenomenon that the universe, from every point, appears to be expanding outwardly, directed radially *away from each point*; thus, in the space–time universe, the center is everywhere:

> Relativity assumes that the universe will appear much the same no matter where the observer happens to be situated. The nebulae appear to be rushing away from our particular position, and they will appear to be rushing away from any other position in which an observer is located. [367]

Thus we hypothesize this Bohmian holospheric plenum, like some sea-floor bed of existence, to be discoverable at the center of every conceivable coordinate in space–time; the concept can be seen resonating vibrantly in the title of Jean Gebser's magnum opus, *The Ever-Present Origin*. [368] We can find the same image resonating in T. S. Eliot's "still point of the turning world." [369]

> O hidden under the dove's wing, hidden in the turtle's   breast,

---

[366] Ibid., 191.

[367] Kuehn, *A Student's Guide Through the Great Physics Texts: Vol 1*, 332.

[368] Gebser, *The Ever-Present Origin: Part One: Foundations of the Aperspectival World*.

[369] Eliot, *Four Quartets*, 15.

Under the palm tree at noon, under the running water
At the still point of the turning world. O hidden.[370]

                           –T. S. Eliot, "Coriolan," (1931)

We also hypothesize that this center of the cosmos, the origin, located everywhere throughout the cosmos, is the same origin that Teilhard defines as "point Omega."[371] Having established the ontological basis of a plenum, Bohm goes further to envision what he terms "the holomovement," the dynamics of energy processing within this plenum, an "immense sea of energy," flowing within and between the non-time-space domains of the implicate and the explicate orders:

> This sea is to be understood in terms of a multidimensional implicate order, while the universe of matter as we generally observe it is to be treated as a comparatively small pattern of excitation. This excitation pattern is relatively autonomous and gives rise to approximately recurrent, stable and separable projections into a three-dimensional explicate order of manifestation, which is more or less equivalent to that of space as we commonly experience it.[372]

---

[370] Eliot, *Collected Poems 1909–1962*, 126.

[371] Teilhard, "Life and the Planets," 122. Essay written in 1945.

[372] Bohm, *Wholeness and the Implicate Order*, 192.

This region of implicate order, the holoplenum (Fig. 19), is here visualized as consisting of close-packed holospheres, each a sphere bounded by the Planck limit of 10⁻³³ cm.

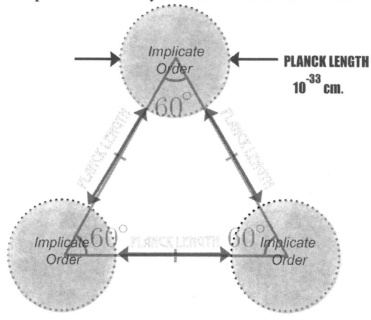

Figure 19. Holoplenum formed by implicate order. Graphic by author.

Because each holosphere can come no closer than one Planck length to neighboring holospheres, simple geometry insures that in a single plane these holospheres form equilateral triangles, and in three dimensions the holospheres of the holoplenum would thus form regular tetrahedrons in close-packed configuration (Fig. 20). This geometry aligns with the prediction of the architect and systems theorist Buckminster Fuller, who wrote that the natural analytic geometry of the universe is based on arrays of tetrahedra; Fuller supported his conjecture with the fact that the strongest possible homogeneous truss is cyclically tetrahedral.[373]

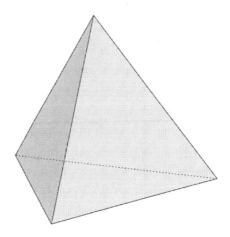

Figure 20. A regular three-dimensional tetrahedron. Graphic by author.

Fuller's idea, that a three-dimensional tetrahedron may be a natural underlying geometry of nature, has been reinforced by the discovery, in 2013, that DNA strands at the nanostructure level form stable three-dimensional tetrahedrons and therefore are suitably scalable for nanotechnology engineering:

> The physicochemical stability of DNA makes it a desirable candidate for the design of nanostructure materials as DNA is inherently nanoscalable . . . . The DNA nanostructure consists of six single-stranded oligonucleotides

[373] Edmondson, *The Synergetic Geometry of R. Buckminster Fuller*, 19.

that hybridize to form a *three-dimensional tetrahedron.*[374]

In addition to operating within a geometrically maximally stable plenum, any phenomena at the Planck dimension would also operate at the highest frequency rate possible in space–time, simply because at this smallest dimension would also be found the smallest wavelength, both being equal to one Planck length. According to Wien's law (the higher the frequency, the higher the energy), at the smallest wavelength possible, at the Planck length, would also be found the highest energy.[375]

Wheeler's Self-Observing U

"Truth is less than truth until it is made known."[376]
–John Archibald Wheeler

In the context of consciousness, another visual metaphor is revealing, congruent with Bohm's cosmology. The metaphor can be seen in a relational diagram drawn by the Princeton physicist John Archibald Wheeler (1911–2008). Wheeler had worked closely with Bohr in the late 1930s, was a Princeton colleague of Bohm's in the late 1940s, and thesis advisor to a young Richard Feynman, who received the Nobel Prize in Physics in 1965.[377]

---

[374] Rendek, Fromme, Grotjohann, and Fromme, "Three-Dimensional DNA Nanostructure," 141.

[375] Bohm, *Quantum Theory*, 6.

[376] Wheeler, *A Journey into Gravity and Spacetime*, v.

[377] Baggott, *The Quantum Story*, 242.

Wheeler used a visual metaphor (Fig. 21), which he termed the "Self-Observing U," to help understand the quantum theoretical observation and creation of an actual entity, within an explicate (space–time) universe. As Wheeler explains here in his 1998 memoir, *Geons, Black Holes, and Quantum Foam*, he views the universe as a self-excited circuit:

> Not all potentiality is converted to actuality in any finite time . . . . My diagram of a big U (for universe) attempts to illustrate this idea. The upper left end of the U represents the Big Bang, when it all started. Moving down along the thin left leg and up along the thick right leg of the U symbolically traces the evolution of the universe, from small to large—time enough for life and mind to develop. At the upper right of the U sits, finally, the eye of the observer. By looking back, by observing what happened in the earliest days of the universe, we give reality to those days. The eye could as well be a piece of mica. It need not be part of an intelligent being. The point is that the universe is a grand synthesis, putting itself together all the time as a whole.[378]

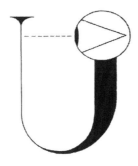

---

[378] Wheeler, *Geons, Black Holes, and Quantum Foam*, 338.

Figure 21. Wheeler's self-observing U. Graphic by author.[379]

The figure also supports Bohm's conjecture that there is no separation between the observing instrument and what is observed, as he elaborates here:

> For example, you are looking at this table; the form of this table has been built up by your experience which you are projecting into the table. Is the table you, or is it something separate from you? You appreciate it as a table with a certain form and a certain subsistence, but that form and that subsistence are as much you as the table. If you probed it with a very high energy machine, say with neutrinos, they would go right through, and the table would be a vaporous nebula. So the form of the table as a solid substance, or subsistence, comes from the human brain with its own particular mode of interacting. In a sense, the observer is the observed.[380]

That this paragraph on perception sounds a great deal like passages from Karl Pribram's 1972 *Languages of the Brain* is likely no coincidence, as Bohm had previously met Pribram at a Krishnamurti conference in Ojai, and the two had become personal acquaintances and shared many ideas over the preceding five years.[381]

---

[379] Modified from figure captioned, "Does looking back 'now' give reality to what happened 'then'?"; see Wheeler, *Geons, Black Holes, and Quantum Foam*, 339.

[380] Bohm, *A Question of Physics: Conversations in Physics and Biology*, 132.

[381] Pribram, *The Form Within*.

Creation and Dissolution of the Universe

In the same sense that a digital computer system has a clock-cycle to which all events are synchronized, what might be the underlying clock-cycle of the universe? According to quantum theory, the clock-cycle can be no less than the Planck second, for, as previously discussed, any time unit smaller than Planck time has no meaning. As Bohm's colleague, the physicist Hiley states:

> The explicate "moments" that unfold have a certain temporal thickness, a certain duration. Moments are temporal segmentations of unfoldment.... This is "a moment where *what has been* is separated from *what is yet to come.*" Within this brief duration time becomes nonlocal.[382]

Thus there is separation, and a cycling between local and nonlocal time, and this can be no less than the Planck length. Figure 22 illustrates such a hypothetical clock-cycle with a Planck-limited value of 5.39106×10^{-44} seconds as the clock cycles the cosmos on and off, in and out, forming the digital holoflux.

---

[382] Globus, *The Transparent Becoming of World*, 132.

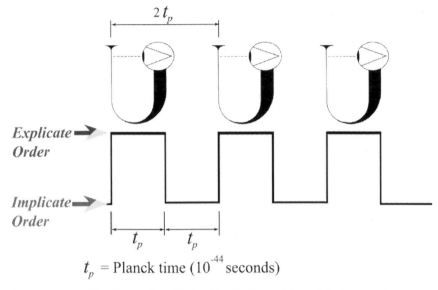

t_p = Planck time (10^{-44} seconds)

Figure 22. Clock-cycle: digital holoflux. Graphic by author.

This theoretical explicate/implicate digital clock cycle is supported in quantum theory by the concept of "quantum fluctuations," described here by Wheeler:

> Space—pure, empty, energy-free space—all the time and everywhere experiences so-called quantum fluctuations at a fantastically small scale of time, of the order of 10^{-44} second and less. During these quantum fluctuations, pairs of particles appear for an instant from the emptiness of space—perhaps an electron and an antielectron pair or a proton and an antiproton pair. Particle–antiparticle pairs are in effect all the time and everywhere being created and destroyed. Their destruction is so rapid that the particles never come into evidence at any everyday scale of observation.[383]

---

[383] Wheeler, *A Journey into Gravity and Spacetime*, 223.

This accords well with Bohm's ontological model, in that each quantum tick reveals a new explicate order:

> As with consciousness, each moment has a certain explicate order, and in addition it enfolds all the others, though in its own way. So the relationship of each moment in the whole to all the others is implied by its total content: the way in which it "holds" all the others enfolded within it.[384]

This holoflux clock-cycle process or oscillation between an implicate order and an explicate order is also remarkably congruent with Dewey's previously-mentioned theory of laminated space–time. [385] Going further, in considering that, within an explicate space–time order, any frequencies in time imply the existence of corresponding frequencies in space, Bohm's comments:

> These ideas are connected with our ontological interpretation by means of a model of a particle as a sequence of incoming and outgoing waves, with *successive waves very close to each other.*[386]

These "very close" waves find their successive limit, as we have discussed, at the bounding Planck length of 10^{-33} cm, and the bounding Planck time value of 10^{-44} sec time

---

[384] Bohm, *Wholeness and the Implicate Order*, 207.

[385] Dewey, *Theory of Laminated Spacetime*.

[386] Bohm and Hiley, *Ontological Interpretation of Quantum Theory*, 9–10.

can also be viewed as a total of 10^{44} successive alterations ("incoming and outgoing waves") per (human) second.

Temperature/Energy of a Quantum Black Hole

Looking at a calculation of the theoretical temperature of an "object" of the size of holosphere which is assumed, for purposes of calculation, to be a black hole, we can use an equation derived by Stephen Hawking to calculate the temperature at the surface of such a quantum black hole (Equation 2, "Hawking's temperature of a black hole"):

> Notice that Hawking's formula, the mass of the black hole is in the denominator. That means that the larger the mass, the colder the black hole, and conversely, the smaller the mass, the warmer the black hole.[387]

$$T = \frac{1}{16\pi^2} \frac{c^3 h}{GMk}$$

Equation 2. Hawking's temperature of a black hole.[388]

According to the Hawking equation and Wien's law, we see that the highest temperature, the greatest energy and highest frequency of electromagnetic energy possible, all issue from the very heart of each and every "point" in space–time, from within the theoretical locus of a holosphere of diameter 10^{-35} m, the Planck length. Thus the quantum wave, or Planck wave of quantum number one, enters the space–time continuum at maximum

---

[387] Susskind, *The Black Hole War*, 173.

[388] Ibid.

temperature, from every holospheric point in the holoplenum, at a cyclic frequency of 10^{44} Hz, a frequency limit set by the Planck time of 5.39106 x 10^{-44} seconds.

Wheeler's "It from Bit" Black Hole

Even beyond timing considerations, Wheeler also developed a theory of information storage, in which he finds at the upper limit the Planck length, deep within the physical world:

> "It from bit" symbolizes the idea that every item of the physical world has at bottom, at a very deep bottom, in most instances an immaterial source and explanation.[389]

Wheeler's explanation was to digitize the cosmos by assigning one "bit" of information to the smallest physical area possible in space–time: an area equal to that of a square having each side the Planck's limiting length of 10^{-35} meters.[390]

In 1970 one of Wheeler's graduate students, Jacob Bekenstein, proposed a novel idea, that there is a maximum amount of information that can be stored in a finite region of space, and that quantum theory points to that area:[391]

> One unit of entropy (information), one unit of randomness, one unit of disorder, Bekenstein

---

[389] Wheeler, *Information, Physics, Quantum: The Search for Links*, 361.

[390] Wheeler, *Geons, Black Holes & Quantum Foam: A Life in Physics*, 297.

[391] Wheeler, *A Journey into Gravity and Spacetime*, 222.

explained to me, must be associated with a bit of area of this order of magnitude . . . . Thus one unit of entropy is associated with each 1.04 x 10⁻^{69} square meters of the horizon of a black hole.[392]

This proposed upper limit to the information that can be contained upon the surface of a specific, finite volume of space has come to be known as the "Bekenstein bound."[393] Figure 23 is Wheeler's depiction of information bits stored on the surface of a sphere.

---

[392] Ibid.

[393] Bekenstein, "Black Holes and Entropy."

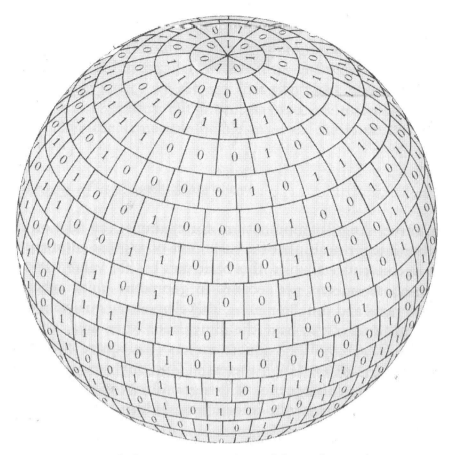

Figure 23. Symbolic representation of the Bekenstein
number of bits. Wheeler (1990), A Journey into Gravity and
Spacetime, 220; reprinted with permission.

Using this concept, we can calculate the maximum
amount of information that might be stored in a one-
centimeter radius sphere located in the human brain. To
obtain this limiting number of bits, we simply calculate the
surface area on a sphere of one-centimeter radius, and then
divide the result by 1.04×10^{-69} square meters (a square of
Planck length).
Using simple geometry, we use the equation for the surface
area of a sphere $4\pi r^2$. We can then approximate the area to
be, $4\pi r^2 = 4 \times 3.14 \times (10^{-2})^2$ or 1.256×10^{-5} square meters.

If we divide this value by 1.04 x 10^{-69} square meters we obtain the following answer for the number of bits of information stored in a one-centimeter radius sphere: 1.256 x 10^{-5} / 1.04 x 10^{-69} = 1.207 x 10^{64} bits of information.

By contrast, if we perform the same calculation using the surface area of a holosphere (quantum black hole), the surprising answer (perhaps not so surprising) is that there are π qubits per holospherical surface, which implies that the universe, in terms of information computation, is not based on two-state binary computing, but that it operates on π-based computational algorithms at the base level of the holoplenum.

The enormous amount of information that might be physically stored in the holoplenum accords well with the holographic principle described by the theoretical physicist Paola Zizzi, the proponent of a quantum gravity theory in which space is considered to be granular. According to Zizzi, the universe should be regarded as a kind of super computer:

> The holographic principle states that all the information enclosed in a region of space with volume V, is encoded on the surface S, bounding V. More precisely, each pixel of area (a pixel here is one unit of the Planck area) of S encodes one bit of information. In a more sophisticated (quantum) version of the holographic principle the encoded information is quantum, and each pixel encodes one quantum bit (or "qubit") of information .... At this point every quantized horizon can be viewed as a quantum register (a

quantum register is the memory of a quantum computer, built with qubits).[394]

The problem remains, however, *how* this information might be stored, and more importantly, in order to address Chalmers' "hard problem," what is the mechanism for comprehension of this information? How is such information experienced? To answer "how" for either of these problems first requires a clear understanding of how information is encoded, transmitted, and received via twenty-first-century human technology. We begin with the concepts of frequency and the frequency domain.

Fields, Frequency, and the Frequency Domain

An understanding of fields and frequency, their measurement and dynamics, are of central importance to an understanding of the holoflux field theory of consciousness. It was Michael Faraday (1791–1867) who first conceived of the reality of an invisible electromagnetic "field" during his observation of magnetic lines of force around a conductor carrying a direct current.[395] But while Faraday had the ability to conceptualize a certain ontological reality, he did not have sufficient mathematical training to formalize the dynamics of his theorized field. Thus it was James Clerk Maxwell (1831–1879) who in 1861, through a series of interlocking equations, subsequently known as the "Maxwell equations," was able to model the dynamics of electric and magnetic energy, in waves of various

---

[394] Zizzi, "Consciousness and Logic in a Quantum Computing Universe," 460.

[395] Crease, *The Great Equations*, 135.

frequencies, flowing through space–time in an ocean of vibrating flux.[396]

Figure 24. James Clerk Maxwell at Trinity College, Cambridge. Graphic by Tjlaxs (2005). Public domain image published in the US before 1923. Retrieved from Wikimedia Commons.

His discovery was a mathematical one, based upon his development of a set of four interlocking partial differential equations with which he was able to predict the dynamics of electric charges and how they are generated by oscillating magnetic fields. Ironically, though Maxwell's equations predicted electromagnetic waves, their existence was not accepted as real until nearly 25 years later, when Heinrich Hertz (1857–1894) experimentally detected electromagnetic waves.[397] Nevertheless, Hertz was forever in awe of the equations that led him to his discovery, and here he speaks,

---

[396] Cook, *The Theory of the Electromagnetic Field.*

[397] Hertz, *Electric Waves.*

190

with almost mystical reverence, of the "wisdom" that he has found in Maxwell's equations:

> One cannot escape the feeling that these mathematical formulae have an independent existence and an intelligence of their own, that they are wiser than we are, wiser even than their discoverers, that we get more out of them than was originally put into them.[398]

In the 1800s, frequencies were measured in units of "Cycles Per Second," a convention which was adopted for many decades into the twentieth century. With the development of quantum mechanics, it was realized that units of frequency often needed to be dimensionless for certain calculations to make sense. In 1930, a dimensionless frequency unit named, appropriately, "Hertz," was adopted by the International Electrotechnical Commission, officially replacing the misleading concept implied in units of "cycles per second."[399] Karl Pribram, commenting on the confusion, here suggests using the term "spectral density" in lieu of the term "frequencies":

> When we deal with a spectrum of frequencies per se, we often substitute the term "spectral density" to avoid a common confusion that Gabor pointed out in his paper: non mathematicians, even physicists, often think of frequencies as occurring only in time, but when mathematicians deal with vibrations as in the Fourier transform,

---

[398] E. T. Bell, *Men of Mathematics*, 16.

[399] Ruppert, *History of the International Electrotechnical Commission*.

frequencies are described as composing spectra and devoid of space and time.[400]

Perhaps Pribram is reacting here to the confusion in terminology that has muddled some critics of Pribram's holographic paradigm, leading them to believe that frequency by definition (as units of cycles per second) can only exist in space–time. Here for example, Ken Wilber exhibits this fallacy, apparently misled by the term "cycles/second," in his dismissal of Pribram's holographic paradigm:

> The transform of "things" into "frequencies" is not a transform of space/time objects into space/time frequencies. Frequency does not mean "no space, no time"; it means cycles/second or space per time. To read the mathematics otherwise is more than a quantum leap; it is a leap of faith.[401]

Sine Wave and Frequency Motion of an Exoplanet

It is useful to visualize the path of a sine wave in nature. Assume we are measuring the brightness of an exoplanet circling around a distant star, and that we are viewing it almost edge-on to its planar orbit. When the planet is closest to us, it will be brightest, and when it is on the opposite side of its central star, it will appear maximally dim, being at its furthest distance from our viewing point. If we were to plot the intensity of this visual image of an exoplanet over the period during which it makes one orbital

---

[400] Pribram, *The Form Within*, 105.

[401] Wilber, *The Holographic Paradigm*, 181.

cycle, it would appear, graphed on two-dimensional Cartesian coordinates, as the sine wave in Fig. 25. Where the graph crosses the zero axis corresponds to the exoplanet being at right angles to its star and our vantage point.

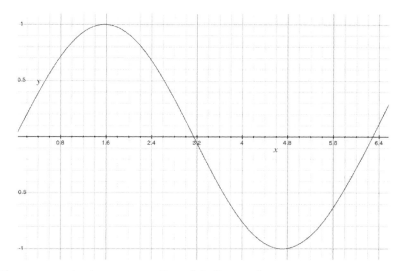

Figure 25. A sine wave. Graphic by author.

According to the Bohr model of atomic theory, electrons spinning around their nuclei emit similar sine wave patterns as they orbit, and accordingly, space–time is replete with sinusoidal electromagnetic waves of an almost infinite number of different frequencies, corresponding to orbiting photons.[402] The frequency of radiation emitted is the inverse of the orbital time; for example, an orbit that takes one second to complete would emit electromagnetic radiation of 1 Hz, while an orbit of an electron with smaller radii would exhibit a higher frequencies of radiant of energy. The closer to the center, they faster the orbit and the less time expired.

---

[402] Baggott, *The Quantum Story*, 30.

The wavelength of a sine wave is a measurement of the distance, in space, between any two points with the same phase of a frequency, such as between troughs, crests, or zero crossing in the same direction. Figure 26 illustrates the concept of wavelength, depicting the graph of a sine of wavelength λ.

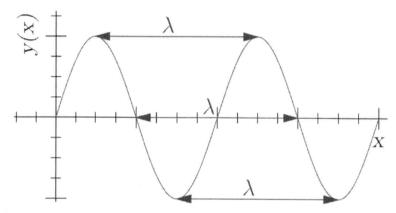

Figure 26. Wavelength. Graphic by Richard F. Lyon (2009). Reprinted under the terms of a Creative Commons Attribution ShareAlike 3.0 Unported license.

Frequency charts of radiant electromagnetic energy are commonly depicted as a spectrum displayed on two-dimensional Cartesian coordinates with named ranges, some of which are listed in Table 3, "Ranges of the Electromagnetic Field."

Table 3

Ranges of the Electromagnetic Field

Named range	Approximate wavelengths	Frequency (Hz)
Radio waves	10^3 or 1 kilometer	10^6
Microwaves	10^0 or 1 meter	10^9
Infrared	10^{-8} meters	10^{13}

Visible light	10^{-9} meters	10^{14}
UV rays	10^{-10} meters	10^{16}
X rays	10^{-11} meters	10^{18}
Gamma rays	10^{-12} meters	10^{19}

Note. Data adapted from Benenson et al., *Handbook of Physics*, 227.

The ubiquitous word "heat" tends to confuse an actual phenomenon with an epiphenomenon. The actual the sensation termed "heat" is a measure of human neurosensory reaction to the physically radiant energy phenomenon of electromagnetic energy interacting with neurons in the skin cells. The actual energy in question is invisible electromagnetic radiation in the infrared band of the spectrum. Similarly, when we use the word "light," we tend to fall into the same potentially specious obfuscation. The term "light," like heat, pertains to the bio-sensory phenomenon of visual perception, while the primary phenomenon is actually pure radiant electromagnetic energy, precisely the same kind of energy as "heat," though of a higher frequency (a shorter wavelength) in the significantly broader electromagnetic spectrum.[403]

What is less commonly considered is that the living human body itself broadcasts a unique, narrow spectrum of electromagnetic radiation in the infrared band of radiation. [404] Wien's Law states that the maximum electromagnetic wavelength generated by a theoretically

---

[403] Feynman, Leighton, and Sands, *The Feynman Lectures on Physics*, 72.

[404] Becker and Selden, *The Body Electric: Electromagnetism and the Foundations of Life.*

perfect "black body" at a specific given temperature is given by the following equation:

$$\lambda_{\text{max}} = \frac{b}{T}$$

Equation 3. Wien's Law.[405] Graphic by author.

Here "b" in the equation is a constant discovered by Wilhelm Wien in 1893 and is equal to 2.897768551 x 10³ m K, and T is the temperature.[406] If we substitute the core human body temperature of 98.6 F for T, we obtain the maximum wavelength to be **9.34 micrometers**. Electromagnetic energy vibrating at this wavelength lies within the range of the infrared region, just below the range of humanly visible light frequencies. It is of interest to note that human bodies generate electromagnetic radiation at frequencies with a wavelength approximately five times smaller than the diameter of a human hair, but the approximate size of a human red blood cell.[407]

Energy vibrating in the infrared band of radiation also has a unique relationship with water. It is within the infrared range that water molecules exhibit their maximum transmittance or transparency to electromagnetic radiation, as can be seen in Fig. 27, "Water Response to Infrared Electromagnetic Radiation." A sharp dip in the absorption coefficient of atmospheric water vapor can be seen in the

---

[405] Feynman, Leighton, and Sands. *The Feynman Lectures on Physics, Vol. 1*, 74.

[406] Crease, *The Great Equations*, 128.

[407] Becker, *Cross Currents: The Perils of Electropollution*.

graph at about 10 microns on the horizontal axis. Such a dip is what communication engineers call a "passband." Earth's atmosphere exhibits a passband to radiation in the 10 micron range, the infrared. What is important to note here is that this atmospheric passband closely matches the human peak wavelength of electromagnetic radiation, previously calculated as 9.34 microns.[408]

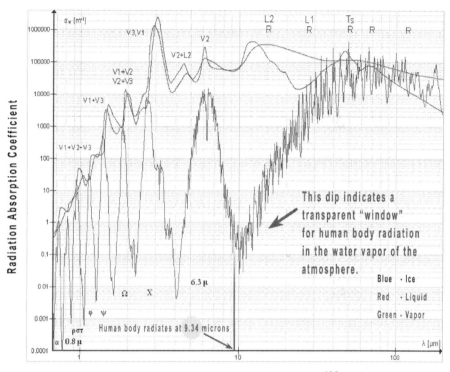

Figure 27. Water response to infrared radiation.[409]
Annotation added by author to image by Darekk2 (2012).

---

[408] Warren and Brandt, "Optical Constants of Ice from the Ultraviolet to the Microwave," 1049.

[409] Water absorption spectrum; absorption coefficient for water—liquid (red line), vapor (green) and ice (blue) between 667 nm and 200 μm (red and most important part of infrared).

If the dynamics of human consciousness has evolved to broadcast and receive in this frequency range, then it would be a very convenient thing indeed that the atmosphere of our planet is transparent in this range. At 9.34 microns, the atmosphere with its gasses and water molecules does not absorb our radiant energy but allows it to pass relatively unrestricted and unattenuated in the biosphere. The passbands of the Earth's atmosphere can be seen in a graph of atmospheric electromagnetic opacity by wavelength, plotted by NASA (Fig. 28).

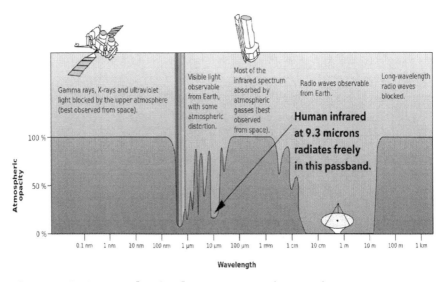

Figure 28. Atmospheric electromagnetic opacity. Annotation added by author to NASA image by Mysid (2008). Public domain image retrieved from Wikimedia Commons.

As early as 1939 military engineers began exploiting the fact that the electromagnetic radiation emitted by

198

human bodies is transparent to the atmosphere. This realization enabled them to develop electro-optic night vision devices specifically to observe human infrared radiation travelling through the atmosphere at wavelengths between 9 and 10 microns.[410]

Water molecules themselves, as vapor in the atmosphere, may act as magnetically resonant dipole "highways," providing infrared channels and currents in the air, even among the clouds, for electromagnetic bio-networking around Earth's globe. Such bio-communication possibilities for human infrared radiation have been widely ignored in the neuroscience community, where such energy is understandably dismissed as "heat," or "noise," or "random thermodynamic activity," while the focus continues to be primarily upon the search for bands of human consciousness within the relatively slow, "brain-wave" frequency passband regions that are recorded by scalp-affixed electroencephalographic (EEG) sensors, generally detected in a range from 8 Hz to 50 Hz.[411]

In contrast to this low frequency range (8–50 Hz) detected by sensors on the exterior of the human scalp, the human body continuously radiates, internally and externally, in the "thermal infrared" or "long-wavelength infrared" band, which is tuned to wavelengths from 8–15 microns, in a frequency range from 27–30 THz (1 THz = 10^{12} Hz). Table 4 compares the detected ranges of human EEG frequency and human infrared frequency. The much higher frequency band of infrared as compared to EEG

---

[410] Clark, *Photography by Infrared—Its Principles and Applications*, 78.

[411] Nunez, *Brain, Mind, and the Structure of Reality*, 104–5.

would translate to vast differences in information processing and storage capacity, discussed later in this chapter.

Table 4
Frequency Range: Brain Waves Versus Plasma Waves

Wave type	Frequency (Hz)
EEG "Brain Wave"	$0.8-5 \times 10^1$ Hz
Infrared "Plasma Wave"	$2.7-3 \times 10^{13}$ Hz

Note. Data from Nunez. *Brain, Mind,* 216. Author's table.

Potentially significant biological correlations can now be established. The human emission of radiation wavelengths in the 9.34 micron range not only lies within the infrared band, but also is dimensionally the same size as the prokaryote (basically, a bacteria), believed to be the first living organism on planet Earth. [412] This human electromagnetic wavelength of 9.34 microns also matches the average diameter of human blood capillaries, the smallest of the body's circulatory structures, on the average 8–10 microns in diameter; it has been estimated that there are approximately 25,000 miles of capillaries within each adult human body.[413] To appreciate the significance of the correlation of the human infrared radiation wavelength and the inner diameter of the human capillary system, it is important to understand the concept of waveguides in communication engineering.

Waveguides have been used for over a century, both commercially and in research, to channel and guide vibrating energy of specific limited frequency ranges. It was

---

[412] Zimmer, "Origins: On the Origin of Eukaryotes," 667.

[413] Romanes, *Cunningham's Textbook of Anatomy,* 840.

discovered late in the nineteenth century that circular metallic tubes, or hollow metal ducts, similar to A/C ventilation ducts, but much smaller, could be used to channel and guide either sound vibrations in air, or electromagnetic energy in air or vacuum. Without the waveguide, the vibrational energy field is transmitted in all directions, which may be visualized as magnetic lines, arrows emerging from a point at the center of an expanding sphere. This energy disperses outwardly, the magnetic vectored arrowheads pushing into the inside of an infinitely expanding sphere. A waveguide, however, constrains the magnetic component of the wave-front of vibrating energy to one specific linear direction, in parallel with the center of the waveguide, and thus, conceptually, the wave itself loses very little power while confined to propagate down the center of the waveguide, like a stream of water emerging from the pinprick of a large, taut, water balloon.[414]

In the mid-twentieth century, scientists began to develop microwave devices for radar and high information, bi-directional communication. In general, the inner dimension (diameter) of the waveguide must be of the same order of magnitude as the wavelength being "guided." Electrical engineers during World War II developed radar technology by using metal waveguides to channel, modulate, and detect frequencies in the microwave band.[415]

Contemporary data networks are increasingly channeled through optical waveguides using the properties of thin transparent fiber optic materials. High-speed network optical fibers currently used in the global Internet

---

[414] Dorf, *The Electrical Engineering Handbook*.

[415] Ibid.

confine light to their core, most commonly using a glass fiber with a core diameter of 8–10 microns, designed for laser communication in the near infrared, the frequency band in which the ubiquitous carbon dioxide laser (CO_2 laser) emits coherent radiation. The CO_2 laser is one of the most widely used lasers due to its ability to reliably operate at the highest-power efficiency currently found among laser systems.[416]

Perhaps it should not come as a surprise then that living human blood cells operate within their energy environment in the same infrared band as does our Internet data, and that the blood system is saturated with carbon dioxide gas. If conscious information processing in the human bio-system uses electromagnetic energy as a medium, then waveguide networks might also be identified within human physiology. Dimensional analysis, developed in the following section, would indicate the possibility of two systems of enclosed, tubular structures that might act as waveguides for bands of networked human electromagnetics.

A recent proposal by the University of California Los Angeles neuroscientist N. J. Woolf goes so far as to identify the site of memory storage in the locus of microtubule channels:

> Most contemporary models of consciousness posit synaptic activity as the primary basis of consciousness . . . . The view I propose is that the site of memory storage is not within the synapse, but in the sub-synaptic zone, in the microtubules of the dendrite shaft . . . the logic to this proposal

---

[416] Kachris, Christoforos, Bergman, and Tomkos, *Optical Interconnects for Future Data Center Networks.*

is that the synapse is a channel transmitting information, much like a radio receiver . . . . In this analogy, the receiving channel is the synapse or spine.[417]

Such waveguides might be a function of the blood capillary system and/or the microtubule system, as indicated in Fig. 29.

---

[417] Woolf, "Microtubules in the Cerebral Cortex," 83–84.

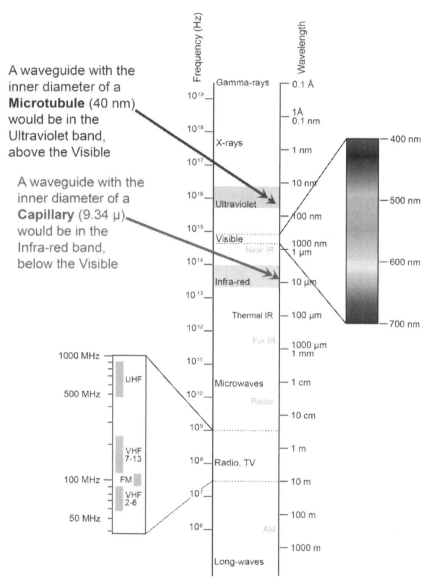

A waveguide with the inner diameter of a **Microtubule** (40 nm) would be in the Ultraviolet band, above the Visible

A waveguide with the inner diameter of a **Capillary** (9.34 µ) would be in the Infra-red band, below the Visible

Figure 29. Microtubules and capillaries as waveguides. Annotations by author; graphic by Jahoe (2012). Reprinted under the terms of a Creative Commons Attribution ShareAlike 2.5 Generic license. Image retrieved from Wikimedia Commons.

204

Information, Communication, and Meaning

Before discussing the mathematics of electromagnetic communication at the heart of holoflux theory, it is useful to examine the distinction between information, communication, and meaning. David Bohm stressed that meaning is found embedded in structure:

> Meanings are seen to be capable of being organized into ever more subtle and comprehensive over-all structures.[418]

Bohm also posits that there is a direct connection between *energy* and *meaning*, that in a sense they are aspects of the same thing:

> I would like to suggest then that the activity, virtual or actual, in the energy and in the soma is the meaning of the information, rather than to say that the information affects an entity called the mind, which in turn operates somehow on the matter of the body.[419]

As discussed in Chapter 3, Bohm went on to develop a theory he termed *active information*. [420] A similar description of information and meaning has been expressed by Rollin McCratey:

> The most basic definition of *information* is data which *in-form*, or give shape to, action or

---

[418] Bohm, *Unfolding Meaning*, 75.

[419] Bohm, "Meaning and Information," 46.

[420] Bohm, "Meaning and Information," 1.

behavior, such as a message that conveys "meaning" to the recipient of a signal (Bradley & Pribram, 1998). In human language, abstract symbols like words, numbers, graphical figures, and even gestures and vocal intonations are used to encode the meaning conveyed in a message. In physiological systems, changes in chemical concentrations, the amount of biological activity, or the pattern of rhythmic activity are common means by which information is encoded in the movement of energy to inform system behavior.[421]

Communication involves three things: information, meaning, and energy transfer. For communication to occur, three things must happen: (1) an initial process in which there is an energetic transformation of meaning (understanding) into information encoded in some media, (2) an energetic transmission of the information to a receiver or receiving entity remote in space and/or time, and finally, (3) an extraction of the received information and an energetic transformation of the information (i.e., its interpretation) into meaning.

For two-way communication, the reverse must happen, the previous receiving entity encodes meaning (perhaps in response to the original meaning) into information, transmits the information through some medium (possibly the same medium, but not necessarily) to the original sender, and the information received is then translated or interpreted (understood) by the original sender. This process constitutes a full circle, a cybernetic loop, between sender and receiver.

---

[421] McCraty et al., *The Coherent Heart*, 16.

In the spatial dimension, communication can be carried by yelling across a room. Visually, smoke signals, semaphores, or moving lips have all been used as effective means of communication. In the time dimensions, simple sticky note messages can be sent to one's self in the future (though this is one-way communication).

It was Claude Shannon (a cousin of Thomas Edison) who applied thermodynamic equations to relate the flow of thermal energy to the flow of information encoded in any medium. [422] His work led to enhanced methods of modulating information signals in different media, from electromagnetic "radio wave" energy to visible and infrared "light" energy.

Two domains, the time domain (t_d) and the frequency domain (f_d), are of essential importance in the field of information theory and signal communication. On the first page of an undergraduate electrical engineering textbook on network analysis and synthesis, Kuo states:

> In describing signals, we use the two universal languages of electrical engineering—*time* and *frequency*. Strictly speaking, a signal is a function of time. However, the signal can be described equally well in terms of *spectral* or *frequency* information. As between any two languages, such as French and German, translation is needed to render information given in one language comprehensible in the other. Between time and frequency, the translation is effected by the *Fourier series* and the *Fourier integral*.[423]

[422] Shannon, "A Mathematical Theory of Communication."

[423] Kuo, *Network Analysis and Synthesis*, 1.

In his book *Brain and Perception*, Pribram used almost the same words as Kuo in discussing methods by which a Fourier transform operates in mathematical physics. Here Pribram reaches the same conclusion as Kuo:

> It is reasonable to ask: What advantage does the organism gain by processing in the spectral transform domain? The answer is efficiency: The fact that correlations are *so easily achieved* by first convolving signals in the spectral domain and then, inverse transforming them into the space–time domain. Thus Fast Fourier Transform (FFT) procedures have become the basis of computerized tomography, the CT scans used by hospitals.[424]

This emphasis on the significant role of Fourier transform mathematics in electrical engineering and neurophysiological research can also be found in quantum physics (e.g., on page 1 of Bohm's own 646-page textbook, *Quantum Theory*):

> The development of the special mathematical techniques that are necessary for obtaining quantitative results in complex problems should take place, for the most part, either in a mathematics course or in a special course concerned with the mathematics of quantum theory. It seems impossible, however, to develop quantum concepts extensively without Fourier analysis. It is, therefore, presupposed that the

---

[424] Pribram, *Brain and Perception*, 73.

reader is moderately familiar with Fourier analysis.[425]

Accordingly it is worthwhile to examine in detail the nature of the Fourier series and Fourier integrals, and in particular to explore their relation to imaginary numbers and the Maxwell equations that map the flow of electromagnetic energy in space–time.

Leonhard Euler and Imaginary Numbers

The two domains related by the Fourier transform, the time domain and frequency domain, had been "discovered," explored and developed as early as 1735 by Leonhard Euler (1707–1783), a Swiss mathematical genius who not only defined the concept of a "function," (Euler was the first to write $f(x)$ to denote a function driven by a variable), but also named and defined numerous mathematical symbols widely used today including the constant "pi," in Greek, the letter π; he had determined through calculation that if the diameter of a circle is 1, then its circumference must be the irrational number, 3.14159265 which "for the sake of brevity" he labeled π.[426] Euler's most important work published work is a two-volume textbook written in 1748, *Introductio ad Analysin Infinitorum (Introduction to Infinite Analysis)*.[427]

In the *Introductio*, Euler announced the dramatic discovery of a deep connection between

---

[425] Bohm, *Quantum Theory*, 1.

[426] Crease, *The Great Equations*, 100.

[427] Ibid., 98.

exponential functions, trigonometric functions, and imaginary numbers ... Euler unveiled numerous discoveries about functions involving infinite theories . . . and proposed definitions and symbols that have since become standard, including π and e.[428]

An example can be seen here in his choice of a base for an exponential function, which he called e, created by adding up a simple infinite series:

$$e = 1 + \frac{1}{1!} + \frac{1}{2!} + \frac{1}{3!} + \frac{1}{4!} + \frac{1}{5!} + \frac{1}{6!} + \frac{1}{7!} + \frac{1}{8!} + \frac{1}{9!} + \frac{1}{10!} + \frac{1}{11!} + \frac{1}{12!} + \cdots$$

This number e became Euler's base for what he called "natural logarithms," and one of the most important mathematical constants. [429] However Euler's greatest contribution to mathematical physics was his proof of a direct mathematical connection between the *time domain* and the *frequency domain*. The Nobel Prize winning physicist, Richard Feynman, has called Euler's discovery, "the gold standard for mathematical beauty," and "the most remarkable formula in mathematics."[430]

Mathematicians in the early eighteenth century, following Newton, sought for expressions and patterns in pure mathematics that could be shown to mirror physical phenomena observed in nature. With his photographic memory and "rare ability for concentration," Euler was able

---

[428] Ibid., 98–99.

[429] Ibid., 100.

[430] Feynman, Leighton, and Sands, *The Feynman Lectures*, 211.

to perceive patterns in mathematical series and relationships that resulted in a prodigious number of proofs (at his death Euler had published more than 40 folio volumes on mathematics). Euler's biographer put forth his own theory on the spectacular success of this prodigy:

> The phenomenon of Euler is essentially tied to three factors: first to the gift of a possibly unique memory . . . at an advanced age, he demonstrated that he could repeat the Aeneid of Virgil from beginning to end without hesitation, and for every page in the edition he could indicate which line was the first and which the last. Secondly, his enormous mnemonic power was paired with a rare ability of concentration. Noise and hustle in his immediate vicinity barely disturbed him in his mental work: "A child on his knees, a cat on his back, this is the way he wrote his immortal works" reports his colleague, Thiebault. The third factor of the "mystery Euler" is simply his steady, quiet work.[431]

Prior to Euler's discovery, there had never been a way to mathematically connect the timespace (t_d) dimension with the nontemporal frequency (f_d) dimension. His discovery resulted from his investigation into an obscure field of mathematics (discovered by Greek mathematicians, but first called "imaginary numbers" by Descartes by way of ridicule) in which Euler defined the square root of minus

---

[431] Fellmann, *Leonhard Euler*, xv.

one as the letter "i" (for "imaginary").[432] Thus the letter i designates the square root of minus one:

$$i = \sqrt{-1},$$

or conversely, $i^2 = -1$.

Euler found this imaginary number to be a great mathematical tool because multiplying "i" times "i" (i.e., squaring "i"), simply reverses the sign of an expression. This feature can be used to reverse the signs of various elements in a series expansion, and thus allowed Euler to develop and explore a wide range of equalities in mathematical expansion series. Use of this imaginary number as an operator, combined with his copious memory led directly to his discovery, in 1735, of what is now called Euler's Law: a direct relationship between real numbers and imaginary numbers. Depicted in Cartesian coordinates, the horizontal axis of real numbers, commonly labeled the "time" axis, is widely used in physics and mathematical charting, while the vertical, "imaginary" axis, is widely used in electrical engineering because it governs so well the mathematics of complex-plane calculations which are ubiquitous in contemporary electronic devices, during the translation of digital to analog signals and vice versa.[433]

In his *Introductio ad analysin infinitorum*, Euler announced the discovery of a connection between exponential functions, trigonometric functions, and

---

[432] While the "i" symbol continues to be used by mathematicians and physicists, electrical engineers use the letter "j" to designate imaginary numbers, primarily because they use the letter "i" to designate electrical current flow; Kuo, *Network Analysis and Synthesis*, 16.

[433] Kuo, *Network Analysis and Synthesis*, 77.

imaginary numbers.[434] Perhaps the best way to appreciate the beauty in the discovery of Euler's Law is to go through its derivation.[435]

Derivation of Euler's Law

Euler was fascinated by what are called "infinite series," expressions by which trigonometric values can be expressed, and more importantly, calculated. By summing a series of arithmetical terms, the value of a sin or cos of an angle can be calculated to any degree of precision by approximating them as the sum of a series of arithmetic values. Obviously an entire infinite series could not be calculated, but approximations were acceptable because it allowed the creation of large tables of values that were in widespread demand for use by engineers in the sixteenth century throughout Europe.[436]

Euler spent countless hours developing various infinite series, in the attempt to discover connections and relationships among the patterns. Two of these series especially intrigued him, the Scottish mathematician Colin Maclaurin's infinite series expansion of the sine and the cosine functions, both shown partially expanded as follows:

$$\sin x = x - \frac{x^3}{3!} + \frac{x^5}{5!} - \frac{x^7}{7!} + \frac{x^9}{9!} - \frac{x^{11}}{11!} \cdots$$

---

[434] Crease, *The Great Equations*, 99.

[435] Material in the following section is taken from Crease, "Euler's Equation," in *The Great Equations*, 91–110; mathematical expressions in this section are by author.

[436] Crease, *The Great Equation*, 100.

$$\cos x = 1 - \frac{x^2}{2!} + \frac{x^4}{4!} - \frac{x^6}{6!} + \frac{x^8}{8!} - \frac{x^{10}}{10!} \cdots$$

Note that the "factorial sign" (!) represents the product of all numbers starting from the indicated number down to 1, (i.e., 3! = 3 x 2 x 1 = 6), and also that the ellipsis (...) in each of the expressions above indicate an infinite series of additional factors, which follow the same pattern of progression. When Euler discovered an infinite series expansion for his own natural logarithm (the base used widely in nuclear physics, was later named "e" for Euler), he noticed how the Maclaurin's series seemed similar to the pattern of expansion of his own discovery of the e^x expansion:

$$e^x = 1 + x + \frac{x^2}{2!} + \frac{x^3}{3!} + \frac{x^4}{4!} + \frac{x^5}{5!} + \frac{x^6}{6!} \cdots$$

Euler noticed that this was strangely similar to the Maclaurin expansions for cos x and sin x added together; the result of such an addition (shown below, the sum of the two series at the top of this page) is identical to the expansion of e^x, except where minus signs appear.

$$\sin x + \cos x = 1 + x - \frac{x^2}{2!} - \frac{x^3}{3!} + \frac{x^4}{4!} + \frac{x^5}{5!} - \frac{x^6}{6!} - \frac{x^7}{7!}$$
$$+ \frac{x^8}{8!} + \cdots$$

For many months Euler struggled to unlock the secret of what seemed to be a remarkably close connection. Finally, it dawned on him that the relationship might find closure if he could find a way to use his imaginary number "i," the square root of minus 1 to change signs.

Substituting "ix" for "x" everywhere in his equation (an allowable substitution, since by the rules of algebra any valid expression can be substituted for "x"), he found that wherever "i^2" could be identified and factored out, the sign for that expression would reverse, and he quickly saw that his expansion would then more closely match that of the expansion of $\cos x + \sin x$.

To recapitulate, here again is Euler's original infinite expansion of the natural logarithm that he had previously discovered:

$$e^x = 1 + x + \frac{x^2}{2!} + \frac{x^3}{3!} + \frac{x^4}{4!} + \frac{x^5}{5!} + \frac{x^6}{6!} \cdots$$

Wherever there is an "x" in the above equation, Euler substituted "ix,"

$$e^{ix} = 1 + ix + \frac{(ix)^2}{2!} + \frac{(ix)^3}{3!} + \frac{(ix)^4}{4!} + \frac{(ix)^5}{5!} + \frac{(ix)^6}{6!} \cdots$$

Wherever he found an "i^2" he converted it to its computed value of "-1":

$$e^{ix} = 1 + ix - \frac{x^2}{2!} - \frac{ix^3}{3!} + \frac{x^4}{4!} + \frac{ix^5}{5!} + \cdots$$

Rearranging the results slightly, we can see the original patterns of $\cos x$ and $\sin x$ expansion on the left, now seen as equal to Euler's e^{ix} (on the right): this equation is known as "Euler's Law":

$$e^{ix} = \left(1 - \frac{x^2}{2!} + \frac{x^4}{4!} + \cdots \right) + \left(ix - \frac{ix^3}{3!} + \frac{ix^5}{5!} + \cdots \right)$$

Now the i can be factored out from the right side of the equation:

$$e^{ix} = \left(1 - \frac{x^2}{2!} + \frac{x^4}{4!} + \cdots \right) + i * \left(x - \frac{x^3}{3!} + \frac{x^5}{5!} + \cdots \right)$$

The expressions now within the brackets are simply the Maclaurin expansion series for cos x and sin x, and the entire expression can now be written as:

$$e^{ix} = \cos x + i * \sin x$$

The amazement generated by this discovery was that for the first time a solid, derivable mathematical link had been established between e, the natural exponential function, the imaginary number i, and trigonometric geometry; the discovery was published in 1735 by Euler (Eqn. 4).

$$e^{ix} = \cos x + i * \sin x$$

Equation 4. Euler's Law.[437] Graphic by author.

Notice how both sides of Euler's Law contain both real numbers (**x**) and imaginary numbers (**i**). Euler's Law maps the intersection of the axis of real numbers with the angular frequency axis of imaginary numbers on a single intersecting plane, allowing us to model mathematically the real world of timespace/frequency phenomena of quantum electrodynamics. Euler's Law has since become the basis of electronic communication technology within which our society is currently enmeshed.[438]

During the eighteenth century this field, "complex mathematics," remained an obscurity, until "rediscovered" by physicists such as Maxwell, Tesla, and Marconi in the

---

[437] Crease, *The Great Equations*, 102.

[438] Blakeslee, *The Radio Amateur's Handbook*, 23.

late nineteenth century; the mathematics of imaginary numbers became an essential tool for modeling an invisible electromagnetic reality, and more importantly, provided a direct way of calculating, predicting, and modulating the electromagnetic energy oscillations and waves associated with the newly emerging technologies of alternating current. [439] Nevertheless, it was Euler who first established the mathematical beachhead into the Real–Imaginary domain, and this relationship was eventually found, perhaps mysteriously, to mirror electromagnetic realities in space–time. [440]

The Integral Operator and the Fourier Transform

Seventy-four years after Euler published his famous theorem, Jean Baptist Joseph Fourier (1768–1830), expanding upon Euler's mathematical discovery, published what came to be known as the Fourier series and the Fourier Transform, in a paper entitled *The Analytic Theory of Heat*. [441] Before describing the Fourier Transform, it is useful to begin by examining the word "integral" through the perspective of history. The word integral itself stems from a mathematical sign, a convention that was first introduced by Gottfried Wilhelm von Leibniz (1646–1716) as a stylized, elongated letter *S* which he used as shorthand for the Latin word *Summa* (translates "sum" or "total") to denote something that originates from a summation. [442]

---

[439] Kuo, *Network Analysis and Synthesis*, 14.

[440] Crease, *The Great Equation*, 108.

[441] Fourier, *The Analytic Theory of Heat*.

[442] Crease, *The Great Equations*, 96.

Both Leibniz and Isaac Newton (1643–1727) seem to have developed the fundamental concepts of integral calculus simultaneously, but Newton's notation of using a vertical mark to indicate summation became the cause of considerable notational confusion (a vertical slash is "easily confused with the numeral, '1,' or with a bracket, or with the letter 'I'"), and over the next 15 years, Leibniz's elongated letter S found preference among mathematicians to denote "summation."[443] The word "integral" itself was coined by Jacob Bernoulli (1654–1705), so that the S notation could more easily be discussed in mathematical conversation and in lectures.[444]

However it was not until 1822, when Jean Baptiste Joseph Fourier introduced the notation of upper and lower limits to the integral operator symbol, that the full power of integral calculus was unleashed, making possible the development of his "Fourier series."[445]

A full century after Euler, it was Fourier, working at the time as Napoleon's governor of Egypt, who managed to link the real and imaginary axes by building upon Euler's Theorem. While Euler had provided the initial link between the frequency and timespace domains, it was Fourier, during his experimental investigation of heat flow, who developed the mathematics to model the thermodynamic properties of energy, and was able to derive a mathematical operation of integral calculus that expressed accurately the

---

[443] Browder, *Mathematical Analysis: An Introduction*, 121.

[444] Livio, *The Golden Ratio: The Story of Phi*.

[445] Feynman, Leighton, and Sands, *The Feynman Lectures on Physics*, 271.

energy transformations between a time domain (l_d) and a frequency domain (f_d).[446]

However, the mathematics expressed in the Fourier transform can also be understood as a link between a physics of space–time (t_d) and an actual, ontologically real frequency domain (f_d).

The Fourier transforms are shown in Equation 5:

$$f(t) = \int_{-\infty}^{+\infty} X(F)e^{j2\pi Ft} \qquad f(F) = \int_{-\infty}^{+\infty} x(t)e^{-j2\pi Ft}$$

Fourier integral transform of a continuous time function into the frequency domain (f_d).	Fourier integral transform of a continuous frequency function into the time domain (t_d).

Equation 5. Fourier Transform/Inverse Transform.[447]

These Fourier transform expressions indicate that any arbitrary function in the timespace domain, $f(t)$, can be transformed into and expressed by an infinite series of frequency spectra functions $X(F)$ in the frequency domain, and conversely, that any arbitrary function in the frequency domain, $f(F)$ can be transformed into and expressed by an infinite series of time functions, $x(t)$.

These Fourier transforms are themselves derived from an underlying series of alternate pure sine and pure cosine waves, as depicted in Equation 6.

---

[446] Ibid., 286.

[447] Stein and Shakarchi, *Fourier Analysis*, 134–36.

$$f(t) = a_0 + \sum_{n=1}^{\infty} \left(a_n \cos \frac{n\pi t}{L} + b_n \sin \frac{n\pi t}{L} \right)$$

Equation 6. The Fourier Series.[448]

A century after Fourier's death, Norbert Wiener made use of Fourier's transform to model and analyze brain waves, and he was able to detect frequencies, centered within different spatial locations on the cortex, that exhibited auto-correlation. Specific frequencies were found to be attracting one another toward an intermediate frequency, thus exhibiting resonance or "self tuning" within a narrow range of the frequency domain (f_d).[449] This discovery led Wiener to conjecture that the infrared band of electromagnetic flux may be the loci of "self-organizing systems."[450]

> We thus see that a nonlinear interaction causing the attraction of frequency can generate a *self-organizing system*, as it does in the case of the brain waves we have discussed.... This possibility of self-organization is by no means limited to the very low frequency of these two phenomena. Consider self-organizing systems at the frequency level, say, of infrared light.[451]

---

[448] Kuo, *Network Analysis and Synthesis*, 40.

[449] Wiener, *Cybernetics: Control and Communication in Animal and Machine*, 198.

[450] Ibid.

[451] Ibid., 202.

Wiener goes on to discuss such possibilities in biology, where he focuses upon the problems of communication at molecular and primitive cellular levels, specifically on the problem of how substances produce cancer by reproducing themselves to mimic pre-existing normal local cells. Molecules do not simply pass notes to one another, and they do not have eyes, so how do they perceive and how do they communicate? Wiener conjectures:

> The usual explanation given is that one molecule of these substances acts as a template according to which the constituent's smaller molecules lay themselves down and unite into a similar macromolecule. However, an entirely possible way of describing such forces is that the active bearer of the specificity of a molecule may lie *in the frequency pattern of its molecular radiation*, an important part of which may lie *in infrared electromagnetic frequencies* or even lower. It is quite possible that this phenomenon may be regarded as a sort of attractive interaction of frequency.[452]

At the end of his classic book on cybernetics, in the chapter, "Brain Waves and Self-Organizing Systems," Wiener suggests further possible studies to "throw light on the validity of my hypothesis concerning brain waves."[453] Wiener goes on to describe the widespread observations of seemingly simultaneous behavior of groups of living organisms such as crickets, tree frogs, or fish, activity that

---

[452] Ibid. Italics added.

[453] Ibid., 200.

might be attributable to simultaneous synchronization of neuronal networks through resonant tuning within the frequency domain (f_d):

> It has often been supposed that the fireflies in a tree flash in unison . . .
> I have heard it stated that in the case of some of the fireflies of Southeastern Asia this phenomenon is so marked that it can scarcely be put down to illusion . . . . Could not the same supposed phenomenon of the pulling together of frequencies take place? However this process occurs, it is a dynamic process and involves forces or their equivalent.[454]

The Real–Imaginary Domain and the Mandelbrot Set

In early explorations of the real–imaginary domain model in the nineteenth century, the Danish mathematician Caspar Wessel, and the mathematical physicist and astronomer Johann Carl Friedrich Gauss independently discovered that two-dimensional Cartesian plots or graphs could be made of the real–imaginary axes, with one axis of real numbers (traditionally illustrated by a straight horizontal line with values increasing from left to right) and a vertical axis of imaginary numbers drawn at a 90-degree angle to the real number axis.[455] In the twentieth century this two-dimensional model has been adopted by electrical engineers to model, analyze, and solve complex problems dealing with transformations between the time (t_d) and

---

[454] Ibid.

[455] E. T. Bell, *Men of Mathematics*.

frequency (f_d), domains in electrical power and communication engineering.[456] The concept remains at the essential core of engineering calculations for transforming electromagnetic energy into information encoded in light, sound, and multidimensional images.[457]

Perhaps the most fascinating tool for exploring the nature of the interface between the Real–Imaginary domains was developed in 1980 when the Polish–American engineer, Benoit Mandelbrot, created the software to plot an actual image of the two-dimensional interface between space–time and frequency domains close to the origin (defined as the intersecting point where the Real axis equals zero and the Imaginary axis equals zero). His initial impression, upon seeing the first image, was that the computer program had malfunctioned. [458] Subsequent computer plots assured him that these visual patterns were truly there. Images of this region about the time frequency origin have gained interest worldwide and the region itself has come to be known as the Mandelbrot set (fig. 30). The English mathematical physicist Sir Roger Penrose was so taken by the resulting images that he described them with a sense of almost reverential awe:

---

[456] Kuo, *Network Analysis and Synthesis*.

[457] Ibid., 389.

[458] Mandelbrot, "Fractals and the Rebirth of Iteration Theory," 151.

The Mandelbrot set is not an invention of the human mind: it was a discovery. Just like Mount Everest, the Mandelbrot set is just *there!*[459]

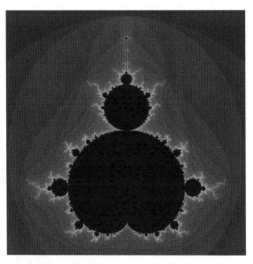

Figure 30. Mandelbrot: Origin of real–imaginary axis. Graphic by author.

The Mandelbrot set exhibits remarkable properties. As calculations are done on ever smaller regions on the time–frequency plane, the images appear similar but never completely repeatable, and the viewer begins to sense some sort of biological shapes emerging from this strange world of pure mathematical being. Penrose goes on to say, "The very system of complex numbers has a profound and timeless reality which goes quite beyond the mental constructions of any particular mathematician."[460]

---

[459] Penrose, *Concerning Computers, Minds and the Laws of Physics*, 124.

[460] Ibid., 127.

Exploitation of the basic properties of this mysterious real–imaginary domain have led directly to twenty-first century digital device systems, and accordingly, it is entirely conceivable that they might also be involved in some space-time-frequency spectrum of the psyche, as theorized by Jung: "Psychic processes therefore behave like a scale along which consciousness 'slides.'"[461]

> Using the analogy of the spectrum, we could compare the lowering of unconscious contents to a displacement towards the red end of the colour band, a comparison which is especially edifying in that red, the blood colour, has always signified emotion and instinct . . . . The dynamism of instinct is lodged as it were in the infra-red part of the spectrum . . . . Psychologically, however, the archetype as a spiritual goal toward which the whole nature of man strives . . . as such is a psychoid factor that belongs, as it were, to the invisible, ultraviolet end of the psychic spectrum.[462]

Using Fourier analysis and the Fourier transform, signals can be described either in the time domain or the frequency domain, and they can be quickly transformed back and forth between the two domains. It can be said that they are two different aspects of one and the same thing, energy signals encoded with information content, but potentially existing in either one, or both, of two categorically distinct dimensions. Jung observes the relationship of psyche to matter with the same pattern,

---

[461] Jung, "On the Nature of the Psyche," 207.

[462] Ibid., 187–213.

noting that they are two different modes of one and the same thing:

> Since psyche and matter are contained in one and the same world, and moreover are in continuous contact with one another and ultimately rest on irrepresentable, transcendental factors, it is not only possible, but also fairly probable, even, that psyche and matter are two different aspects of one and the same thing.[463]

If we assume that the energy of the psyche expresses itself in some category of spectral frequency range within the human biosystem, as Jung has speculated, then a mathematical model of psychic energy activity might be found in the Fourier transform. Humans in contemporary society experience the fruits of the mathematics of the Fourier transform reliably every time a digital communication device is operated.[464]
For example, signal processing chips in cell phones are encoded with what are called fast Fourier transform algorithms, which filter audio voice speech frequency patterns in the space–time domain into a relatively small set of pure frequencies, the individual amplitudes of which are then digitized and transmitted. On the receiving end, a reverse fast Fourier transform unpacks the frequency domain data, transforming them into space–time frequency waves of low voltage circuits, which then drive the vibrating speaker devices by which humans "hear" the re-created audio space–time spectral energy.[465]

---

[463] Jung, "On the Nature of the Psyche," 215.

[464] Brigham, "The Fast Fourier Transform."

[465] Ibid.

Pribram describes this same process as it occurs in the brain, while emphasizing the difference between waves and spectra:

> Waves occur in space–time. Spectra do not. Spectra result from the interference among waves—and, by Fourier's insightful technique, the locus of interference can be specified as a number that indicates the "height" of the wave at that point. The number is represented by a Gabor function (or other wavelet.) Frequency in space–time has been converted to spectral density in the transform domain.[466]

Resonance in the Frequency Domain: Faraday Waves

An understanding of the phenomenon of *resonance* is of fundamental importance in any physical approach to communication and information transfer. Rollin McCraty, in discussing his research measuring the energy frequencies transmitted by the beating human heart, describes the phenomenon of resonance. He notes that remarkably large vibrations are observed when specific external frequencies occur close to what have been termed *resonant* frequencies of a beating heart:

> In physics, resonance refers to a phenomenon whereby an unusually large vibration is produced in a system in response to a stimulus whose frequency is identical or nearly identical to the natural vibratory frequency of the system. The frequency of the vibration produced in such a

---

[466] Pribram, *The Form Within*, 109.

state is said to be the *resonant frequency* of the system.[467]

Michael Faraday (1791–1867) discovered resonance in what he believed to be invisible waves of electricity and magnetism vibrating in what he thought to be a solid plenum, the "ether." Faraday not only discovered the laws of electromagnetic induction, and that magnetism can affect light, but also explored the resonance phenomenon in physical systems.[468]

Faraday reported, in 1831 at the Royal Society of London, an unexpected observation during his experiments with the properties of liquids on a vibrating surface. While experimenting with thin films of liquid on the flat heads of vertically vibrating pistons, he observed distinct geometric patterns emerging on the surface of the liquid at specific fixed frequencies. The image below (in fig. 31, "Faraday Wave Patterns") presents twelve examples of these resonant patterns, corresponding to 12 different resonant frequencies in the vibrating fluid; the images are composed of micro-scale polystyrene beads, 200 microns in diameter, each floating on a thin layer of liquid. The distinctly unique geometric surface patterns are formed by the accretion of beads at nodal intersections, where the resonance of standing waves are at a minimum, and are similar to Prigogine's "valleys of minimum potential attractors," in his dissipative structure experiments.[469] It is interesting to

---

[467] McCraty, *The Energetic Heart*, 4.

[468] Crease, *The Great Equations*, 135.

[469] Prigogine, *Thermodynamics: From Heat Engines to Dissipative Structures.*

228

observe here naturally occurring resonance patterns that appear identical to abstract symbols used in various human cultures throughout history, such as the circle, the cross, and the swastika.[470]

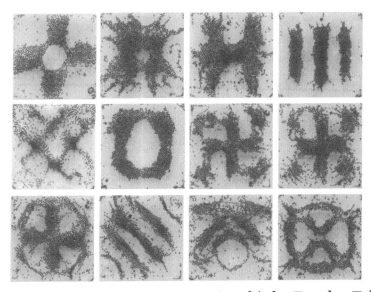

Figure 31. Faraday wave patterns. Graphic by Faraday Telsa (2012). Reprinted under the terms of a Creative Commons Attribution ShareAlike 3.0 Unported license. Image retrieved from Wikimedia Commons.

Since Faraday's time, the concept of resonance has become conventionally associated with music and acoustic phenomena, as in "he had a resonant voice," implying some perceived richness in harmonic acoustic overtones. However in physics, the resonance effect is found to have a more precise meaning, as applied to mechanical and electromagnetic systems, and in fact the phenomenon of resonance has become a fundamental tool in communication theory and the design of electrical

[470] Aigner, *The Swastika Symbol in Navajo Textiles.*

circuits.[471] Resonance is a phenomena characteristic of physical objects extended in space–time, in which objects often exhibit remarkable frequency sensitivity to particular input frequencies, flowing in, through, and around the object, which approach the object's natural frequency (Fig. 32). Perfect resonance occurs where the input frequency and the natural frequency are one.[472]

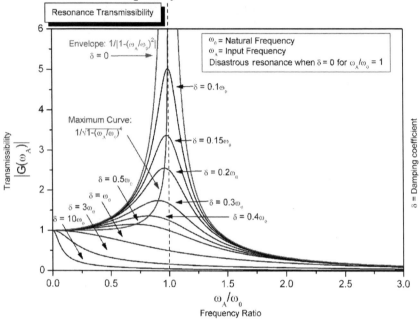

Figure 32. Resonance effect. Graphic by Amuecki (2008). Reprinted under the terms of a Creative Commons Attribution ShareAlike 3.0 Unported license. Image retrieved from Wikimedia Commons.

This principle of resonance governs the design of antennas in electromagnetic transmitting and receiving

---

[471] Dorf, *The Electrical Engineering Handbook*, 41.

[472] Feynman, Leighton, and Sands, *The Feynman Lectures on Physics*, 78.

systems. The goal of antenna design is to construct an antenna that is maximally resonant with an incoming electromagnetic signal; the input frequency and the natural frequency of the antenna must be the same frequency for resonance to occur:

> A fundamental form of antenna is a single wire whose length is approximately equal to half the transmitting wavelength. It is the unit from which many more-complex forms of antennas are constructed. It is known as a *dipole antenna*.[473]

As can be seen in the figure of a sine wave (Fig. 25), the distance between the maximum and minimum values of the sine wave, the maximum distance between peak and trough, is one half of the complete waveform cycle, or exactly the length of a dipole antenna which has been constructed to match, "tuned" to that sine wave frequency.[474]

Resonant electronic components are ubiquitous building blocks in the operation of electronic devices, and resonant mechanical systems frequently exist in the natural world. Resonant conditions in a system exhibit one of two behaviors; the resonance either (1) restricts or blocks the flow of energy into the system, or (2) enhances the flow of energy into the system. In signal analysis the resonance conditions are mathematically termed "poles and zeros"; poles are seen "as being the roots of the denominator" of a signal function, while zeros are "defined as the roots of the

---

[473] Blakeslee, *The Radio Amateur's Handbook*, 580.

[474] Ibid.

numerator" of a signal function.[475] A *resonant pole* in the numerator takes the signal power to infinity, while a *resonant zero* in the denominator, numerically approaching infinity, causes signal power to approach zero. [476] One example of the phenomenon of a resonant pole can be seen in the effect that has been demonstrated by an opera singer acoustically shattering a wine glass by sustaining a high frequency note which happens to be the natural resonant frequency of the crystal (a *pole* in the numerator of a signal function).[477]

Superposition in the Frequency Domain

Also of importance to an understanding of signal communication in the frequency domain is the concept of *superposition*. The combination, or superposition, of multiple frequencies in the frequency domain can create unique patterns in the space–time domain. The Berkeley physicist Henry Stapp explains the importance of superposition in his model of brain dynamics:

> The rudiments of brain dynamics must be understood. In a normal computing machine, the currently active information is stored in a generally small number of registers. But in the brain a huge number of separate patterns of neural excitations can be present at one time. These patterns can become correlated to stimuli and response, and can mediate the behavior of

---

[475] Kuo, *Network Analysis and Synthesis*, 183.

[476] Ibid.

[477] Schrock, "An Opera Singer's Piercing Voice Can Shatter Glass."

the organism .... The main postulate of the model is that every conscious event is the psychological counterpart of a certain special kind of Heisenberg event in the brain, namely an event that actualizes a pattern of neuronal activity that constitutes a *representation* of this general kind. However, any such representation must be *formed before it can be selected*: the representation must be constructed by unconscious brain activity before it can be actualized. During this preliminary mechanical phase, a **superposition** of many such representations must inevitably be generated. During the subsequent actualization phase, only *one* of these representations will be selected.[478]

An example of the superposition principle can be seen in Fig. 33 where the sum of a number of sine waves, shown at the bottom of the figure, results in the "sawtooth wave" seen in the top of the figure.

At the bottom half of the figure are five different frequencies mapped on Cartesian coordinates; the combination of these frequencies, superimposed and translated through a Fourier transform, reveals the sawtooth pattern seen in the upper half of the figure in the time domain.[479]

---

[478] Stapp, *Mind, Matter and Quantum Mechanics*, 25. Emphasis added in bold by author.

[479] Howell, *Principles of Fourier Analysis*.

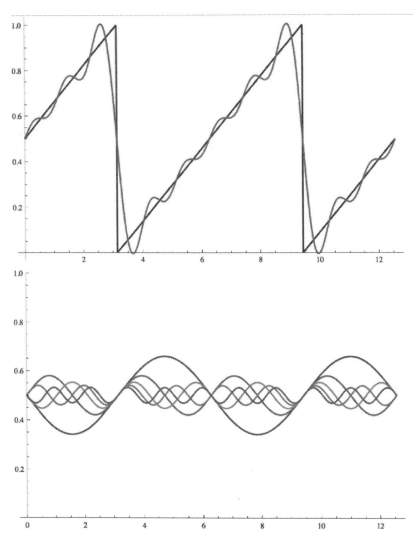

Figure 33. Sawtooth wave pattern created from five
frequencies. Graphic by Differenxe (2010). Reprinted under
the terms of a Creative Commons Attribution ShareAlike 3.0
Unported license. Image retrieved from Wikimedia
Commons.

At this point it is useful to explore a key question
regarding the ontological reality of mathematical functions

operating in the frequency domain: does the frequency domain have an ontological reality, does it exist, or is it simply a mathematical fiction, a fabrication? The many working products of electrical engineering indicate that frequency domain calculations do mirror something real in the cosmos, and experimental evidence that the Schrödinger wavefunction has its own reality gives credence to regarding the frequency domain as also having a cosmological existence beyond that of space–time.

Reality of Schrödinger Wavefunction (ψ)

The applicability of the Schrödinger wavefunction (from which Bohm's quantum potential wavefunction was subsequently derived) may be said to be at the heart of quantum mechanics, but the ontological reality of this wavefunction has not until recently been tested.[480] In 2015, a research team in Australia, at the Centre for Quantum Computer and Communication Technology at the University of Queensland, published results of a series of experiments to explore the nature of the primary mathematical tool used in quantum mechanics, Schrödinger's quantum wavefunction. In describing their research objective, they state, "It is still unclear what the quantum wavefunction actually is: does it merely represent our limited knowledge of a system, or is it an element of reality?"[481] Analyzing four-dimensional states of photons, their experiment *detected the reality of the wavefunction,* and experimental results

---

[480] See Equation 1, "Equation of the Quantum Potential."

[481] Ringbauer et al., "Measurements on the Reality of the Wavefunction," 249.

strengthened the probability that the wavefunction is part of the ontological cosmos, not simply a conceptual tool:

> Our results suggest that, if there is objective reality, the wavefunction corresponds to this reality. These results strengthen the view that the entire wavefunction should be real. The only alternative is to adopt more unorthodox concepts such as backwards-in-time causation, or to completely abandon any notion of objective reality.[482]

These results, strengthening the premise that Schrödinger's wavefunction is ontologically real, also increase the likelihood that Bohm's quantum potential wavefunction, derived directly from Schrödinger's equation, is similarly "real," and that the frequency domain of electrical engineering is also "real." The implications support Bohm's vision, described here, of information being carried by an explicate level of activity (space–time), while being seen from "a finer, subtler implicate level":

> In analogy to what has been said about human experiences, the particles constituting matter in general may be considered to represent a more gross (explicate) somatic level of activity, while the Schrödinger wave field corresponds to a finer, subtler, more implicate and "mind-like" level. In human experience however, it has been proposed that each "mind-like" level can be regarded as a somatic bearer of form when seen from a yet finer and more subtle level. This would imply firstly that the information represented by the Schrödinger wave field is

---

[482] Ibid.

being "carried" by a finer and subtler level of matter that has not yet been revealed more directly. But even more important, it also implies that there may be a finer and more subtle level of information that guides the Schrödinger field, as the information on the Schrodinger field guides the particles.[483]

As discussed in Chapter 4, it is Bohm's quantum potential (Q) of "active information" that provides the guidance that subtly influences the larger effects of the Schrödinger quantum wavefunction (ψ) in the much larger world of particle physics.[484] It is the thesis of this book, backed by current quantum theory, that Bohm's quantum potential manifests as a holoflux process of frequency-phase energy within the frequency domain (the implicate order), resonating with and so influencing electromagnetic energy waves within the space–time domain (the explicate order).

Holoflux in The Holoplenum

Holoflux, as defined in this thesis, is a transformational process of modulated energy flowing into, out from, and within a holoplenum of holospheres in frequencies as high as 10^{44} Hz. This holoflux manifests a flowing field of consciousness, the modulation of which is information embedded in the waves and frequencies of space–time energy. Within each holosphere, below the Planck length of 10^{-35} meters—though the words "within" and "below" are clearly inappropriate for a region that is nonlocal—lies what Bohm calls the *implicate order*.

---

[483] Bohm, "Meaning and Information," 59.

[484] Bohm and Peat, *Science, Order, and Creativity*, 80–81.

Holoflux can be regarded as a type of plasma energy that manifests consciousness in two different modes within two different domains: (1) In the space–time domain, where it manifests in electromagnetic waves, the holoflux process consists of reflective, time-sequenced snapshots of awareness, like glass beads on a thread, and (2) In the frequency domain of the nonlocal, the implicate order, holoflux manifests as immediate awareness (a timeless-sense, the "consciousness-without-an-object" experienced by the mathematician–philosopher Franklin Merrell-Wolf).[485]

Holoflux, as a total manifestation, is a dual process of reflective consciousness and transcendent awareness. Communication, and consciousness flow between and within the two domains: the implicate and the explicate. Another way of regarding holoflux is to see it as a two-way moving flux: (1) It is an explicate energy (E) moving *inward* into the implicate order at the holospheric event horizon of a quantum black hole, and (2) Moving in the opposite direction, it is an implicate energy (Q) moving *outward* as quantum potential from the event horizon, as holoflux energy transforms from out of the implicate order into the explicate order. My thesis rests upon the assumptions that Bohm's implicate order is real, that the frequency domain is real, and that his active information wavefunction is real, affecting our world of "particles" as it springs from the virtually infinite nonlocal information holoflux within the implicate order.

Like Bohm, electrical engineers separate the world into two domains, which they term the *complex-frequency*

---

[485] Merrell-Wolff, *The Philosophy of Consciousness Without an Object.*

domain and the *time domain*. It is our normally perceived space–time that electrical engineers identify as the *time domain*, but it is in the *frequency domain* that they see the operation of communication signals.[486]

Franklin F. Kuo, an American computer scientist and communications engineer at Bell Laboratories, wrote an electrical engineering textbook, developing the mathematics of communication in *Network Analysis and Synthesis*. In the first chapter of his classic textbook, Kuo describes the two domains, and the mathematical advantage of creating and receiving communication signals within the *frequency* domain as opposed to the *space–time* domain:

> In the *complex-frequency domain*, the voltage–current relationships for the elements are expressed in *algebraic* equations. Algebraic equations are, in most cases, more easily solved than differential equations. Herein lies the raison *d'être* for describing signals and networks in the *frequency domain* as well as in the *time domain*.[487]

These two orders of electrical engineering theory can be seen to reflect David Bohm's explicate and implicate orders. Bohm's explicate order is associated with the engineering *time* dimension through which signals are transmitted and received sequentially in time, while Bohm's implicate order can be identified with the electrical engineering *frequency* dimension as a timeless, spaceless domain of pure frequency-phase information.

---

[486] Kuo, *Network Analysis and Synthesis*, 13.

[487] Ibid.

It has been discovered that these two domains are strongly linked, mathematically, with the operation of the Fourier transform. As Kuo says, "between time and frequency, the translation is effected by the Fourier series."[488] As we have seen in Chapter 4, the Fourier series has also become the bedrock of quantum theoretical calculations, as expressed by David Bohm in the opening of his textbook, *Quantum Theory*:

> It seems impossible to develop quantum concepts extensively without Fourier analysis.[489]

Our thesis, then, is that Kuo's frequency domain, bridged to time by Fourier's mathematics in our twenty-first-century information technology, has an ontological reality, and that there does exist an actual frequency domain, which we also identify with Bohm's hypothesized implicate order.

The Dynamics of Holoflux

Having established the basic architecture of the holoflux theory, it is possible to go further by imagining the cycle nature of holoflux information as it manifests in and between the two domains, from a Bohmian perspective.

During each inward (implicate) interval (of 10^{-44} seconds), Bohm's quantum potential undergoes reconfiguration calculations within the nonlocal frequency domain. These internal calculations use information that has been feeding inwardly from the explicate (space–time)

---

[488] Ibid., 3.

[489] Bohm, *Quantum Theory*, 1.

order during previous "cycles." The sub-quantum calculations within the implicate yield solutions involving frequency superposition and fractal pattern formation, likely far beyond our current mathematical capabilities, within the frequency domain. The results of this holoflux superposition-calculation are then posted into space–time, and incorporated into the outflowing modulation of holoflux as the quantum potential Q, of active information. These manifest in waveforms entering space–time as fields of modulated electromagnetic energy.

Conversely, information flowing within space–time, not only travels outward, but moves (in-folds and enfolds) towards the center, back into the implicate order, to be captured by the quantum black hole of the Planck holosphere at its event horizon. Such enfolding information is immediately available within the implicate order/frequency domain for superposition-calculation of the next out-going quantum wave into space–time. The resulting outgoing wave of quantum potential (Q) of "active information" is encoded with information to nudge every photon in the universe in space–time.

Holoplenum Plasma Display

It is possible to comprehend the emerging projection of space–time reality from the holoplenum by expanding upon the metaphor of a flat-panel plasma display. The human visual threshold for detecting separate images lies somewhere between 10 to 12 separate images per second, and accordingly the industry standard in the motion picture industry is 24 frames per second, a standard which ensures that the presentation of a sequence of completely static images appear to the human observer as smooth and continuous motion.[490] By contrast, if the entire universe flashes in and out of existence at the limiting Planck time of 5.3×10^{-44} seconds, equivalent to a "frame" rate of almost 10^{44} "frames per second," the cosmos would obviously *appear* to be smooth and continuous in all respects, certainly to any human observer of the cosmos, even at quantum dimensions.[491]

The approximate image resolution of a "holoplenum display" obtained by dividing one inch by the Planck length, yields a maximum resolution of 1.584×10^{34} holopixels per inch. At such hyper-fine resolution, even a proton in the 10^{-15} meter dimensional range would appear to be moving smoothly through space.

Quantum Biology and the Holoflux Field

Quantum mechanics and the concepts of the holoplenum and the holoflux field provide tools for understanding the biological basis for human modes of consciousness. The anesthesiologist and consciousness researcher Stuart Hameroff has, along with the British physicist Sir Roger Penrose, proposed a quantum theory of human consciousness based upon quantum field activity within microtubule structures within the human body.[492] It is notable that in a recent paper, Hameroff argues for an

---

[490] Dorf, *The Electrical Engineering Handbook*, 1538.

[491] Planck time is a constant set by the speed of light and the gravitational constant, at a value of 5.39106×10^{-44} seconds; Runehov and Oviedo, eds., *Encyclopedia of Sciences and Religions*, 1772.

[492] Hameroff and Penrose, "Conscious Events as Orchestrated Space–Time Selections."

approach to consciousness studies in terms of quantum mechanics, and refers to his own contribution in terms of an emerging "quantum biology:"

> At the turn of the 20th century, physics was perceived by its practitioners to be as solid as rock, only to be shaken to the core by the discovery of quantum mechanics. Today, perhaps the most dynamically expanding branch of science is molecular and cellular biology, which is amassing impressive reams of data well ahead of its proper integration and deep analysis. Quantum biology is emerging gradually as a response to the challenge of explaining such important, yet poorly understood phenomena as photosynthesis, bioenergetics, vision, olfaction, bird navigation, etc. Yet, the grandest challenge of all is to explain how our brains work and, in particular, how does conscious behavior emerge from the structure and function of the human brain and its cellular and sub-cellular components.[493]

Quantum Brain Dynamics

Quantum brain mechanics, and in particular, *Quantum Brain Dynamics*, a field pioneered by the physicists Hiroomi Umezawa and Herbert Fröhlich in the late 1960s, is one such contribution to Hameroff's proposed quantum biology.[494] As early as 1978, Stuart, Takahashi, and Umezawa proposed a mechanism of human memory

---

[493] Hameroff, Craddock, and Tuszynski, "Quantum Effects in the Understanding of Consciousness," 230.

[494] Jibu and Yasue, *Quantum Brain Dynamics and Consciousness*, 147.

and consciousness, consistent with quantum field theory, which they called "quantum brain dynamics (QBD)."[495]

Based on Umezawa's original research, Mari Jibu and Kunio Yasue at Seishin University in Japan put forward a detailed model of consciousness based upon the quantum dynamics of the electromagnetic field, which they describe as follows:

> The long-standing difficulty of understanding the origin and mechanism of unity of consciousness (as a unified self) has been called the "binding problem" in neurophysiology. The binding problem may be solved . . . by investigating the usually neglected quantum electromagnetic phenomena taking place in the dynamically ordered regions (i.e., perimembranous regions) of intracellular and extracellular water. There, each brain cell is enfolded within a common field of macroscopic condensation of evanescent photons and all the physico-chemical processes taking part in the stratified society of brain cells are subject to the control and unification by quantum electrodynamics. Unity of consciousness thus arises from the existence of the global field of condensed evanescent photons overlapping the whole brain tissue in the cranium.[496]

In extending Umezawa's theory of QBD, Jibu and Yasue describe how they have discovered that, through dynamic resonance (spin), polarized dipole water molecules

---

[495] Stuart, Takahashi, and Umezawa, "Mixed System Brain Dynamics."

[496] Jibu and Yasue, "Quantum Brain Dynamics and Quantum Field Theory," 288.

throughout the blood stream produce the activity, in effect, of a single resonant water dipole, a "macromolecule" in the bodies of all living, water based creatures. The macromolecular-dipole, offering an exceptional information highway for electromagnetic fields on the macro level, manifests as a plasma. It should be noted that it was the physics of plasma that captivated David Bohm during his thesis research under Oppenheimer, and it is useful here to clarify the definition of plasma:

> A state of matter in which a significant portion of the particles are ionized. Plasmas are by far the most common phase of matter in the universe, both by mass and by volume. All stars are made of plasma, and interstellar space is filled with plasma. Common forms of plasma include lightning, St. Elmo's fire, the polar aurorae, the solar wind, neon signs, and plasma displays in modern home television.[497]

Within this polarized, nonlocal, H_2O quantum field is embedded an electromagnetic field described here by Jibu and Yasue:

> There are two basic fields in QBD: the water rotational field and the electromagnetic field. The two must be described simultaneously by quantum field theory because they interact with each other.... The water rotational field extending over the whole assembly of brain cells manifests an overall domain structure in which the whole region occupied by water is divided into many domains.... In other words, they are

---

[497] Chen, *Introduction to Plasma Physics*, 56.

bound to each other quite strongly by a quantum theoretical nonlocal coherence.[498]

In 1995, building upon their earlier paradigm, Jibu and Yasue published the mathematics to support their theory that the creation and annihilation dynamics of "corticons" points to an "energy quanta of the water rotational field extending to the whole assembly of brain cells, and photons, that is, energy quanta of the electromagnetic field."[499] Their theory focuses upon the nonlocal quantum field that is generated within the human circulatory system, embedded in an electromagnetic field manifesting throughout the contiguous ionized , blood plasma system.

That our blood might act as an electromagnetic plasma should not be surprising— the first line in a textbook on plasma physics reads, "It has often been said that 99% of the matter in the universe is in the plasma state."[500] Jibu and Yasue go further by explaining how QBD explain how life itself can be seen to be equivalent to "the unity of water" in the human body, or as "a single molecule" in the human blood system:

> All H_2O molecules bound together in a QBD vacuum domain form a single, extensive molecule of water in a macroscopic domain. That is, water throughout the entire region of the

[498] Jibu and Yasue, *Quantum Brain Dynamics and Consciousness*, 164–65.

[499] Jibu and Yasue, "Quantum Brain Dynamics and Quantum Field Theory," 293.

[500] Chen, *Introduction to Plasma Physics*, 1.

cerebral cortex is thought to be composed of many macroscopic water molecules whose sizes are all comparable to the coherence length of the QBD vacuum, that is, about 50 microns. This remarkable feature of water in living matter might provide us with quantum field theoretical support for the idea that life is nothing but the unity of water as a single molecule in living matter.[501]

Quantum brain dynamics supports the model of a locus of consciousness beyond that of the nervous system and brain. The supporting pattern can be found in the QBD manifestation of a "single extensive molecule of water," dipolar in geometry like an antenna, generating a complex magnetic field through the circulation of hydrogen ions in blood plasma.

In such a model, the blood system of the human body can be seen as an extensively polarized "super cell" of nonlocal electromagnetic plasma energy, which can then be differentiated from the neuronal brain body of consciousness, itself generated by sequential electrical patterns flowing as pulses in the nervous system pathways. Moving charges generate magnetic fields, and ionized human blood flow is no exception: flowing blood plasma results in creation of a magnetic field, and this is in accord the conjecture of QBD.[502] The circulatory system can be seen as a magnetic plasma composed primarily of ionized red blood cells (referred to as erythrocytes) and water molecules, flowing together in complex vortices of blood

---

[501] Jibu and Yasue, "Quantum Brain Dynamics and Quantum Field Theory," 293.

[502] Dorf, *The Electrical Engineering Handbook*, 27.

plasma around every cell and through every capillary of the body.[503] Each erythrocyte is a flexible, annular, bio-concave disk shaped like a doughnut (in geometry, a torus), having a thin webbed center where the hole in a pastry doughnut would be located (Fig. 34).

Mammalian erythrocytes are unique among vertebrates for having no nucleus at all; each blood cell sheds its nucleus and internal organelles as it reaches maturity. The typical outside diameter of a red blood cell is approximately 9 microns, close to the infrared wavelength of 9.6 microns generated by the human body.[504]

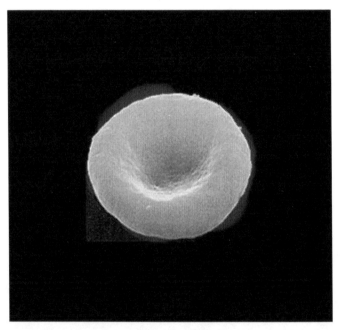

Figure 34. Red blood cell. Graphic by Svdmolen (2005). This work is in the public domain under the terms of Title 17, Chapter 1, Section 105 of the US Code.

---

[503] McCraty, *The Energetic Heart*.

[504] Turgeon, *Clinical Hematology*.

The adult human body contains approximately 6 grams of iron, of which 60% is stored throughout the 10^{12} erythrocytes, each of which contains approximately 270 million atoms of ionic iron embedded in transparent hemoglobin.[505] Thus each erythrocyte, replete with iron ions embedded in hemoglobin, creates in effect, an ionized iron toroid.[506] One of the best-known applications of the toroid shape is called the "Tokamak device," which uses a magnetic field to confine plasma in the shape of a torus in experiments to produce controlled thermonuclear fusion power. Andrei Sakharov, who eventually became known internationally as a Soviet dissident, first designed the Tokamak enclosure device in the Soviet Union in the 1950s.[507]

Holoflux Analysis of Human Red Blood Cell

Let us step through a holoflux analysis of the possible functions of a red blood cell as a locus of consciousness and the possible use of the erythrocyte as a locus of memory storage at the human biological scale. If, as previously conjectured, the red blood cell has an ideal diameter to resonate electromagnetic radiation in its ferrite-embedded ring at the human infrared wavelength of 10 microns, then we can ask if this configuration could accommodate a unique isospheric frequency (wavelength) for each of the

---

[505] Romanes, *Cunningham's Textbook of Anatomy.*

[506] Wick, Pinggera, and Lehmann, *Clinical Aspects and Laboratory Iron Metabolism,* 6.

[507] Nishikawa and Wakatani, *Plasma Physics.*

currently 7 billion living humans on the planet. Figure 35 outlines the feasibility of this approach.

Assuming each unique frequency would match its radially unique isosphere, separated by only one Planck length, Figure 35 suggests how seven billion unique isospheres, each of quantum discrete frequency, might be nested within the geometry of a typical human red blood cell (in the image we have multiplied 7 billion times the Planck length of approximately 10^{-35} m to obtain an estimated shell thickness of 10^{-26} meters). This implies that each living human being might have a unique holospheric frequency, detectable by other human blood cells via the implicate order about which each is centered, and thus provides a possible mechanism for communication, via the mechanisms of resonance and superposition in the frequency domain of the implicate order.

How 7 billion unique human frequencies can be accommodated within the ring diameter of an erythrocyte.

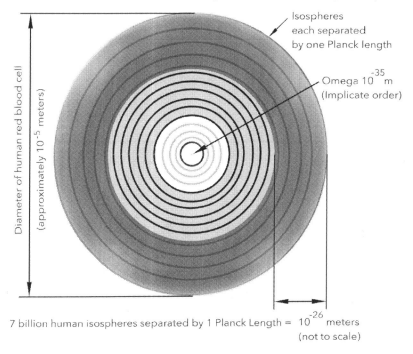

Isospheres each separated by one Planck length

Omega 10^{-35} m (Implicate order)

Diameter of human red blood cell (approximately 10^{-5} meters)

7 billion human isospheres separated by 1 Planck Length = 10^{-26} meters (not to scale)

Figure 35. Isospheric capacity of red blood cell. Graphic by author.

A calculated estimate of the memory storage capacity of a single red blood cell can now be made, using Wheeler's approach to determine the number of Bekenstein equivalent bits on the surface of an isosphere the diameter of a typical red blood cell.[508] Here we take 8.1 microns, (or 8.1 x 10^{-5} meters), as the average diameter of a typical human red blood cell, and proceed to calculate the maximum possible storage capacity on the surface of a hypothetical holosphere associated with a single red blood.[509] To obtain the limiting

---

[508] Wheeler, *A Journey into Gravity and Spacetime*, 222.

[509] Romanes, *Cunningham's Textbook of Anatomy*, 137.

number of bits, we simply calculate the surface area on a sphere of 8.1 microns diameter, and then divide the value obtained by 1.04 x 10^{-69} square meters (which is the Bekenstein unit of entropy, or approximately the square of the Planck length, 1.616199 x 10^{-35} meter).[510] The surface area of the erythrocyte-bisected sphere is $4\pi r^2$ or $4\pi(8.1$ x $10^{-5})^2$ = $4\pi(6.561$ x $10^{-9})$ = 8.24 x 10^{-9} square meters. Dividing this by the qubit area of 1.04 x 10^{-69} square meters yields the estimated maximum storage capacity of 8 x 10^{60} information bits. This is an extremely large information storage capacity.

Not to be neglected as part of any electromagnetic holoflux process associated with the cardiovascular system is the likely role of the heart:

> The heart generates the largest electromagnetic field in the body. The electrical field as measured in an electrocardiogram (ECG) is about 60 times greater in amplitude than the brain waves recorded in an electroencephalogram (EEG). The magnetic component of the heart's field, which is around 5000 times stronger than that produced by the brain, is not impeded by tissues and can be measured several feet away from the body with Superconducting Quantum Interference Device (SQUID) based magnetometers.[511]

Dimensional Analysis and EMF Wavelength

As previously discussed, a rule of thumb in applying the phenomenon of resonance in any situation indicates

---

[510] Wheeler, *A Journey into Gravity and Spacetime*, 222.

[511] McCraty, *The Energetic Heart*, 1.

that the optimal physical dimensions of the resonant receiving system must approach a half-wavelength of the dimension of the transmitted energy wave. Using dimensional analysis, this fact can be used in the search for possible loci of consciousness in the electromagnetic spectrum. In this section we examine calculated correlations between dimensions of structural bio-components in the human body and corresponding wavelengths in the electromagnetic spectrum.

If we examine human biophysical components and calculate their peak resonant electromagnetic energy frequencies using Wien's Law, and then identify the frequency bandwidth within which we find these resonances for the biological components being examined, two possible systems emerge: the near infrared and the near ultraviolet (the use of the word "near" implies frequencies adjacent to the visible spectrum).

The following dimensional analysis correlations support the possibility of a conscious electromagnetic– holoflux information system active within a 10 micron wavelength band throughout the human bio-system:

- The human body at 98.6 F emits wavelengths of 9.6 μm.
- Earth has an atmospheric pass-band at wavelengths of 9–10 μm.
- Inner diameters of blood capillaries are 10 μm.
- Outside diameter of a typical blood cells is 9 μm.

- CO_2 laser outputs between wavelengths of 9.4 –10.6 μm.[512]

Data is presented in Table 5, ranking physical components by increasing size, along with their calculated Wien blackbody peak wavelengths and corresponding theoretical waveguide resonant frequency ranges.

As indicated in Table 5, the average diameter of human blood capillaries of 10 μm coincides with a major "passband" of the planetary atmosphere itself. As previously discussed, a simple Wien's law calculation show that the normal human body radiates most strongly in the near infrared, measured at a macro level as "heat" at a temperature of 91.6 F, which again, using Wien's Law, exhibits a peak spectral energy response at wavelengths of approximately 10 μm. It is accordingly to this wavelength that the maximum sensitivity of military night-vision goggles is tuned.[513]

A physiological waveguide candidate in another frequency range can be found in the inner diameter of the microtubule system, located throughout neurons and also within cilia.[514] At 15 nm in dimension, microtubules would be especially sensitive to an electromagnetic wavelength in

---

[512] The carbon dioxide laser is one of the earliest gas lasers to be developed (invented by Kumar Patel of Bell Labs in 1964), and is still one of the most useful. Carbon dioxide lasers are the highest-power continuous wave lasers that are currently available; Milonni and Eberly, *Laser Physics*.

[513] Clark, *Photography by Infrared—Its Principles and Applications*, 78.

[514] Pizzi et al., "Evidences of New Biophysical Properties of Microtubules."

the ultraviolet bandwidth, just above visible light frequencies in the electromagnetic spectrum.

Table 5
Physical Correlations with Electromagnetic Frequency Bands

Physical component	Range (physical dimension)	Calculated blackbody wavelength peak	Calculated electromagnetic resonant waveguide frequency range
Passband of Earth's atmosphere	1 to 11 microns	3 to 50 microns = "Mid-Infrared Spectrum"	$10^{12}–10^{13}$ Hz
Blood capillary system	10 microns	3 to 50 microns = "Mid-Infrared Spectrum"	$10^{12}–10^{13}$ Hz
Red blood cell	6 to 8 microns	3 to 50 microns = "Mid-Infrared Spectrum"	$10^{12}–10^{13}$ Hz
Cerebral neuron nucleus	3 microns to 18 microns	3 to 50 microns = "Mid-Infrared Spectrum"	$10^{12}–10^{13}$ Hz
Unmyelinated cortical axons in the brain	80 nm to 400 nm	10 to 400 nm = "Ultraviolet Spectrum"	$10^{16}–10^{17}$ Hz
Microtubule in neuron and in cilia	15 nm to 25 nm	10 nm to 400 nm is the "Ultraviolet Spectrum"	$10^{16}–10^{17}$ Hz

Note. nm = nanometer (10^{-9} meter); Hz = Hertz. Data adapted from Romanes, *Cunningham's Textbook of Anatomy.* Author's table.

Biosphere, Magnetosphere, Chromosphere

In searching for energies of consciousness, it is important to explore the possibility of consciousness as having a component (if not comprising) the Earth's magnetic field, also known as the geomagnetic field, the magnetic field of energy flux extending from the Earth's inner core out to its interaction with that stream of high energy particles emanating from the Sun, the solar wind. This enormous magnetic field in which we find ourselves is generated by a magnetic dipole, powerfully driven by a spiraling ocean of liquid metal in the outer core, spinning around the enormous copper-magnesium crystal of the Earth's inner core. A supercomputer at the Los Alamos National Laboratory has created a model of flow patterns of geomagnetic energy within and around the Earth, illustrated in Fig. 36. Each line represents the locus of an intense magnetic field component. The dense clusters of magnetic lines are within the Earth's core.

Figure 36. Supercomputer model of magnetosphere. Graphic by Glatzmaier (2007). This work is in the public domain under the terms of Title 17, Chapter 1, Section 105 of the US Code.

The dipole axis of the Earth is tilted at an approximate angle of 11 degrees with respect to the rotational axis, as if there were a bar magnet placed at that angle along the central axis of the Earth. However, unlike the static field of a bar magnet, Earth's geomagnetic field quivers and resonates over time in synch with the motion of molten iron alloys in the Earth's outer core, the geodynamo. If the universe is alive and sentient, then these vibrations could be replete with frequency modes of consciousness, communication signals yet to be deciphered by human technology, filling bandwidths that have perhaps only thus far been explored by mystics, shamans, and cybernauts.[515]

Where might there be found other electromagnetic energies of the earth, candidates for some holoflux-driven form of consciousness? Geophysicists have determined that two fundamental energy sources are to be found in the earth's crust: geothermal and geoelectric energy, respectively. We are all aware of geothermal energy, spectacularly displayed in enormous glowing lava flows from volcanic activity, erupting geothermal energy rising from below the crust of the Earth. But what is not widely known is that while the amount of *geothermal* energy in the world is estimated to be approximately equal to 2×10^7 Megawatt-hours (MWh), this is dwarfed by the amount of *geoelectric* energy, which is equal to 1.14×10^8 MWh, a surprisingly tenfold magnitude greater than the geothermal energy.[516]

---

[515] Lilly, *The Deep Self: Consciousness Exploration in the Isolation Tank.*

[516] Booth, Koren, and Persinger, "Increased Feelings of the Sensed Presence During Exposures to Weak Magnetic Fields."

This geoelectric energy, which can be seen in the atmosphere discharging in lightning strikes and in ionized aurora borealis displays, flows in vast currents of electromagnetic energy, rivers of flowing electrons, both in the sea and within the Earth's crust, in enormous rivers of electricity. [517] These geoelectric flows are called telluric currents (from Latin *tellūs*, "earth"), and they occur both in the Earth's crust as well as within the much deeper mantle. These geomagnetically induced currents are generated by the daily enormous magnetic interactions of the sun's magnetic field and the spinning Earth's geomagnetic field at the geopause, the area where the sun and the earth meet in ever-changing resonant magnetic vibrations of enormous power that induce the aurora borealis and the telluric currents flowing in and around the surface of the planet. [518]

Nikola Tesla, who invented the alternating current electrical grid system, in spite of Thomas Edison's attempt to make his direct current distribution system the standard, began to fabricate a system that would tap telluric currents for electrical power and use the currents themselves to transmit the power in wireless electrical energy grids, affording free power distributed over the face of the Earth by the planet itself. [519] Mysteriously, his pilot experimental station which would have tapped the Telluric currents was burned to the ground, some say by Thomas Edison's supporters. [520]

---

[517] Allaby and Allaby, "Telluric Current."

[518] Ibid.

[519] M. Cheney, *Tesla: Man Out of Time.*

[520] Ibid, 78.

This enormous geoelectric energy is spread all over the earth's crust, most concentrated in wet rocks located in the earthquake belt zones.[521] If human consciousness does have an energy component in the electromagnetic spectrum, then it must be affected by, and interact to some degree with, this geoelectric energy environment of the earth. Many animals possess a "magnetic sense" and appear to be able to track the magnetic field of the earth, which is generated by the flow of molten material in the earth's core and the corresponding flow of ions in the atmosphere. [522] Magnetoreception is an accepted phenomenon among a wide range of animals: birds, fruit flies, honeybees, turtles, lobsters, sharks, stingrays, whales and even bacteria.[523]

Even animals not normally known for their migration habits have been discovered to possess such a sense:

> Recent publications from a German research group (Begall et al., 2008), made the discovery that cattle (and other herd animals, such as red and roe deer) tend to situate themselves on a magnetic North–South axis, as if involuntarily directed by the earth's magnetic field. These surprising results were discovered when satellite images provided by Google Earth were used to analyze herding patterns and behavior. However, the built-in magnetic compass gets out of alignment the closer the cattle get to high voltage

---

[521] Vejvoda, *17th International Conference on Reactor Technology*, 17.

[522] Ruhenstroth-Bauer, "Influence of the Earth's Magnetic Field," 336.

[523] Wiltschko and Wiltschko, "Magnetoreception in Birds and Other Animals," 675.

power lines, and the cattle then align with the power lines instead.[524]

Contemporary research in electrophysiology indicates that human bodies may be more involved in sensing electromagnetic fields than has previously been acknowledged. Research at Cal Tech has discovered traces of magnetite in the human brain and heart, in about the same density as that found in migrating animals, and has proven that onset of rapid eye movement in sleeping humans is shortened in the E–W directional orientation of sleepers as compared to the N–S position.[525]

On the average there are from about one hundred lightning discharges per second around the globe.[526] It is known that one of the physical characteristics of the earth is that an effective waveguide cavity exists between the ionosphere and the surface of the earth, and this cavity resonates at 7.8 to 8.0 Hz, in what is called the Schumann resonance frequency peak.[527] The same frequency peak found in high end Theta waves and low end Alpha waves as measured on the human scalp.[528] In studying this Schumann cavity resonance phenomenon, the neurophysiologist Michael Persinger hs concluded:

---

[524] Ibid, 677.

[525] Ruhenstroth-Bauer, "Influence of Earth's Magnetic Field," 195.

[526] Persinger, "Schumann Resonance Frequencies," 25.

[527] Sentman, "Schumann Resonances," 271.

[528] Allaby and Allaby, "Telluric Current," 43.

Because of the very small attenuation rates within the cavity, electromagnetic patterns are generated for megameters without appreciable loss of amplitude. In general, the expansion and return of the "ringing" around the earth's circumference can occur between 4 and 5 times. The latency for the return of the circular wave is about 125 milliseconds.[529]

These lightning discharges, within the geophysical cavity, emit energy waves that travel around the globe and return in 125 ms cycles. In one second, each wave circles the planet eight times (8 x 125 ms = 1 second). This in effect results in an ongoing lightning driven pulse rate equal to the cranial wave frequency of 8 Hz. The question then becomes, is this match of the predominant human Alpha wave with the planetary Schumann resonances of electromagnetic energy coincidence, or evolutionary design? If the psyche has a spectral frequency component, then is it possible that there have evolved in the human biosystem physiological modulators of this frequency component?

Microwave cavities are to the invisible frequency energy spectrum what lenses are to visible light energy.[530] In a biomedical engineering class lecture discussing the electrophysiology of the nervous system, I noticed the striking similarities between the waveguide horn antennas designed in another class, a microwave communication lab, and the images of the ventricular cavities within the human cranial cavity. I mentioned this to my professor and was assured that the ventricular system, as understood, had only

---

[529] Persinger, "Schumann Resonance Frequencies," 25.

[530] Warren and Brandt, "Optical Constants of Ice from the Ultraviolet to the Microwave."

two functions, that it existed to help maintain thermal equilibrium in the brain, and that it acted as mechanical protection for the brain, by attenuating sudden shock trauma to the skull. Nevertheless, the ventricular cavities (Fig. 37) are seen to be dimensionally consistent with the microwave band, which covers a range of frequencies with wavelength from one millimeter to one meter.[531]

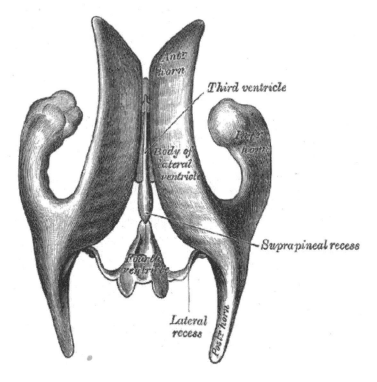

Figure 37. Drawing of ventricular cavities. Graphic by Gray (1918). Reprinted under the terms of a Creative Commons Attribution ShareAlike 3.0 Unported license. Image retrieved from Wikimedia Commons.

---

[531] Dorf, *The Electrical Engineering Handbook*.

Another clue may be seen in cerebrospinal fluid itself, conventionally dismissed as being understood simply to act as a shock absorber or nutrient circulation system for the brain:

> Cerebrospinal fluid (CSF) is a clear, colorless liquid that bathes the brain and spinal cord. While the primary function of CSF is to cushion the brain within the skull and serve as a shock absorber for the central nervous system, CSF also circulates nutrients and chemicals filtered from the blood and removes waste products from the brain.[532]

Comparing the drawing of the ventricular cavities (Fig. 37) with the image of a waveguide system for microwaves used in radar (Fig. 38), it can be concluded that perhaps within the cavities of the ventricular system can be discovered another instance of Deacon's "something that is not there."[533]

---

[532] National Multiple Sclerosis Society. "Cerebrospinal Fluid (CSF)."

[533] Deacon, "What Is Missing from Theories of Information," 140.

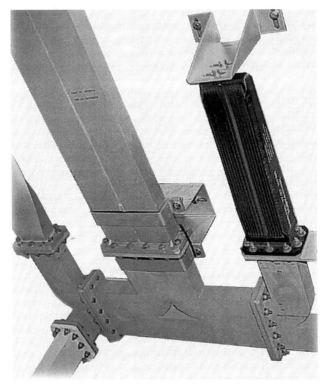

Figure 38. Microwave radar circuitry. Graphic by Averse (2007). Reprinted under the terms of a Creative Commons Attribution ShareAlike 3.0 Unported license. Image retrieved from Wikimedia Commons.

Chapter 6: The Hyperphysics of Teilhard

> In spite of all the theoretical objections that would seek to discourage the belief, our minds remain invincibly persuaded that a certain very simple fundamental rule lies hidden beneath the overpowering multiplicity of events and beings: to discover and formulate this rule, we believe, would make the universe intelligible in the totality of its development.[534]
>
> > –Pierre Teilhard de Chardin

Early in the twentieth century, Marie Joseph Pierre Teilhard de Chardin,[535] a geologist, paleontologist, and priest by training, developed a model of consciousness, which he referred to as "hyperphysics."[536] He conceived of this model in the context of his knowledge of physics, his keen observational skills as a geo-paleontologist, and his own specific introspective experience over a 40-year period of careful observation and consideration. In developing hyperphysics, Teilhard conducted an integral exploration of a region inclusive of and yet beyond the conceptual boundaries of physics or paleontology or the priesthood. His theories of consciousness, detailed in his many essays, are examined and interpreted here through the lens of the

---

[534] Teilhard, "Centrology: An Essay in a Dialectic of Union," 99. Essay written in 1944.

[535] In this dissertation, I refer to him as Teilhard de Chardin, or simply Teilhard.

[536] Teilhard, *The Human Phenomenon*, 2.

Pribram—Bohm holoflux theories examined previously. The objectives of this chapter are to interpret and extend Teilhard's theories of hyperphysics in general, and to discover how Teilhard's theories can be reconciled with holoflux theory.

In a letter to Henri de Lubac[537] dated 1934, Teilhard uses the word *hyperphysics*, describing it as a kind of metaphysics springing from the hard sciences, a metaphysics based upon science, yet "another sort of metaphysics which would really be a hyperphysics."[538] In the first sentence of the Author's Note to *The Human Phenomenon*, Teilhard states that the nature of his theories of hyperphysics is scientific, "purely and simply":

> If this book is to be properly understood it must be read not as a work on metaphysics, still less as a sort of theological essay, but purely and simply as a scientific treatise . . . only take a closer look at it, and you will see that this "hyperphysics" is not a metaphysics. [539]

It can be assumed that, trained in the sciences of geology and paleontology, Teilhard would have been an astute observer, constantly seeking and discerning patterns in the natural world. His published professional papers led to significant recognition in the field of paleontology; when published in 1971, a collection of his scientific papers filled

---

[537] de Lubac, *The Religion of Teilhard de Chardin*; Henri de Lubac, eventually Cardinal de Lubac, was a Jesuit friend and correspondent of Teilhard's for more than 30 years.

[538] Teilhard, *Lettres Intimes*, 269.

[539] Teilhard, *The Phenomenon of Man*, xix.

eleven volumes.[540] Yet, in spite of the time constraints of his dual career as priest and scientist, he was able to develop, through a long series of unpublished essays written over his lifetime, a coherent theory describing a general physics of consciousness. Fueled by a lifelong practice of introspective observation, often alone in the silence of nature, Teilhard elaborated his map of the dynamics of consciousness, hyperphysics.

It is likely that Teilhard never knew how his life work in hyperphysics and the evolution of consciousness would be judged by mainstream science; the English edition of *The Phenomenon of Man* was only published in 1959, four years after his death, and was received somewhat critically both by the philosophical and the scientific community, as can be seen in this 1965 review:

> Is his proposed "hyperphysics" science? . .There has been considerable confusion both in the United States and in Europe, where it appeared in French four years earlier, over what it is— physics, metaphysics, theology, mysticism, prophecy?[541]

Rarely has a scientist, formally trained and active in a demanding technical profession, found time and interest (under the tacit threat of ridicule or censure) to develop a theory of consciousness based upon the data of first-hand participatory experience and observation. Pierre Teilhard de Chardin was one of the few: a trained scientist, holding a

---

[540] Teilhard, *L'oeuvre Scientifique.*

[541] B. Cheney, "Has Teilhard de Chardin 'Really' Joined the Within and the Without of Things?," 217.

doctorate in geological paleontology from the Sorbonne, who wrote regularly and extensively to produce a science-based model of the evolutionary dynamics of consciousness, an "ultraphysics of union."[542] For over 40 years, through direct experience, observation, and keen analysis, Teilhard laid down a foundation and a legacy that he hoped would forge a new science-based understanding of the dynamics of consciousness in an evolving cosmos.[543]

Teilhard's Integral Life Experience

It is easy to see how the region of his birth, Auvergne in south central France, instilled in Teilhard a passion for geology and nature (Fig. 39).

Figure 39. Auvergne landscape. Graphic by Romary (2006). Reprinted under the terms of a Creative Commons Attribution ShareAlike 3.0 Unported license. Image retrieved from Wikimedia Commons.

---

[542] Ibid.

[543] Teilhard, "The Stuff of the Universe," 383. Essay written in 1953.

The most volcanic, mineral-rich region of France, Auvergne is also home to the largest oak forest in Europe, and it was here, a few miles from the highest volcanic summit in the region, that Pierre Teilhard de Chardin was born on May 1, 1881, the fourth of 11 siblings, in his family chateau, Sarcenat.[544]

Teilhard was a direct descendent of Voltaire, on his mother's side, and his father, descended from a noble family, was one of the largest landowners in the province, affording him ample free time to "build up sizeable collections of regional insects, birds, stones, and plants."[545] It was into this rich environment that Teilhard was born, soon becoming entranced with nature; he embraced his father's passion for geology, and at an early age began collecting and classifying specimens. But it was his mother's influence that instilled in her young son a love of the spiritual life, and he was introduced to regular family prayer, and a contemplative practice, the prayer on the Sacred Heart of Jesus. Following family tradition, Teilhard was sent to a Jesuit boarding school at the age of 11.[546]

Of all the Catholic religious congregations, the Jesuit order is especially known for its emphasis on intellectual research and scholarship, and in this environment Teilhard excelled academically. But it was here, also, that Teilhard began his daily practice of sitting for an hour in silent contemplation:

---

[544] King, *Spirit of Fire: The Life and Vision of Teilhard de Chardin*, 1.

[545] Ibid., 4.

[546] Ibid.

It was at the school that he became an ascetic who voluntarily rose at dawn every day and went to sit in the chapel, often in freezing temperatures before the rest of the students awoke. He would follow a similar habit throughout his life, wherever he might be: in an Asian desert, in a prehistoric cave, or aboard a ship in rough seas.[547]

In 1899, at the age of 17, he made the decision to join the Jesuit order, and was formally accepted as a Jesuit novice, a candidate for eventual priesthood. After completing Jesuit secondary school, as part of his training as a novice, he was assigned abroad to teach physics and chemistry for a three-year period. Teilhard was sent to a Jesuit-run school in Cairo, Egypt, and it was there that he first experienced the fascination of an exotic new culture, an attraction to the mystery of surrounding antiquities, and most of all, perhaps, in the experience of profound silence in the vastness of a desert.[548]

It was immediately after I had experienced such sense of wonder in Egypt that there gradually grew in me, as a *presence* much more than as an abstract notion, the consciousness of a deep-running, ontological, total Current which embraced the whole Universe in which I moved; and this consciousness continued to grow until it filled the whole horizon of my inner being.[549]

---

[547] Aczel, *The Jesuit and the Skull*, 72.

[548] Ibid., 24.

[549] Teilhard, *The Heart of Matter*, 25.

Upon returning from Egypt, in 1909, Teilhard spent several years studying philosophy and theology at a Jesuit center in Hastings, on the coast of England, 60 miles southeast of London. It was during this time that he carefully read and reread *Creative Evolution*, a recently published work by the popular French philosopher Henri Bergson (1859–1941), a book the Vatican would soon place on its Index of Forbidden Books.[550] Previously, Teilhard had uncritically accepted the currently held theory of the *fixity* of species, and though he knew of Darwin's theories, they had seemed to him only an interesting hypothesis, one certainly suspect in the eyes of his Jesuit community. But after a careful reading of Bergson's *Creative Evolution*, Teilhard found himself suddenly a "convinced evolutionist," in strong agreement with Bergson's arguments for evolution, while yet disagreeing with Bergson's vision of a "pre-existing and obdurate matter" being operated upon by a life-force energy, which Bergson named *élan vital*. Teilhard himself felt that this life-force, referred to by Bergson, was never to be found remote from matter, but from inception is at the very heart of matter.[551]

The dynamics of evolution, according to Bergson, is powered by a "vital" force of energy that animates not only life but the unfolding of the cosmos, and that fundamentally connects consciousness and body, an idea in radical contrast to widely accepted belief in the *dualism* of matter and consciousness, set forth by the seventeenth century philosopher–scientist René Descartes.[552]

---

[550] Ibid., 74.

[551] Raven, *Teilhard de Chardin: Scientist and Seer*, 164–65.

[552] Bergson, *Creative Evolution*.

The young Teilhard was especially impressed with Bergson's emphasis on the importance of *intuition* and *immediate experience*, as these were Teilhard's own tools, developed and honed during his daily contemplative practices. Through immediate experience he was able to observe directly the structure and dynamics of his own inner space, his own complexity-consciousness in process, and he says that this has led to "a new intuition that totally alters the physiognomy of the universe in which we move, in other words, in an awakening."[553] Near the end of his life Teilhard comments on the early influence of Bergson's book:

> I can remember very clearly the avidity with which, at that time, I read Bergson's *Creative Evolution* . . . I can now see quite clearly that the effect that brilliant book had upon me was to provide fuel at just the right moment . . . for a fire that was already consuming my heart and mind. And that fire had been kindled.[554]

The effect of Bergson's ideas upon Teilhard's worldview was significant indeed. In 1930, Teilhard wrote of Bergson, in a letter to his close friend Leontine Zanta (the first French woman to receive a doctorate in philosophy), "I pray for that admirable man and venerate him as a kind of saint."[555] After reading *Creative Evolution*, according to Teilhard's biographer Ursula King:

---

[553] Teilhard, *The Human Phenomenon*, 149.

[554] Teilhard, *The Heart of Matter*, 25.

[555] Teilhard, *Letters to Leontine Zanta*, 102.

The magic word "evolution" haunted his thoughts "like a tune"; it was to him "like an unsatisfied hunger, like a promise held out to me, like a summons to be answered." Evolution was vital. It was the necessary condition of all further scientific thought.[556]

In 1912, Teilhard began formal graduate studies in geology and paleontology, eventually leading to his doctorate, though interrupted by World War I; as a student, he also began working at the Museum of Natural History in Paris. In 1914 he was called up for service by the French Army and quickly trained as a medical orderly.[557] After serving for some time behind the lines, he volunteered to be reassigned to the Western Front, as a stretcher bearer rather than as an army chaplain, and on January 22, 1915, he was assigned to a regiment of Moroccan light infantry, where "on arrival Teilhard made himself look like an Arab by exchanging his field-service blue for the khaki colors of the African troops, and his kepi for a red fez."[558]

It was here, alongside members of this regiment of Algerian tribesmen that Teilhard served for over three years in the trenches of the front lines. Teilhard was the only Christian in his regiment, but by the end of the war he was referred to affectionately by the North African Muslim soldiers he lived with in the trenches as *"Sidi Marabout,"* an acknowledgement of his spiritual power as a man closely bound to God, protected from all injuries by divine

---

[556] King, *Spirit of Fire*, 38.

[557] King, *Spirit of Fire*, 47.

[558] Ibid., 49.

grace."[559] After the war, at the request of his war-time regiment, Teilhard was awarded the French Legion of Honour for bravery.[560] His citation reads:

> An outstanding stretcher-bearer, who during four years of active service was in every battle and engagement the regiment took part in, applying to remain in the ranks in order that he might be with the men whose dangers and hardships he constantly shared.[561]

Teilhard thus witnessed first-hand, for a protracted period of his life, the enormous suffering and destruction of human life that was the characteristic brutality of the war. Such experience was in sharp contrast to his academic life.

> It was in Belgium that Teilhard experienced the true horror of World War I. When they arrived at Ypres, the troops found a town that had just been burned down. Hundreds of soldiers lay on the ground, dead or dying. And after the Germans were through with their conventional weapons strike, they attacked their enemy with poison gas.[562]

---

[559] King, *Pierre Teilhard de Chardin*, 52; *Sidi Marabout*: An Arabic title of great esteem and honor; *Sidi* refers to a North African settled in France; *Marabout* designates a saint and ascetic blessed with divine favor.

[560] Aczel, *The Jesuit and the Skull*, 82.

[561] Ibid.

[562] Ibid., 77.

Yet the young scholar/priest seemed to display no fear, at least to his closest colleagues. One of his fellow soldiers at the time, Max Bégoüen, wrote the following, describing an event he witnessed on the Belgian front, in 1915:

> The North African sharpshooters of his regiment thought he was protected by his *baraka* (an Arabic word meaning "spiritual stature" or "supernatural quality"). The curtain of machine gun fire and the hail of bombardments both seemed to pass him by. During the attacks of September 2 at Artois, my brother was wounded, and, as he wandered on the battlefield, he saw a single stretcher bearer rising up in front of him, and he, for it was Teilhard, accomplished his mission quite imperturbably under terrible ire . . . "I thought I had seen the appearance of a messenger from God."
>
> I once asked Father Teilhard, "What do you do to keep this sense of calm during battle? It looks as if you do not see the danger and that fear does not touch you."
>
> He answered, with that serious but friendly smile which gave such a human warmth to his words, "If I am killed, I shall just change my state, that's all."[563]

During this time and under these conditions he began to experience, observe, and ultimately write about, his own direct awareness of nonordinary states of consciousness. For example, it was at the front that he began to perceive, directly, for the first time, a sense of collective consciousness over and above his own. In his 1917 essay

---

[563] Corte, *Pierre Teilhard de Chardin*, 15.

"Nostalgia for the Front," Teilhard asks, "Is it not ridiculous to be so drawn into the magnetic field of the war . . . more than ever the Front casts its spell over me . . . . What is it, then, that I myself have seen at the front?"[564] And he answers himself, "it is above all something more, something more subtle and more substantial, I might define it as a superhuman state to which the soul is borne." Having left the front lines, he experiences a feeling of loss: "I have the feeling of having lost a soul, a soul greater than my own, which lives in the trenches and which I have left behind."[565]

It trying to understand the impact of these experiences on the young Teilhard, it is worthwhile to consider that at Verdun, where Teilhard served during one of the most protracted battles of the war, the single battle continued for over nine months, and the human losses approached apocalyptic proportion:

> A French estimate that is probably not excessive places the total French and German losses on the Verdun battlefield at 420,000 dead, and 800,000 gassed or wounded; nearly a million and a quarter in all.[566]

It was at Verdun, the night before the attack on Fort Douaumont, on October 14, 1916, that Teilhard experienced an extraordinary vision, which he recounted afterwards in the short essay, "Christ in Matter."[567] Here, in the visual

---

[564] Teilhard, "Nostalgia for the Front," 172.

[565] Ibid.

[566] Horne, *The Price of Glory: Verdun 1916*, 328.

[567] Teilhard, "Christ in Matter," 61. Essay written in 1916.

imagery alone, one can only imagine that Teilhard was experiencing a major psychotropic vision, perhaps brought on by fatigue, synesthesia from the constant bombardment, or from the stress of being continually at the front on the eve of a major offensive attack.

The Powerful Vision

The imagery of Teilhard's vision is so intense and specific here that one wonders, even, if he might have ingested ergot-infected rye bread (ergot mold on rye bread has been reported to induce LSD-like symptoms; in 1951 an entire French village became infected with the ergot alkaloid, experiencing hallucinations).[568] Here is Teilhard's description of this pivotal, altered-state experience that occurred in an abandoned chapel, at night, during the battle of Verdun:

> Suppose, I thought, that Christ should deign to appear here, in the flesh, before my very eyes— what would he look like? Most important of all, in what way would he fit himself into Matter and so be sensibly apprehended? . .Meanwhile, my eyes had unconsciously come to rest on a picture that represented Christ with his Heart offered to men. This picture was hanging in front of me, on the wall of a church into which I had gone to pray . . . I was still looking at the picture when the vision began. (Indeed, I cannot be certain exactly when it began, because it had already reached a certain pitch of intensity when I became aware of it.) All I know is that as I let my eyes roam over the outlines of the picture, I

---

[568] Tudzynski, Correia, and Keller. 2001. "Biotechnology and Genetics of Ergot Alkaloids."

suddenly realized that they *were melting*. They were melting, but in a very special way that I find it difficult to describe.

If I relaxed my visual concentration, the whole of Christ's outline, the folds of his robe, the bloom of his skin, merged (though without disappearing) into all the rest . . . the edge which divided Christ from the surrounding World was changing into a layer of vibration in which all distinct delimitation was lost . . . I noticed that the vibrant atmosphere which formed a halo around Christ was not confined to a narrow strip encircling him, but radiated into Infinity. From time to time what seemed to be trails of phosphorescence streamed across it, in which could be seen a continuous pulsing surge which reached out to the furthest spheres of matter— forming a sort of crimson ganglion, or nervous network, running across every substance. *The whole Universe was vibrating* . . . . It was thus that the light and the colours of all the beauties we know shone, with an inexpressible iridescence . . . these countless modifications followed one another in succession, were transformed, melted into one another in a harmony that was utterly satisfying to me . . . I was completely at a loss. *I found it impossible to decipher* . . . . All I know is that, since that occasion, I believe I have seen a hint of it once, and that was in the eyes of a dying soldier.[569]

Decades later, Teilhard refers to this epiphanic experience, this "particular interior event" of 40 years prior.[570] He describes how it has been that, ever since this

---

[569] Teilhard, "Christ in Matter," 61–65. Essay written 1916.

[570] Teilhard, "The Christic," 83. Essay written in 1955.

early revelation, he has had "the capacity to see two fundamental psychic movements or currents," which, when he first perceived them in his 1916 epiphany, "reacted endlessly upon one another in a flash of extraordinary brilliance, releasing . . . a light so intense that it transfigured for me the very depths of the World."[571] In his final essay, completed a month before his death, Teilhard stresses the *objective validity* of this initial evidence that had led directly to his new understanding of consciousness and the universe, evidence which had presented itself to him experientially in 1916:

> What follows is not a mere speculative dissertation in which the main lines of some long-matured and cleverly constructed system are set out. It constitutes the evidence brought to bear, with complete objectivity, *upon a particular interior event, upon a particular personal experience* . . . . Today, after forty years of continuous thought, it is still exactly the same fundamental vision that I feel I must present, and enable others to share in its matured form— for the last time.[572]

It is this subsequent "forty years of continuous thought" which makes the uniqueness of his observations, expressed in his essays, so significant for the development of consciousness studies. Four sides of Teilhard's nature reinforced one another, integrally it would seem: scientific training, mystical vision, exceptional intelligence, and a

---

[571] Ibid.

[572] Ibid., 82–83. Italic emphasis added.

passionate enthusiasm for discovery and understanding. While he was formally a scientist, highly trained and experienced in the observation, collection, classification, and written interpretation of geological and anthropological data, yet he was also a Jesuit priest, deeply immersed in observing the internal phenomena of spirit during his daily contemplative period. His was a quest to bring scientific reasoning and understanding to bear upon a direct vision, one that has been described by his biographer as:

> a powerful vision linked to experiences of a deeply mystical, or what might be called pan-entheistic, character although he often simply called them "pantheistic." These experiences occurred over many years.[573]

Throughout his writing, one encounters passages that can only be seen to refer directly to personal experience of a sort of perception that he himself categorized as pantheism and mystical vision (which, along with his fascination with evolution, caused him enduring conflict with more conservative forces in the Vatican). Teilhard states that his perception, "as experience shows, is indeed the result . . . of a mystic absorbed in divine contemplation."[574] Elsewhere Teilhard regards this special psychic perception as a natural ability, but one that requires practice and cultivation in order to catalyze the required change of state in consciousness:

> This perception of a natural psychic unity higher than our "souls" requires, as I know from

---

[573] King, *Spirit of Fire*, 59.

[574] Ibid., 116.

280

experience, a special quality and training in the observer . . . once we manage to affect this change of viewpoint then the earth, our little human earth, is draped in a splendor. Floating above the biosphere, whose layers no doubt gradually merge into it, the world of thought, the noosphere, begins to let its crown shine. The noosphere![575]

Teilhard's contemplative, mystical interests began at an early age, during which he searched to discern some "Absolute" in his experience of prayer with his large Catholic family, described here in, "My Universe," written on the battlefield of the Marne, three weeks after the beginning of a major attack by the Germans:

> However far back I go into my memories (even before the age of ten) I can distinguish in myself the presence of a strictly dominating passion: the passion for the Absolute. At that age, of course, I did not so describe the urgent concern I felt; but today I can put a name to it without any possible hesitation. Ever since my childhood, the need to lay hold of "some Absolute" in everything was the axis of my inner life.[576]

During 1926 and 1927 Teilhard wrote *The Divine Milieu* while working in China, where he had effectively been banished by the Jesuit authorities; it is in the middle of this essay that he describes what can be only understood as a personal experience of deep contemplation in which, through a process of increasing centro-complexity, he began

---

[575] Teilhard, "Human Energy," 118. Essay written in 1937.

[576] Teilhard, "My Universe" 197. Essay written 14 April, 1918.

to travel consciously toward an encounter with a heretofore unimagined depth of inner being:

> And so, for the first time in my life perhaps (although I am supposed to meditate every day!), I took the lamp and, leaving the zone of everyday occupations and relationships where everything seems clear, I went down into my inmost self, to the deep abyss whence I feel dimly that my power of action emanates. But as I moved further and further away from the conventional certainties by which social life is superficially illuminated, I became aware that I was losing contact with myself. At each step of the descent a new person was disclosed within me of whose name I was no longer sure, and who no longer obeyed me. And when I had to stop my exploration because the path faded from beneath my steps, I found a bottomless abyss at my feet, and out of it came— arising I know not from where—the current which I dare to call *my* life. What science will ever be able to reveal to man the origin, nature and character of that conscious power. . .? Stirred by my discovery, I then wanted to return to the light of day and forget the disturbing enigma in the comfortable surroundings of familiar things.[577]

In the development of Teilhard's mystical sense, the possibility cannot be ruled out that Teilhard in midlife had the occasion to experience consciousness-expanding drugs, which would have provided new material for development of his theories of consciousness. On an ocean passage from France to China in 1926, Teilhard had befriended a French couple with a homestead in East Africa, Henry de Monfried

---

[577] Teilhard, *The Divine Milieu*, 76–77.

and his wife, Armgart.[578] Monfried has been variously described as "a pirate, a smuggler, and an arms dealer."[579] Nevertheless the three immediately developed strong bonds that lasted for decades, and Teilhard would often visit them in their East African home during his many voyages between Asia and France. As one of Teilhard's biographers comments:

> Teilhard was so attracted to this couple that, still aboard the *Angkor*, he confessed to Armgart, "I have full faith in Henry, in what he says about himself; but even more truly, I love you, you and him."

On a return voyage from China, three years later, Teilhard stopped in East Africa to join Henry and Armgart for a visit, with apparently no reservations at all concerning the use of opium: according to Teilhard's biographer, Jacques Arnould, "Teilhard brought Monfried opium from China—'for his personal use.'"[580] On another occasion, Teilhard saved Monfried from arrest by local authorities in China when Monfried was trying to pick up a shipment of hashish in Chinese Turkistan.[581] It should be noted that the use of hashish and opium was widespread in China during this time, and we can assume that the European enclave of intellectuals and artists in Peking in the "roaring 20s" may likely have experimented with psychotropics such as

---

[578] Aczel, *The Jesuit and the Skull*, 123–24.

[579] Ibid., 124.

[580] Ibid., 132.

[581] Ibid.

hashish and opium, particularly as the practice was not illegal during Teilhard's years in Peking:

> Ma Fuxiang [a Chinese warlord in the early 20th century] officially prohibited opium and made it illegal in Ningxia [included Peking], but the Guominjun reversed his policy; by 1933, people from every level of society were using the drug.[582]

In such an environment, during his decade long friendship with the American artist, Lucile Swan, it is not beyond consideration that Teilhard may have experienced the psychotropic effects of hashish and/or opium, which would have only provided rich psychic material for self-observation and development of his ideas concerning a hyperphysics of consciousness, noosphere, and the Omega point.

Our thesis holds that over his lifetime, it is Teilhard's mystical sense aligned with his rigorous scientifically trained skill in observation as a geologist and paleontologist, coupled with his Jesuit training in logic, clarity, and expressive writing that gave him the ability to record his ideas so prolifically; in addition to *11* volumes of scientific publications published during his lifetime, there now exist *13* volumes of speculative philosophy, all published after his death.[583] In 1951 he wrote a short essay entitled "Some Notes on the Mystical Sense: An Attempt at Clarification," which begins with the sentences:

---

[582] Association for Asian Studies, Southeast Conference, *Annals, Volumes 1–5*, 51.

[583] King, *Spirit of Fire*, 233–34.

The mystical sense is essentially a feeling for, a presentiment of, the total and final unity of the world, beyond its present sensibly apprehended multiplicity: it is a cosmic sense of "oneness." It enables us to become one with all by co-extension "with the sphere": that is to say, by suppression of all internal and external determinants, to come together with a sort of common stuff which *underlies* the variety of concrete beings. It is access to Aldous Huxley's "common ground."[584]

It is clear that Teilhard as geologist/paleontologist was in an ideal position for observing, documenting, and interpreting the direct experiences of the inner life of Teilhard the contemplative priest. This integral configuration underlies the development of his "hyperphysics," his "physics of centration."[585]

After World War II, having just spent six years in relative isolation under the Japanese occupation, Teilhard gave a lecture at the French Embassy in Peking, in which he talks about the "growing importance with which leading thinkers of all denominations are beginning to attach to the phenomenon of mysticism." [586] He goes on to describe mysticism in the perception of the Omega point:

Let us suppose that from this universal centre, this Omega point, there constantly emanate radiations hitherto only perceptible to those

---

[584] Teilhard, "Some Notes on the Mystical Sense: An Attempt at Clarification," 209. Essay written in 1951.

[585] Teilhard, *The Human Phenomenon*, 2.

[586] Teilhard, "Life and the Planets," 123. Lecture delivered in 1945

persons whom we call "mystics." Let us further imagine that, as the sensibility or response to mysticism of the human race increases with planetisation, the awareness of Omega becomes so widespread as to warm the earth psychically.[587]

It is my contention that Teilhard's hyperphysics emerged as a product of multiple factors: a deep contemplative mystical sense combined with extensive scientific training, intense experience, and high intelligence, acting together in Teilhard to provide a truly integral perspective. In Fig. 40 can be seen a symbolic diagram of these factors in Teilhard's unique multiperspectival consciousness.

---

[587] Ibid., 122.

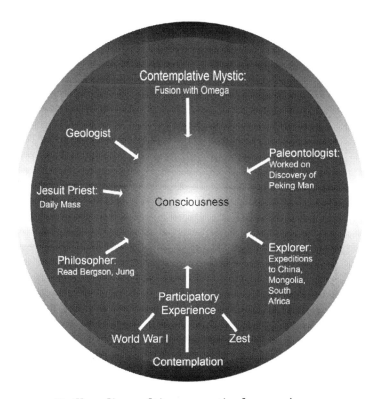

Figure 40. Teilhard's multiperspectival consciousness. Graphic by author.

That Teilhard's understanding grew over the arc of his lifetime is evident in essays striving to express his vision, beginning in World War I and continuing until his death in 1955. In all of his essays can be detected his motivated energy to express as clearly as possible in words the framework of his understanding:

> It seems to me that a whole lifetime of continual hard work would be as nothing to me, if only I

could, just for one moment, give a true picture of what I see.[588]

In 1922 Teilhard was awarded his doctorate, defending his thesis on mammals of the Lower Eocene (56 to 33.9 million years ago) in France.[589] According to a biographer, "The board of examiners had no hesitation in conferring on him the title of doctor, with distinction."[590] In that same year, the British psychologist Conway Lloyd Morgan (1852–1936) presented a series of radical new ideas at speaker at the Gifford Lectures, in which he extended the ideas of Henri Bergson.[591] Morgan described how an observed increase of complexity in the evolutionary process often results in discontinuous leaps with the past, rather than through a more gradual, steady process, as had been predicted by the theory of Darwinian natural selection.[592] Lloyd Morgan's theory can be seen as a precursor to an expression of the dynamics of complexity-consciousness in Teilhard's own hyperphysics. The direct effect of centro-complexification, according to Teilhard, catalyzes transformation in the organization and functioning of consciousness, causing a phase shift, as when water

---

[588] Teilhard, "My Fundamental Vision," 164. Essay written in 1948.

[589] Ibid., 83. Note that the Eocene Epoch lasted from 56 to 33.9 million years ago.

[590] Ibid., 84.

[591] Morgan, *Emergent Evolution: Gifford Lectures, 1921–22.*

[592] Haisch, *The Purpose-Guided Universe: Believing in Einstein, Darwin, and God.*

crystallizes into ice, or transforms into steam. It is this principle of centro-complexity that drives, that initiates this catalysis.

Unfortunately, essays such as "Centrology," which develops the theory of centro-complexity in detail, were never published in Teilhard's lifetime. Conservative elements in the Catholic hierarchy made it difficult if not impossible for him to publish much of his work, in great part because the Church had not yet reconciled the science of evolution with doctrinal Catholicism, and Teilhard's essays and lectures soared unchecked on a wave of evolutionary ideas.

Though Teilhard was forbidden to teach, lecture, or publish outside of a narrow range of scientific material, yet his strictly scientific publications fill 11 volumes, indicating the extent of his output and providing an indication of his professional stature as a world-class paleontologist. Teilhard's books and essays on speculative philosophy and the evolution of consciousness, on the other hand, though published between 1955 and 1976, only after his death, fill another 13 volumes.[593]

Certainly being forbidden to publish had its effect on Teilhard. To keep him out of Paris, where the Church saw his ideas as attracting too much enthusiasm among young seminarians, he was virtually banished from Paris, ordered to an assignment in China early in his career, and then banished again, to America, after the war and near the end of his life.[594] These challenges (some might say affronts) to the expression of his richest ideas, coupled perhaps with the

---

[593] King, *Spirit of Fire*, 233–34.

[594] Ibid.

horror and suffering he had experienced at first hand during two world wars, all must have taken a toll on his emotional side, and must surely have contributed to his frequent bouts of despondence and depression. Pierre Leroy, his friend and colleague throughout their years of confinement in Peking, who, at 20 years Teilhard's junior, had first met Teilhard in 1928 in Paris, writes of Teilhard's bouts of depression:

> Many have rightly been struck by Pere Teilhard's great optimism. He was indeed an optimist, in his attribution to the universe of a sense of direction in spite of the existence of evil and in spite of appearances ... but how often in intimate conversation have I found him depressed and with almost no heart to carry on .... During that period he was at times prostrated by fits of weeping, and he appeared to be on the verge of despair .... Six years thus went by in the dispiriting atmosphere of China occupied by the Japanese and cut off from the rest of the world.[595]

Yet when Teilhard was finally able to leave China, at the war's end, he wrote, during the sea passage on his return to France, "These seven years have made me quite grey, but they have toughened me—not hardened me, I hope—interiorly."[596] He retained the passion and motivation to write extensively, particularly in his later years, and he continued the development of his observations and conclusions regarding consciousness and the dynamics of energy in an evolving universe. He himself would likely have

---

[595] Leroy, "Teilhard de Chardin: The Man," 32.

[596] Teilhard, *Letters from a Traveller*, 291

characterized the gift of this persevering energy with the term "zest," which he defines it here a 1950 essay:

> By "zest for living" or "zest for life," I mean here, to put it very approximately, that spiritual disposition, at once intellectual and affective, in virtue of which life, the world, and action seem to us, on the whole, luminous—interesting—appetizing.[597]

It is almost as if the restriction placed upon him by the Church against publication gave him free rein to explore his ideas in essays that were freely distributed among his closest friends and many acquaintances. In spite of the censorship of the Church, many unofficial copies of his writings were made, and most have been published in posthumous collections.[598] One of his most profound essays, "Centrology: An Essay in a Dialectic of Union," discussed in detail later in this chapter, was written in his period of isolation in Peking during Japanese wartime occupation.[599] Soon after emerging from his seclusion in China, Teilhard was deeply disappointed when the Vatican forbade him to publish what he considered to be his major work, *The Human Phenomenon*, while simultaneously refusing him permission to accept the offer of a prestigious teaching Chair at the College de France. Yet in spite of such opposition to his visionary understanding of the energy of consciousness, it has been noted that, "he wrote *more*

---

[597] Teilhard, "The Zest for Living," 231.

[598] King, *Pierre Teilhard de Chardin*, 17.

[599] Teilhard, "Centrology: An Essay in the Dialectic of Union," written in 1944.

religious and philosophical essays in the years 1946–1955 than during any other period of his life—his bibliography lists over ninety titles for this time."[600]

Energy: Axial and Tangential

Energy is the central element in Teilhard's technical modeling of the cosmos. He says that while "in metaphysics the notion of being can be defined with a precision that is geometric," things are not so clear in physics, where the notion of energy is "still open to all sorts of possible corrections or improvements."[601] Teilhard's essays on the energy of consciousness, spanning four decades, systematically introduce a coherent range of such corrections and improvements. In the last page of his essay, "Activation of Energy," Teilhard states, "there are two different energies one axial, increasing, and irreversible, and the other peripheral or tangential, constant, and reversible: and these two energies are linked together in 'arrangement.'"[602] Thus Teilhard's hyperphysics posits two modes, domains, or dimensions of energy, not only of a *tangential component* of energy that operates within space–time dimensions, and which is measured and explored by modern physics, but also a *radial* or *axial component* of energy. It is this axial energy that provides the direct link with the center termed Omega by Teilhard, which guides,

---

[600] King, *Spirit of Fire*, 213.

[601] Teilhard, "The Energy of Evolution," 361–62. Essay written in 1953.

[602] Teilhard, "The Activation of Human Energy," 393. Essay written in 1953.

informs, and maintains the evolutionary process throughout the space–time cosmos. [603] He describes this radial component of energy as "a new dimensional zone" that brings with it "new properties," and he describes how increasing centration along the radial component leads to increasing states of "complexity-consciousness." [604]

As Teilhard stated,

> science in its present reconstructions of the world fails to grasp an essential factor, or, to be more exact, an entire dimension of the universe . . . all we need to do is to take the inside of things into account at the same time as the outside. [605]

Energy, for Teilhard, is not simply regarded as a mathematical abstraction. He views energy as the matrix of consciousness, the driver of evolution, and as a living, communicating radiation or flux. For Teilhard energy is "a true 'transcosmic' radiation for which the organisms . . . would seem to be precisely the naturally provided receivers."[606]

Teilhard is critical of the one-dimensional approach to energy taken by contemporary research. He asks, "What is the relationship between this interior energy . . . and the goddess of energy worshipped by physicists?"[607] His answer

---

[603] Teilhard, *Activation of Energy*.

[604] Teilhard, "The Atomism of Spirit," 29. Essay written in 1941.

[605] Teilhard, *The Human Phenomenon*, 109.

[606] Teilhard, "The Zest for Living," 242. Essay written in 1950.

[607] Ibid.

is that there are two fundamental categories or modes of energy, and implies that physicists deal with but one mode. In his own words, "We still persist in regarding the physical as constituting the 'true' phenomenon in the universe, and the psychic as a sort of epiphenomenon."[608]

He also describes these two components of energy in physical and the psychic terms: "*physical energy* being no more than *materialized psychic energy*,"[609] but he is not able to posit a mathematical or physical relationship between these two dimensions, other than to express the hope that "there must surely be some hidden relationship which links them together in their development."[610]

A Thinking Earth: The Noosphere

Despite clerical resistance to his ideas, Teilhard continued to be fascinated by what he saw as the emerging evolution of a collective human consciousness upon the planet Earth, the emergence of a "thinking Earth," a phenomenon which he had directly intuited in his intense experiences at the Front in 1917. He continued his dual work in the fields of paleontology and speculative philosophy; for example in January 1923 he finished an essay, "Pantheism and Christianity," only to publish two months later "Paleontology and the Appearance of Man."[611]

---

[608] Teilhard, "The Activation of Human Energy," 393. Essay written in 1953.

[609] Teilhard, footnote 10, "Centrology: An Essay in a Dialectic of Union," 121. Essay written in 1944.

[610] Ibid., 120.

[611] Teilhard, *Christianity and Evolution*, 56; and *The Appearance of Man*, 33.

Intense life experiences led Teilhard to the perception of an emerging planetary consciousness, which he termed the *noosphere*, [612] which after his death has been conceptualized as *"an ultimate and inevitable sphere of evolution . . . a* scientific approach with a bridge to religion."[613]

During the war, Teilhard had given the name "The Great Monad" to his conception and experience of an emerging consciousness.[614] But by 1920, during his doctoral studies, he was using the term "Anthroposphere" in referring to this thinking sphere of the planet.[615] In Paris in 1921, drawn together by similar interests, Édouard Le Roy (1870–1954) and Teilhard de Chardin met and became friends. A mathematician and philosopher by training, Le Roy immediately found in Teilhard an intellectual equal, and the two began a lifetime relationship, leading with the year to the exploration of a new concept, the noosphere.[616] Le Roy had studied with Henri Bergson, and had become known as his protégé; subsequently he had been appointed successor to Bergson at the College de France.[617] Though 10

---

[612] "Over and above the biosphere there is a *noosphere*.";
Teilhard, *The Human Phenomenon*, 124.

[613] Samson and Pitt, *The Biosphere and Noosphere Reader*, 3.

[614] Teilhard, "The Great Monad," 182. Essay written in 1918.

[615] Teilhard, *The Heart of Matter*.

[616] Noosphere: from the Greek νοῦς (*nous*: "sense, mind, wit") and σφαῖρα (*sphaira*: "sphere, orb, globe"); Samson and Pitt, *The Biosphere and Noosphere Reader*.

[617] King, *Spirit of Fire*, 84.

years Teilhard's senior, the two soon began a series of informal weekly discussions:

> Punctually, at 8:30 p.m., on Wednesday evenings Teilhard would call at Le Roy's apartment in the Rue Cassette, and it was not long before the two men were thinking and speaking with a single mind.[618]

Though Le Roy was a decade older than Teilhard, their relationship appears to have been more than simple mentorship; Teilhard says in a letter,

> I loved him like a father, and owed him a very great debt . . . he gave me confidence, enlarged my mind, and served as a spokesman for my ideas, then taking shape, on 'hominization' and the "noosphere."[619]

Over their many months of frequent discussion, the two grew so close in their philosophical thought that Le Roy would later say in one of his books:

> "I have so often and for so long talked over with Pere Teilhard the views expressed here that neither of us can any longer pick out his own contribution."[620]

Their meetings soon included a mutual acquaintance, the brilliant writer Vladimir Ivanovich Vernadsky (1863–

---

[618] Speaight, *The Life of Teilhard de Chardin*, 117.

[619] Teilhard, as quoted in Cuénot, *Teilhard de Chardin: A Biographical Study*, 59.

[620] King, *Spirit of Fire*, 84.

1945), a distinguished Russian geologist from St. Petersburg, who eventually founded the field known as biogeochemistry. Vernadsky popularized his term "the biosphere" in a series of lectures at the Sorbonne during 1922–1923, frequently attended by Le Roy and Teilhard.[621]

Vernadsky viewed the phenomenon of life as a natural and integral part of the cosmos, and not merely some epiphenomenon. Accordingly, he professed that universal physical laws, discovered by science over a wide range of seemingly disparate fields, would eventually find continuation with fundamental principles that are the ground of life.[622]

Not widely acknowledged in the West, Vernadsky was the first to recognize the importance of life as a geological force, an idea that predates the more recent Gaia hypothesis:

> James E. Lovelock, the British inventor and the other major scientific contributor to the concept of an integrated biosphere in this century, remained unaware of Vernadsky's work until well after Lovelock framed his own Gaia hypothesis. Whereas Vernadsky's work emphasized life as a geological force, Lovelock has shown that earth has a physiology: the temperature, alkalinity,

---

[621] Bailes, *Science and Russian Culture in an Age of Revolutions*; the term "biosphere" had been in use since as early as 1900, popularized by the Austrian geologist Eduard Suess.

[622] Samson and Pitt, *The Biosphere and Noosphere Reader*, 94–95.

acidity, and reactive gases are modulated by life.[623]

Teilhard left Paris for China on April 6, 1923, booking inexpensive shipping routes that gave him opportunity to spend time exploring the Suez, Ceylon, Sumatra, Saigon, and Hong Kong, before arriving in Shanghai. During his time at sea, he had ample hours to think about and to observe the biosphere:

> Teilhard spent his time aboard ship reading, writing, and observing nature. He liked to look at the stars at night—so clear and bright when seen from a ship far from the intruding lights of terra firma—and by day observe the state of the ocean, calm at times and stormy at others.[624]

On May 6, 1923, barely a month after departing from Marseille, Teilhard completed the essay, later called "Hominization," which sets forth his first extended exploration of the "Noosphere" concept, which may be considered an outgrowth of recent discussions with Vernadsky and Le Roy in Paris."[625] In the essay, Teilhard begins by making a subtle shift from the usual Cartesian linear approach to paleontological classification toward a more spherical, three-dimensional metaphysical geometry: "We begin to understand that the most natural division of the elements of the earth would be by zones, by circles, by

---

[623] Vernadsky, *The Biosphere*, 16.

[624] Aczel, *The Jesuit and the Skull*, 86.

[625] Teilhard, "Hominization," 61. Essay written in 1923.

spheres."[626] In the last half of the essay, Teilhard develops his understanding of the "Noosphere" concept, and in one section, "The Psychic Essence of Evolution," Teilhard says:

> It has appeared as a possible element in a sort of higher organism which might form itself . . .or else something (someone) exists, in which each element gradually finds, by reunion with the whole, the completion of all the savable elements that have been formed in its individuality.[627]

In this "reunion with the whole" can be seen a foreshadowing of the main theme of one of his final essays, written thirty-two years later, "The Death-Barrier and Co-Reflection," in which is described a process in which each individual human, at least the "savable elements," transcend the physical death barrier, merging with the Noosphere due to "the principles of the conservation of consciousness . . .conceived as the luminous attainment of *a new psychological stage.*"[628]

Teilhard concludes his "breaking the death-barrier" essay with the statement that "the interior equilibrium of what we have called the Noosphere requires the presence *perceived by individuals* of a higher pole or centre that directs, sustains and assembles the whole sheaf of our efforts." [629] The emphasis which Teilhard places on the

---

[626] Ibid., 62.

[627] Ibid., 73–78.

[628] Teilhard, "The Death-Barrier and Co-Reflection," 402. Essay written in 1955.

[629] Ibid., 78.

words "perceived by individuals" can be seen here to underscore the experiential, participatory dimension of his quest to explore and to understand the dynamics of the planet Earth, considering it, certainly from Vernadsky's biospheric view, as an evolving organism at every level.

Upon returning to Paris, after having spent 18 months in his extended expedition to Mongolia, Teilhard resumed teaching classes at the Institut Catholique, from which he had taken a leave of absence.[630]

> Teilhard gave four lectures on evolution during the winter months of 1925; and at the same time continued to develop his theory of the noosphere—a kind of cosmic envelope created by the reflection of the mind. The word was his own invention—it had come to him during the war—but the word and the idea were both adopted later by Le Roy and the Russian geologist Vernadsky, who was in Paris at the time.[631]

One of the earliest discussions of the "nous" or "noos" may be found in the writings of the Pre-Socratic Greek philosopher who introduced philosophy to Athens, Anaxagoras (500–428 BCE). [632] In developing his philosophy of the infinite interconnectedness of an infinite multitude of imperishable small parts, Anaxagoras concluded the following:

---

[630] King, *Spirit of Fire*, 104.

[631] Speaight, *The Life of Teilhard de Chardin*, 135.

[632] Radhakrishnan, *History of Philosophy Eastern and Western*, 57.

A single overarching principle is needed to provide unity to the whole system. This principle is *nous* . . . . *"Nous"* is more related to the concept of mind in the sense of the human mind or reason (though distinct from "logos," which is also sometimes translated as reason). It represents, furthermore, a kind of unity of thought a "thinking thing" in some sense.[633]

The Neoplatonists developed the concept of the *nous* even further 800 years later, and this can be found particularly in Plotinus.[634] According to Plotinus, writing in the third century CE, the original Being, the One, emanates the *nous*, the archetype of all manifestations in the visible world of time and space.[635]

Plotinus presents a philosophy of Unity: unity as unfathomable and transcendent, and unity as omnipresent and immanent.[636]

This Neoplatonist *nous* is accessible to the human mind under certain conditions, and it is what the Neoplatonists termed the *anima mundi*, or "world soul" which bridges the *nous* with the material world of time and space.[637]

---

[633] Skrbina, *Panpsychism in the West*, 30.

[634] MacKenna, *Plotinus: The Enneads*.

[635] Radhakrishnan, *History of Philosophy Eastern and Western*, 115.

[636] MacKenna, *Plotinus: The Enneads*, 712.

[637] Jung, *Psychology and Alchemy*.

The noosphere for Teilhard, as expressed in his numerous essays, corresponds more with the Neoplatonist *anima mundi*, rather than the Anaxagoras *nous*, which appears to be more like Bohm's implicate–explicate "wholeness." [638] Teilhard's concept of the noosphere is indeed part of the phenomenal world while maintaining links to the transcendent; but it is specifically associated with the planets in general, and the Earth in particular, with human consciousness evolving within a planetary sphere. Teilhard goes so far as to discuss the possibility of multiple, numerous noospheres, associated with distant planets, and speculates that there may indeed be communication between these multiple noospheres.[639]

Though there had been some controversy over the origin of the word "noosphere," shortly before his own death Teilhard confirmed that the word was his own in a letter referring to the recent demise of his friend Édouard Le Roy. In the letter, Teilhard writes:

> I believe, so far as one can ever tell, that the word 'noosphere' was my invention; but it was he [Le Roy] who launched it.[640]

In a 1951 essay, almost 30 years after first using the term, Teilhard elaborates his mature understanding of the noosphere:

---

[638] Bohm, *Wholeness and the Implicate Order*, 19.

[639] Teilhard, "Centrology: An Essay in a Dialectic of Union," 127. Essay written in 1944.

[640] Teilhard, as quoted in Cuénot, *Teilhard de Chardin: A Biographical Study*, 59.

It is an amazing thing—in less than a million years the human "species" has succeeded in covering the earth: and not only spatially—on this surface that is now completely encircled mankind has completed the construction of a close network of planetary links, so successfully that a special envelope now stretches over the old biosphere. Every day this new integument grows in strength; it can be clearly recognized and distinguished in every quarter; it is provided with its own system of internal connections and communications—and for this I have for a long time proposed the name of *noosphere*.[641]

In a collection of essays, *The Biosphere and Noosphere Reader*, the editors begin their Preface by characterizing the search for the noosphere:

The noosphere lies at an intersection where science and philosophy meet . . . an interdisciplinary domain of wide interest and high relevance that remains outside the purview of most specialists, but is of major significance for the future of humankind.[642]

Four approaches to Teilhard's concept of the noosphere are presented:

1. The *noosphere* is a product of the biosphere as transformed by human knowledge and action.

2. The *noosphere* represents an ultimate and inevitable sphere of evolution.

---

[641] Teilhard, "The Convergence of the Universe," 285. Essay written in 1951.

[642] Samson and Pitt, *The Biosphere and Noosphere Reader*, xi.

3. The *noosphere* is a manifestation of global mind.

4. The *noosphere* is the mental sphere in which change and creativity are inherent although essentially unpredictable.[643]

Locating the Noosphere

At this point we speculate as to where in the physical space–time universe the noosphere might be found. To find the noosphere let us try a thought experiment and build a likely image of the noosphere. Picture in your mind the geometry of the planet Earth. Imagine the heat, approximately 7200° C in the central core.[644] Place your consciousness at the absolute geometric-gravitational central point of the planetary core. Now begin to move (or to rise) along a radial line slowly outward, toward the cold of space, noting the temperature drop as you move along the line away from the center of the planet, and stop at the moment you arrive at the temperature 98.2° F, the average human core temperature.

Repeating the above procedure multiple times, with many different radii moving away at different angular separation from the core, a three-dimensional surface mapping, like a mathematical brane, or Teilhard's isosphere, will begin to emerge, an infrared energy

---

[643] Ibid., 2–3.

[644] Allaby and Allaby, *A Dictionary of Earth Science*, 72.

isosphere to which each human being is linked through an identical resonance frequency.[645]

The shape of this isosphere will likely be highly organic and fractal in appearance, sometimes hovering above the ground on thermoclimes where the "ambient temperature" reaches 98.2° F, while in arctic regions and below the oceans it will be located hundreds of feet the surface of ice or water.

But the noosphere is more than simply a dynamic location on the surface of an isosphere at or above or below the rocky surface of the earth. It is energy at the same frequency band as the human body, which has been said to generate, with each heartbeat, approximately 1.3 watts of radiant power.[646] While we normally think of each heartbeat as simply a pushing of blood through the arteries, it is also radiantly generating infrared electromagnetic energy (the infrared being a range of the spectrum that we often hear dismissively described as "heat").

How might this information be used to substantiate Teilhard's vision of the reality of the noosphere, which would manifest in some planetary energy of consciousness. In Table 6 three values of energy output are compared.

Table 6
Radiant Energy Outputs, Compared

Source of energy	Power (watts)

---

[645] A brane is a geometrical boundary of higher dimensional dimensions spaces. This concept is used in contemporary superstring theory and M-theory; see Susskind, *The Black Hole War.*

[646] Malinski, *Chemistry of the Heart*, 61.

Most powerful radio frequency transmitter on planet[647]	1,000,000
Maximum output of Three Mile Island nuclear reactor[648]	873,000,000
Combined electromagnetic output of 7 billion human heartbeats[649]	9,100,000,000

A chart of global population growth (Fig. 41) indicates that there are currently approximately 7 billion human beings living on the planet.

---

[647] Radio Ukraine; Berg, *Broadcasting on the Short Waves, 1945 to Today*, 43.

[648] Walker, *Three Mile Island: A Nuclear Crisis in Historical Perspective*, 12.

[649] Assuming 7 billion human beings with average heartbeat output of 1.3 watts.

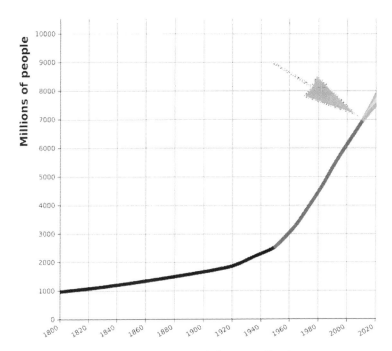

Figure 41. Human population of the Earth since 1800. Graphic by Aetheling (2012). Reprinted under the terms of a Creative Commons Attribution ShareAlike 3.0 Unported license. Image retrieved from Wikimedia Commons.

Accordingly, we multiplying 7 billion humans by the average of 1.3 watts of radiation per human to find the current amount of energy being broadcast by all human hearts as over nine gigawatts (9,100,000,000 watts), as shown previously, at the bottom of Table 6. In the table, this can be seen dwarfing the output power of the most powerful radio transmitter in the world at 1,000,000 watts (one megawatt), and even of the maximum energy output of the Three Mile Island nuclear power plant, which occasionally operated at its maximum output of 873,000,000 watts.

It is possible that the nine gigawatts of electromagnetic energy being continuously broadcast by our collective heartbeats may be taking part in a vast energetic interactive resonance with Gaia. Our own collective energy

307

transmits in the far infrared in the 10-micron wavelength range (predicted by Wien's Law for our body temperature range) is the part of the geomagnetosphere that is us, the noosphere (the "us" sphere).

Evidence of direct interaction of the energy of the geomagnetosphere with human consciousness can be viewed in Fig. 4.

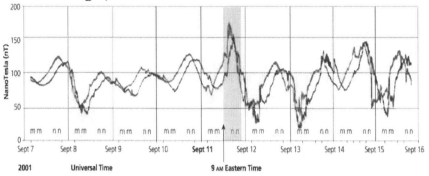

Figure 42. Evidence of a coherent planetary standing wave.[650] Image from McCraty, Deyhle, and Childre, "The Global Coherence Initiative," 75, fig. 10. Reprinted with permission from HeartMath Institute.

This is a chart recording daily data from Geostationary Operational Environmental Satellites and weather satellites in geosynchronous orbit over the United States in the days before, during, and after the September 11, 2001, terrorist attacks on the United States. Continuous readings show a marked peak on September 11, 2001

---

[650] The data in this chart was recorded from the Geostationary Operational Environmental Satellites 8 and 10, weather satellites in geosynchronous orbit over the east and west coasts of the United States in the days before, during, and after the September 11, 2001, terrorist attacks.

308

followed by several days of marked disruption in the observed diurnal rhythm of the geomagnetosphere.[651]

In the conclusion of the paper, the authors state: "The study . . . supports the hypothesis that humanity is connected via a global field." [652] Perhaps the same hypothetical "global field" of radiation can be seen in the one Teilhard describes in a 1953 essay, "A Sequel to the Problem of Human Origins":

> Our minds cannot resist the inevitable conclusion that were we, by chance, to possess plates that were sensitive to the specific radiation of the "noospheres" scattered throughout space, it would be *practically certain* that what we saw registered on them would be a cloud of thinking stars.[653]

In early summer of 1923, Teilhard found himself travelling for the first time on an expedition into the Ordos Desert of Outer Mongolia.[654] It is here that he has another major vision, a peak experience later recounted in "The Mass on the World," and of which he comments:

> I see the same thing as I saw long ago at the "front" (which from the human point of view, was

---

[651] McCraty, Deyhle, and Childre, "The Global Coherence Initiative: Creating a Coherent Planetary Standing Wave," 75.

[652] McCraty, Deyhle, and Childre, "The Global Coherence Initiative: Creating a Coherent Planetary Standing Wave," 76.

[653] Teilhard, *Christianity and Evolution: Reflections on Science and Religion*, 231.

[654] King, *Spirit of Fire*, 97.

the most alive region that existed): one single operation is in process of happening in the world, and it alone can justify our action.[655]

After 18 months in China, Teilhard returned to Paris, only to discover that his earlier essay on "original sin" had been discovered by a Jesuit colleague in one of his desk drawers at the Institut Catholique, and subsequently forwarded to the Vatican, "where the Holy Office and the Jesuit headquarters already held a file on Teilhard."[656] Reproaching him for having dared to discuss new ways of understanding original sin, the Church authorities (1) insisted that he "sign a pledge to keep silent in the future," (2) permanently revoked his license to teach at the Institut Catholique, where he had been an Assistant Professor in geology, and (3) asked him to leave Paris.[657] Teilhard's return to China in 1926 seems to have been at a low point in his career:

> His departure had something of the aspect of a disgrace. He had been removed from Paris by the prudence of his superiors, to whom he had been denounced for propagating dubious ideas, and who feared a censure that would be equally prejudicial to the career of the young scientist and the good name of the Order. Thus he was leaving France under a cloud for an indefinite time, and he saw the momentum of his influence

---

[655] Ibid., 98.

[656] Ibid., 106.

[657] Ibid., 106–8.

broken just as it was beginning to prove fruitful.[658]

Problems with a previous essay only aggravated the situation, one of his earliest essays, "Cosmic Life," a 56-page essay written at Dunkirk on the front during Easter week, April 24, 1916. When he sent it for publishing to the editors of a Jesuit periodical in Paris, *Etudes,* it was rejected for including such sentences as "The life of Christ mingles with the life-blood of evolution."[659] In the rejection letter, one of the editors explained:

> Your thesis is *exciting* [he used the English word, in the midst of French] and interesting to a high degree . . . . It is a rich canvas, full of beautiful images. But it is not at all suited for our peaceful readers.[660]

The essay had then been brought to the attention of officials at the Vatican by Teilhard's Jesuit supervisor, Father Claude Chanteur, who expressed strong reservations about giving Teilhard formal admission into the Jesuit Order, but who eventually, perhaps reluctantly, allowed the 37-year-old Teilhard to take his solemn vows, on May 26, 1918.[661]

Upon his return to China in 1926, Teilhard made the best of his virtual exile, involving himself deeply in running

---

[658] Teilhard, "Letters to Two Friends 1926–1952," 5.

[659] Aczel, *The Jesuit and the Skull,* 78.

[660] Ibid.

[661] Ibid., 79.

the Jesuit museum there, and accompanying Father Licent on extensive paleontological expeditions into the vast interior of Eastern Mongolia.[662] During the next 20 years, Teilhard travelled extensively between China and Paris, but during the years from 1940 to 1946 he found himself in Peking under the Japanese occupation, unable to travel. Instead, he devoted himself to perhaps his most challenging essays on the dynamics of consciousness, including "Centrology," discussed in the following section.

In May of 1946, at the end of World War II, Teilhard returned to Paris, where he tried unsuccessfully to obtain permission to publish a major work he had completed in China over a period of several years, *The Human Phenomenon*. While in Paris awaiting a reply, Teilhard began giving lectures on his latest philosophical ideas after a hiatus of 22 years, and soon he began to attract the interest of young Jesuit students, as well as a more secular public that had become less conservative as a result of the war. While Teilhard scrupulously avoided large venues (he had been henceforth forbidden in 1923 to give large public addresses), he soon fell into a hectic activity alternating between intimate private conversations and semipublic discussions. During one such series of monthly discussions with several Jesuit intellectuals, Teilhard set forth two fundamental points in his philosophy, as recorded by one of the attending priests, Fr. Lejay:[663]

- God acts globally on the whole of evolution and consequently utilizes, in selective fashion, all the possibilities offered by secondary causes.

---

[662] King, *Spirit of Fire*, 93.

[663] Cuénot, *Teilhard de Chardin: A Biographical Study*, 257.

- Evil is a by-product of evolution, for there is no evolution without groping, without the intervention of chance; consequently, checks and mistakes are always possible.[664]

After the war in Europe, the topic of evil was of great interest, not only among intellectuals, but also among the general public.[665] Teilhard's characterization of evil as a part of the process of an evolutionary energy did not set well with conservative Church authorities, nor did his growing popularity among intellectual Jesuits and the public. He was offered a Chair at the College de France, but received word from the Vatican in 1950 that he was not permitted to accept the position. That same year even his close friends and sympathetic colleagues were censured: "Jesuit academics who had espoused Teilhard's ideas, among them his friend Henri de Lubac, were ordered by the Vatican to leave their positions."[666] Teilhard decided that he could no longer reside in Paris, and after securing a position in New York, Teilhard left Paris to travel, and eventually, in virtual exile, to spend the rest of his life in North America.

In 1954 Teilhard mentioned in a letter to a nephew that when he died, he wished that it might be on Easter Sunday, the quintessential day, as a Catholic, for celebrating resurrection transformation into eternal life.[667] Perhaps this

---

[664] Ibid., 258.

[665] Leckie, *Delivered from Evil: The Saga of World War II*.

[666] Aczel, *The Jesuit and the Skull*, 213.

[667] King, *Spirit of Fire*, 230.

can be seen as an example of real psychic precognition, for the next year, on April 10, 1955, Teilhard attended Easter services at St. Patrick's Cathedral and enjoyed the Sunday afternoon in company of his close friend Rhoda de Terra and her daughter.[668] Pierre Teilhard de Chardin died while drinking a cup of tea in the front room: "Suddenly, while standing at her window, he fell full length to the floor like a stricken tree."[669] Only a few friends attended his funeral, and only two people accompanied his body on the journey to the cemetery, 60 miles north of New York City, along the banks of the Hudson River to the Jesuit novitiate of St. Andrews-on-the-Hudson.[670]

> Only Pére Leroy and another priest accompanied Teilhard on his last journey. The coffin had to be laid in a temporary vault because the earth was still too frozen for a grave.[671]

Teilhard is buried near the east bank of the Hudson River, under a simple stone inscribed only with his name, dates, and "R. I. P." The small grave remains, but the seminary was sold in 1970 and is now the headquarters of the Culinary Institute of America.[672]

---

[668] Aczel, *The Jesuit and the Skull*, 221.

[669] King, *Spirit of Fire*, 230.

[670] Aczel, *The Jesuit and the Skull*,

[671] Ibid., 231.

[672] Dunwell, *The Hudson: America's River*, 140.

Teilhard's Hyperphysics

Teilhard sees the current human phenomenon of consciousness to be in the early stages of what he terms a "noogenesis," a change of state in human consciousness into a more powerful union, a "joining with other centres of cosmic life to resume the work of universal synthesis on a higher scale."[673] The dynamics of this change and the architecture of consciousness itself is the subject of Teilhard's hyperphysics. Teilhard's ideas are clear, his writing style is straightforward and his logic transparent. But appreciation of his more detailed observations on the dynamics of an energy of consciousness requires careful examination of his more technical writing. Teilhard was fascinated by the phenomenon of "change of state," such as when water changes state to become ice, and, in particular, of evolutionary changes of state, such as when matter changes state to become life. But his greatest interest can be seen in potential imminent changes of state in consciousness itself, both human and cosmic, as he observed here in 1937 (note in the quote that Teilhard often uses the words "spirit" and "consciousness" interchangeably):

> The phenomenon of spirit [consciousness] is not therefore a sort of brief flash in the night; it reveals a gradual and systematic passage from the unconscious to the conscious, and from the

---

[673] Teilhard, "The Spirit of the Earth," 42. Essay written in 1931.

conscious to the self-conscious. It is a *cosmic change of state.*[674]

Teilhard describes three critical points in the evolutionary arc of consciousness on earth, three changes of state:

- "First the appearance of life whence emerged the biosphere."

- "Then, the emergence of thought which produced the noosphere."

- "Finally, a further metamorphosis: the coming to consciousness of an Omega in the heart of the noosphere."[675]

In his numerous essays Teilhard constructs the picture of a panoramic evolutionary arc: The Earth, having experienced a change of state at the moment when life appeared, experienced another change of state as life erupted into self-reflection (thought) in the biological zenith of *homo sapiens*. Teilhard predicts that this evolutionary arc is now moving toward yet another change of state, and is in the process of transforming human consciousness, collectively, into an even greater "complexity-consciousness,"[676] an "internal centro-complexification,"[677]

---

[674] Teilhard, "The Phenomenon of Spirituality," 96–97. Essay written in 1937.

[675] Teilhard, "The Nature of the Point Omega," 160.

[676] Teilhard, "From Cosmos to Cosmogenesis," 257. Essay written in 1951.

[677] Teilhard, "Centrology: An Essay in a Dialectic of Union," 103. Essay written in 1944.

both in the individual as well as the species, through the process of "centration"[678] or "centrogenesis."[679] These terms have all been constructed and developed by Teilhard to articulate and support his theory, and can be regarded as specific to his theory of hyperphysics. We will examine and clarify these terms by focusing on three essays in which his physics of consciousness, hyperphysics, is set forth: two written in 1937, the third and most technical written in 1944, near the end of Teilhard's long seclusion in Peking under Japanese occupation:

- "The Phenomenon of Spirit" (1937), written during an ocean voyage

- "Human Energy" (1937), written in Peking

- "Centrology" (1944), written in Peking

While major components of Teilhard's hyperphysics are presented in these three essays, additional insights into the same concepts can be found throughout his many other writings, both published and unpublished.

"The Phenomenon of Spirituality" (1937)

In 1937 Teilhard made the long Pacific voyage from Shanghai to the United States, where he had been invited to receive the Mendel Medal in recognition of his work in paleontology, specifically as one of the discoverers of Peking Man.[680] During this voyage he completed an essay, "The

---

[678] Ibid., 106.

[679] Ibid., 104.

[680] King, *Spirit of Fire*, 164.

Phenomenon of Spirituality," in which he not only discusses evolution, consciousness, and morality, but begins to articulate details of a hyperphysics of consciousness.[681] In this essay he joins with panpsychist philosopher–scientists from Plato to William James in affirming that it is impossible to deny that consciousness is a part of the natural universe. [682] He also introduces his concept of *centrology*, a basic building block of hyperphysics, and a seed from which, nine years later, emerged the cornerstone of Teilhard's hyperphysics, the essay "Centrology: An Essay in a Dialectic of Union," written in Peking in 1944.[683] The richness and diversity of ideas developed in "The Phenomenon of Spirituality" are stunning and wide-ranging. The topics move from evolutionary cosmology to consciousness, morality, and future research, and at the conclusion of the essay, he speaks of the possibility of seeking scientific proof of consciousness as a *centre* of energy:

> The possibility of proof obtained by direct observation . . . there must be a means . . . of recognizing . . . some psychic effect (radiation or attraction) specifically connected with the operation of this centre.[684]

---

[681] Teilhard, "The Phenomenon of Spirituality." Essay written in 1937.

[682] Skrbina, *Panpsychism in the West.*

[683] Teilhard, *Activation of Energy.*

[684] Teilhard, "The Phenomenon of Spirituality," 112.

In approaching Teilhard's essay, it is important at the outset to consider his frequent use of the terms "spirituality" and "spirit," as opposed to the term "consciousness." As a Jesuit Catholic priest, Teilhard's free use of the words "spirit" and "spirituality" may be easily understood, though the words are colored with religious overtones. Teilhard often seems to interchange the words "spirit" and "consciousness" in his essays, and often one assumes the terms may be synonymous, but the following passage in another essay, also written in 1937, offers a distinction between "spirit" and "consciousness":

> Human energy presents itself to our view as the term of a vast process in which the whole mass of the universe is involved. In us the evolution of the world towards the spirit becomes conscious.[685]

The first sentence tells us that Teilhard, like Bohm, views the universe as a "process" and as a "whole."[686] In the second sentence, Teilhard sees our human state as one in which the "evolution of the world" is becoming "conscious," and in which our human consciousness itself is evolving "towards the spirit." The relationship of spirit to consciousness for Teilhard is reminiscent of the metaphor of the ouroboros snake chasing its tail (see Fig. 43).

---

[685] Teilhard, *Building the Earth*, 67.

[686] Bohm, *Wholeness and the Implicate Order*.

Figure 43. The Ouroboros. Graphic by Pelekanos (1478). An image from a late medieval Byzantine Greek alchemical manuscript Reprinted under the terms of a Creative Commons Attribution ShareAlike 3.0 Unported license. Image retrieved from Wikimedia Commons.

However, Teilhard often uses the word "spirit" when "consciousness" would appear to be more appropriate, and henceforth in quoting passages from Teilhard we will provide an alternate reading of "consciousness" via angle brackets, where deemed appropriate, as in "the phenomenon of spirit [consciousness] . . . is the thing we know best in the world since we are itself."[687]

In the opening of his essay, "The Phenomenon of Spirituality," Teilhard argues that consciousness, whether a force or an energy, should be regarded as a natural, real phenomenon in the universe, worthy of study alongside other equally "real" phenomena that are taken as objects of

---

[687] Teilhard, "The Phenomenon of Spirituality," 93. Essay written in 1937.

interest in science (e.g., light, heat, electromagnetism, gravity, etc.):

> Around us, bodies present various qualities: they are warm, colored, electrified, heavy. But also in certain cases they are living, conscious. Beside the phenomena of heat, light and the rest studied by physics, there is, just as real and *natural*, the *phenomenon of spirituality*.[688]

Teilhard finds it surprising that humans have never truly come to understand this spirit/consciousness in which we are all glaringly immersed:

> The phenomenon of spirit [consciousness] has rightly attracted human attention more than any other. We are coincidental with it. We feel it from within. It is the very thread of which the other phenomena are woven for us. *It is the thing we know best in the world since we are itself*, and it is for us everything. And yet we never come to an understanding concerning the nature of this fundamental element.[689]

Teilhard describes the two most conventional approaches traditionally taken in regarding the phenomenon of consciousness:

> 1. Religious traditions regard consciousness [spirit], in general, to be of a transcendent nature, not of this physical, space–time world, while by contrast, and

---

[688] Ibid.

[689] Ibid.

2. Modern science regards consciousness as an epiphenomenon, a unique accident in the recent evolutionary history of the planet.

Teilhard tells us that in this essay he will propose and develop an alternative to these two approaches:

> I propose in these pages to develop a third viewpoint towards which a new physical science and a new philosophy seem to be converging in the present day: that is to say that spirit [consciousness] is neither super-imposed nor accessory to the cosmos, but that it quite simply represents the higher state assumed in and around us by the primal and indefinable thing that we call, for want of another name, the "stuff of the universe."[690]

Teilhard tells us that the phenomenon of consciousness has been overlooked as an object of study within physical science because, at first sight, the "consciousness portion of the world presents itself in the form of discontinuous, tiny and ephemeral fragments: a bright dust of individualities," while in truth the dimensions of this consciousness ought to be taken as "the dimensions of the universe itself."[691]

But in order to see this, says Teilhard, we need to develop a new form of perception, a new sense with which we may "educate our eyes to perceiving collective realities." Teilhard predicts the development not only of a new form of

---

[690] Ibid., 93–94.

[691] Ibid.

"direct vision," but the emergence of a previously unsuspected psychic ability, a new sensory mode:

> Men have for long been seeking a means of immediately influencing the bodies and souls around them by their will, and of penetrating them by *a direct vision* .... Nothing seems to me more vital, from the point of view of human energy, than the spontaneous appearance and, eventually, the systematic cultivation of such a "cosmic sense."[692]

Teilhard apparently has sensed evolutionary transformations both through his direct inner vision, as well as through his outer vision, he has critically observed both an internal as well as an external nature. Evolution, claims Teilhard, is often accompanied by sudden changes of state, as in water that is seen to become ice, or a solution in crystallization, change of state in "not only molecular or atomic complexity, but interiorization." [693] Teilhard perceives, both internally and externally, that in consciousness change of state follows a process of centration or compression. This can be compared with and contrasted to entropy, the movement of expansion, diffusion, and dissipation, and together they can be seen as "two fundamental cosmic movements ... which we can grasp experientially."[694] He describes these two contrary movements as the concurrent movement of energy in two directions, the "vitalization" and the "dissipation" of energy

---

[692] Teilhard, "Human Energy," 130–31.

[693] Teilhard, "The Phenomenon of Spirituality," 99.

[694] Ibid., 98.

and says that they "are merely the opposite poles of a single cosmic event."[695] Figure 44 contrasts the two movements of entropy and centration.

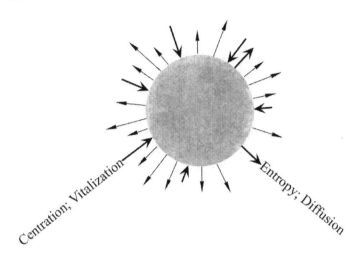

Figure 44. Entropy and centration. Graphic by author.

In words that parallel David Bohm's description of an on-going process of enfolding and unfolding between an implicate and an explicate order, Teilhard describes "the inward furling from which consciousness is born . . . around a centre . . . the All becoming self-reflective upon a single consciousness."[696]

At this point he brings up a theme that will arise repeatedly in his later essays, the transcendence of death by the individual personality.[697] Teilhard says, "to become

[695] Ibid.

[696] Ibid., 101.

[697] Teilhard's final essay, written shortly before his death in 1955, is entitled, "The Death-Barrier and Co-Reflection, or the Imminent Awakening of Human Consciousness to the Sense of Its Irreversibility."

super-conscious the fragmented building blocks of man must unite itself with others," [698] but without losing personalities previously acquired, without losing information. Recall that Teilhard had sensed this phenomenon as a totalization of multiple centres [699] of consciousness, in 1916 at the Front.

He goes on to state that humans in general seem to have lost the "faculty of totalization," with the exception of a few mystics, who have been able to experience union by dissolution, much as salt in the ocean. But it is union by differentiation that interest Teilhard, not union by dissolution.

> We can see a justification ahead for our hope of a personal immortality ... without becoming confused with one another ... to complete ourselves we must pass into a greater than ourselves .... In this convergent universe, all the lower centres unite, but by inclusion in a more powerful centre. Therefore they are all preserved and completed by joining together. [700]

Teilhard now turns to the implications of such a theory for morality, in a section he calls "Moral

---

[698] Teilhard, "The Phenomenon of Spirituality," 103.

[699] Note that the British spelling "centre" is used here and throughout textual discussion in this chapter, not only because it is in accordance with the spelling found in all published translations of Teilhard's work into English, but more specifically because in the context of Teilhard's metaphysics, the word *centre* is used to designate a "center of consciousness," rather than used simply as an adjective, or a location designator.

[700] Teilhard, "The Phenomenon of Spirituality," 104.

Applications." He describes two categories of morality, the "Morality of Balance," and the "Morality of Movement."[701]

Morality of Balance vs. Morality of Movement

Here Teilhard describes two types of morality, the morality of balance, and the morality of movement. The old morality is the morality of balance, an attempt at homeostasis, a "morality that arose largely as an empirical defense of the individual and society."[702] Teilhard goes on to say, "Morality has till now been principally understood as a fixed system of rights and duties intended to establish a static equilibrium." [703] However in light of the modern discovery of the evolutionary nature of everything in the universe, the human being must be seen as "an element destined to complete himself cosmically in a higher consciousness in process of formation," and thus the need for a new morality, a morality of growth (movement), one that will foster and catalyze evolutionary change, a growth into a new formation of being. Teilhard says that new times and a new understanding of the trajectory of life and consciousness implies that while the "moralist was up to now a jurist, or a tight-rope walker," the moralist of the future must "become the technician and engineer of the spiritual [consciousness] energies of the world."[704] He says that for those who see the development of consciousness "as

---

[701] Ibid., 106.

[702] Ibid., 105.

[703] Ibid., 106.

[704] Ibid.

the essential phenomenon of nature … morality is consequently nothing less than the higher development of mechanics and biology. The world is ultimately constructed by moral forces."[705] Having argued the urgent requirement for a new morality, a morality of growth, Teilhard sets forth "three rules that clearly modify or complete the idea we have of goodness and perfection:"[706]

- Good "is what makes for the growth of spirit [consciousness]."

- Good is everything that brings "growth of consciousness to the world."

- "Finally, best is what assures their highest development to the spiritual powers [consciousness] of the earth."[707]

Teilhard summarizes, "many things seemed to be forbidden by the morality of balance which become virtually permitted or even obligatory by the morality of movement." For example, in following a morality of balance, as long as we follow society's rules, we are permitted to waste our lives in any frivolous pursuit (i.e., in sheer entertainment); whereas under a morality of movement such things as research through experimentation with psychotropic drugs and participatory exploration of multiple religions would likely be permissible. With disregard of likely disapproval by Vatican censors, Teilhard urges a new human morality of

---

[705] Ibid., 105.

[706] Ibid., 107.

[707] Ibid.

growth (see Table 7) that "will forbid a neutral and 'inoffensive' existence, and compel him strenuously to free his *autonomy* and *personality* to the utmost," and he urges us "to try everything and to force everything in the direction of the greatest consciousness."[708]

Table 7
Morality of Balance versus Morality of Growth

Morality of balance	Morality of growth
Homeostasis; closed.	Evolutionary movement; open.
Fixed rules, rights, and duties to sustain the present.	Whatever fosters growth of consciousness for the future.
Love is subordinate to procreation.	Love gives incalculable spiritual power.
The old moralities of balance are static, powerless to govern the earth.	What is needed is a new morality of movement, of growth.

Note. Data adapted from Teilhard, "The Phenomenon of Spirituality," 105–10. Author's table.

One can see in Table 7 why the more conservative Church authorities might have had problem with these ideas, but Teilhard is an unapologetic explorer (and a mystic), who states unequivocally:

> The boldest mariners of tomorrow will set out to explore and humanize the mysterious ocean of moral energies ... our goal is to try everything and to force everything in the direction of the

---

[708] Ibid., 107–8.

greatest consciousness ... ever since its beginnings life has been a groping, an adventure, a risk, and general and highest law of morality: to limit force is sin.[709]

At the conclusion of his essay, Teilhard urges us "situate the stuff of the universe in consciousness ... and to see nature as the development of this same consciousness." He regards the idea of a cosmos as "a moving towards personality," and he concludes with a statement that, once more would likely win him no affection among more conservative elements in the Vatican:

> This is the origin of the present crisis in morality ... a powerlessness of (old) moralities of balance to govern the earth. It is necessary for the religions to change themselves ... what we are all more or less lacking at this moment is a new definition of holiness.[710]

Holoflux Theory and Teilhard's "Spirit"

At the heart of this essay, Teilhard introduces a major hypothesis in a key paragraph that is essential to understanding his hyperphysics, and which accords well with Bohm's model in ontological quantum physics, in which the cosmos is seen both as simultaneously unfolding and enfolding:

> Everything that happens in the world, we would say, suggests that the unique centre of consciousness around which the universe is

---

[709] Ibid., 108.

[710] Ibid., 109–11.

furling could only be formed gradually, through a series of diminishing concentric spheres, each of which engenders the next; each sphere being moreover formed of elementary centres charged with a consciousness that increases as their radius diminishes. By means of this mechanism each newly appearing sphere is charged in its turn with the consciousness developed in the preceding spheres, carries it to a degree higher in each of the elementary centres that compose it, and transmits it a little further on toward the centre of total convergence.[711]

This description can be seen as congruent with the theory of holospheres presented in Chapter 5, in which smaller dimensions converge to the limit found at the Planck holosphere, at which point begins the implicate order.

Teilhard concludes this section by telling us that "the final centre of the whole system appears at the end both as the final sphere and as the centre of all the centres spread over this final sphere."[712] This "centre of all centres" can be understood as Bohm's implicate order, transcending space–time. Teilhard also refers to this centre as a "a quantum of consciousness," and tells us that each degree of consciousness at a given moment only exists as "an introduction to a higher consciousness," and that this general process is irresistible and irreversible.[713]

---

[711] Ibid.

[712] Ibid.

[713] Ibid., 99.

If we accept this hypothetical model, says Teilhard, then we are led to two conclusions for the present and for the future:

1. The source of all our difficulties in understanding matter is that it is habitually regarded as inanimate.[714]

2. We are moving towards a higher state of general consciousness . . . other spheres must exist in the future and, inevitably, there exists a supreme centre in which all the personal energy represented by human consciousness must be gathered and "super-personalized."[715]

How might we understand Teilhard's use of the term "spirit" in terms of holoflux theory? It is my contention that Teilhard's "spirit" is equivalent to holoflux energy as it manifests within Bohm's implicate order. In the holoflux theory, spirit has a nonlocal locus embedded within a Planck-length spherical center in space–time, everywhere. Conversely, what is termed consciousness is localized in space–time, manifesting as expanding flux in detectable fields of electromagnetic waves, illustrated in Fig. 45.

Yet they are in relationship, they both exist as part of Bohm's "Wholeness," and there exists a direct connection between spirit and consciousness through the phenomenon of frequency resonance operating through Fourier transform-like mathematical processes.

---

[714] Ibid., 101.

[715] Ibid., 103.

SPIRIT CONSCIOUSNESS

NON-LOCAL   LOCAL

Figure 45. Nonlocal spirit versus local consciousness.
         Graphic by author.

It is useful to go topologically further into the holoflux analogy. Imagine the communal locus of Teilhard's "spirit" as it is found within, at the very center of every "point" within space–time. The holoflux process *is* the implicate order, is *one with* the implicate order; "spirit," as implicate order holoflux, has the advantage of being self-superpositioned, fully interconnected, transcending the limits of time and space, and as has been discussed in Chapter 5, can be identified in electrical engineering terms as the frequency domain.

Let us now move outward in scale, bridging the transition zone, the isospheric shell which divides the implicate order from the explicate order. Here we see holoflux emerging from the implicate order as it transforms into space–time energy, flaring forth as waves of spherically vibrating electromagnetic energy. These waves of energy emerge everywhere into space–time from a holoplenum of Planck diameter isospheres. Each isosphere can be seen to encapsulate the entire implicate order, within which the infinity of frequencies from all time and all space are eternally enfolding into a hyper-harmonic flux.

In terms of Bohmian holoflux theory, the first approach to consciousness, the religious, is focused almost exclusively upon an implicate domain, energy as a transcendent flux, and a focus which generally ignores or rejects as unreal the space–time explicate domain;

conversely, in the second approach to consciousness, the modern scientific, the focus is upon space–time explicate mode phenomena, completely ignoring the possible reality of a non space–time domain.

Teilhard proposes an alternative to these two, seemingly mutually exclusive, approaches:

> I propose in these pages to develop a third viewpoint towards which a new physical science and a new philosophy seem to be converging at the present day: that is to say that spirit is neither super-imposed nor accessory to the cosmos, but that it quite simply represents the higher state assumed in and around us by the primal and indefinable thing that we call, for want of a better name, the "stuff of the universe." Nothing more; and also nothing less. Spirit is neither a meta-phenomenon nor an epi-phenomenon; it is *the* phenomenon.[716]

Teilhard's "spirit," or what he simply calls *"the phenomenon,"* is synonymous with the holoflux model described here that regards the universe as *one whole single energy* processing within and between two primary domains, a space–time domain, and a spectral domain. Figure 46 is a diagram highlighting Teilhard's distinction between "spirit" and "consciousness," drawn in the context of Pribram's original diagram of the Fourier transform (Fig. 46), and Bohm's ontological distinction between an implicate nonlocal order, and an explicate local order.

---

[716] Ibid., 93–94.

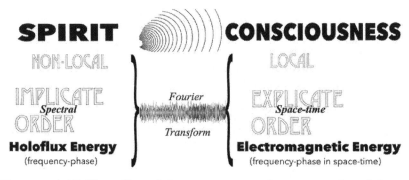

Figure 46. Teilhard's spirit versus consciousness. Graphic by author.

The diagram places "spirit" on the left, in the nonlocal implicate order, manifesting as holoflux energy, possibly the mysterious "dark energy" being sought by physicists.[717] Conversely, "consciousness" can be seen on the right, in the space–time region, manifesting as electromagnetic energy.

The two domains are bridged by mathematical transforms, as indicated symbolically in the diagram by the Fourier transform, which in the Figure represents all of the mathematical transformations in the cosmological process bridging the implicate with the explicate.

"Human Energy" (1937)

It is in an essay written in Peking that same year, "Human Energy," Teilhard describes three forms of energy, and implies that modern science only considers the first two, ignoring the third; these three he identifies as:

- Incorporated energy,

- Controlled energy, and

---

[717] Gao, *Dark Energy: From Einstein's Biggest Blunder to the Holographic Universe.*

- Spiritualized [conscious] energy.

Incorporated energy manifests in rocks, crystals, neurons, etc. Controlled energy is that generated by humans and used to power human devices thermodynamically and electrically. Energy of the third kind, Teilhard's "spiritualized energy," or we would say, the "energy of consciousness," is the primary subject of his essay, "Human Energy."[718]

In this essay Teilhard proposes that each human "represents a cosmic nucleus . . . radiating around it waves of organization and excitation within matter."[719] Teilhard immediately proposes, based it seems upon his own experience, that these radiations can be perceived by human beings, and he makes reference to the need for development of a special psychic mode of perception:

> This perception of a natural psychic unity higher than our "souls" requires, *as I know from experience*, a special quality and training in the observer. Like all broad scientific perspectives it is the product of a prolonged reflexion, leading to the discovery of *a deep cosmic sense*.[720]

Teilhard warns that it is a matter of perception, of tuning, of intent. He says that we are like a cell that can see nothing but other cells, but that there are more complex configurations of being if we only can learn how to join with them. He says that "the thoughts of individuals . . . form

---

[718] Teilhard, "Human Energy." Essay written in 1937.

[719] Ibid., 117.

[720] Ibid., 118. Emphasis added by author.

from the linked multiplicity, a single spirit of the earth," and that he sees humanity continuing to evolve "in the direction of a decisive expansion of our ancient powers reinforced by the acquisition of certain new faculties of consciousness."[721] Teilhard emphasizes that this growth is not a walk of random chance, but that it unfolds within a universe that is alive with an energy that is also synonymous with the mystery we call love or allurement:

> Love by the boundless possibilities of intuition and communication it contains, penetrates the unknown; it will take its place in the mysterious future, with the group of new faculties and consciousnesses that is awaiting us.[722]

Here he expresses a consideration missing in most physical descriptions of energy, the category of "love," something that Teilhard includes as perhaps the most real, fundamental manifestation of energy in his hyperphysical theories. As early as 1931, in "The Spirit of the Earth," Teilhard had referred to an energy of consciousness, of sensation, of love, as manifesting in a spectrum (much as Jung, in 1946, used the imagery of the spectrum to characterize the energy of the psyche).[723] Teilhard says that, "Love is a sacred reserve of energy; it is the blood of spiritual evolution."[724]

---

[721] Ibid., 128.

[722] Ibid., 129–30.

[723] Jung, "On the Nature of the Psyche," 207.

[724] Teilhard, "The Spirit of the Earth," 35. Essay written 1931.

Hominized love is distinct from all other love, because the "spectrum" of its warm and penetrating light is marvelously enriched. No longer only a unique and periodic attraction for purposes of material fertility; but an unbounded and continuous possibility of contact between minds rather than bodies; the play of countless subtle antennae seeking one another.[725]

Teilhard sees this organic love-consciousness energy growing more complex and changing through some natural evolutionary process, currently unknown, but he is confident that there will be an eventual mastery and understanding of this same phenomenon (conscious love) in terms of physics.
Accordingly, he stresses the importance of those engaged in scientific research to turn their focus upon the human phenomenon of consciousness.

He is hopeful, telling us with conviction that "physics will surely isolate and master the secret that lies at the heart of metaphysics," and will accelerate this evolution toward the emergence of a new cosmic sense:

Nothing seems to me more vital, from the point of view of human energy, than the spontaneous appearance and, eventually, the systematic cultivation of such a "cosmic sense."[726]

One in Many: The Noosphere

In a section entitled "Organization of Total Human Energy: The Common Human Soul," Teilhard discusses his

---

[725] Ibid., 33.

[726] Teilhard, "Human Energy," 130–31.

concept of the noosphere, and sees in the process of "raising men to the explicit perception of their 'molecular' nature" that the possibility opens for them to "cease to be closed individuals, to become parts . . . to be integrated in the total energy of the noosphere."[727] But Teilhard is at pains to reassure the reader that this does not imply the loss of individuality, and he points out that individual human souls (the quanta of consciousness) are not like gas molecules, "anonymous and interchangeable corpuscles," but that the formation of the noosphere requires, on the contrary, a "maximum of personality" to be manifest through each human individual sub contribution:

> The utility of each nucleus of human energy in relation to the whole depends on what is unique . . . in the achievement of each.[728]

Assuming that consciousness is evolving and the material universe is evolving, Teilhard wonders where might the energy come from that guides the coalescing centro-complexity into such exquisite configurations, and he wonders what might be the nature of energy within this evolution (i.e., what is "informing" and "powering" this evolutionary process)? His answer can be found in a section he calls, "The Maintenance of Human Energy and 'The Cosmic Point Omega.'" He explains that such energy is axial, that it "is found to be fed by a particular current" flowing from the center, the Omega point, which, he calls a "tension of consciousness."[729] The same phenomenon in

---

[727] Ibid., 131.

[728] Ibid.

[729] Ibid., 138.

338

holoflux theory, this "particular current" flowing from the center, can be seen in Bohm's quantum potential wavefunction, Q, which according to Bohm is also driving the patternings of evolution.

Here Teilhard makes a diversion into a subject he repeatedly brings up, the continuation of the centres of personality after physical death.

> Reflective action and the expectation of total disappearance are *cosmically incompatible*... death leaves some part of ourselves in some way, to which we can turn with devotion and interest, as to a portion of the absolute... as *imperishable*.[730]

He points out that cosmic evolution is a work of "*personal* nature," and that we are each a unique "centre of personal stuff totalizing, in itself, the essence of our personalities... the universal centre of attraction"; at this point he begins to discuss the "centre of psychic convergence," the noosphere, and brings up the image of the sphere.[731]

> The totality of a sphere is just as present in its centre, which takes the form of a point, as spread over its whole surface.[732]

_____

[730] Ibid., 141.

[731] Teilhard, "Cosmic Life," 15; Note that it is here, in Teilhard's earliest known essay, written at Dunkirk in April 1916, that Teilhard first speaks at length about the centres and the sphere: "We are the countless centres of one and the same sphere."

[732] Teilhard, *Human Energy*, 143.

What are the implications in Teilhard's statement, "the totality of a sphere is just as present in its center?" We could say that it implies a sharing of information storage between the isosphere in space–time and the implicate order at the center (Wheeler's qubits of conscious information spread over the surface of a sphere, would be seen here be in resonance with the implicate center). Next Teilhard poses a question whose solution appears to corroborate the concept of an implicate order within the quantum holosophere, and he concludes with his famous dictum, "union differentiates":

> Now why should it be strange for the universe to have a centre, that is to say to collect itself to the same degree in a single consciousness, if its totality is already partially reflected in each of our particular consciousnesses? . .Union, the true upward union in the spirit [consciousness], ends by establishing the elements it dominates in their own perfection. *Union differentiates.*[733]

But not only are each of the centres of consciousness preserved in their union, they are *evolutionarily enhanced*; the n centres join, but in that joining, although they retain their own personalities, an additional personality, $n + 1$, is formed, and "*since there is no fusion or dissolution of the elementary personalities, the centre in which they join must necessarily be distinct from them, that is to say have its own personality.*"[734]

It is at this point in his essay that Teilhard introduces the term Omega, describing it as the cosmic point of total

---

[733] Ibid., 143–44.

[734] Ibid., 144.

synthesis without which "the world would not function," and describing its relationship to the noosphere:

> The noosphere in fact *physically* requires, for its maintenance and functioning ... the unifying influence of a *distinct* center of super-personality ... a centre different from all the other centres which it "super-centres" by assimilation: a personality distinct from all the personalities it perfects by uniting with them .... Consideration of this Omega will allow us to define more completely ... the hidden nature of what we have till now called, vaguely enough, "human energy."[735]

The Omega Point

Central to the architecture of Teilhard de Chardin's hyperphysics is the concept of Omega or the Omega point. According to his close friend Henri de Lubac, Teilhard's first use of the term can be found in one of his earliest essays:

> In the first essay that was entitled *Mon Univers* (1916) he carefully distinguishes, in order to study their relationships, "Omicron, the natural term of human and cosmic progress," from "Omega, the supernatural term of the Kingdom of God" or "Plenitude of Christ." Later, he was to abandon this particular terminology, but he retained the distinction it expressed.[736]

Twenty years later Teilhard was using the term in a more secular, scientific context, as seen here at the close of a

---

[735] Ibid., 145.

[736] de Lubac, *The Religion of Teilhard de Chardin*, 123.

lecture delivered at the French Embassy in Peking on March 10, 1945.[737]

> Ahead of, or rather in the heart of, a universe prolonged along its axis of complexity, there exists a . . . centre of convergence . . . let us call it the *point Omega*.[738]

Teilhard devotes an entire section to "The Attributes of the Omega Point," in his book, *The Human Phenomenon*, begun in Paris in 1939 and completed in China during World War II. In a section that in his first draft had been called, "Spirit and Entropy," Teilhard says of Omega:

> Expressed in terms of internal energy, the cosmic function of Omega consists in initiating and maintaining the unanimity of the world's reflective particles under its radiation. But how could it carry out this action if it were not somehow already . . . *right here and now*? . .Autonomy, actuality, irreversibility and finally, transcendence are the four attributes of Omega . . . Omega is the principle we needed to explain both the steady advance of things toward more consciousness and the paradoxical solidity of what is most fragile . . . . Something in the cosmos, therefore, escapes entropy—and does so more and more.[739]

---

[737] Teilhard, "Life and the Planets." Speech of 1945 published as an essay in 1946.

[738] Ibid., 122.

[739] Teilhard, *The Human Phenomenon*, 191–93.

In "The Heart of Matter," completed in Paris in 1950, Teilhard describes Omega in terms of what can only be seen as a culmination of his own direct personal experience of consciousness. In the first line of the closing section of this essay he states clearly that the discovery of this Omega "brings to a close what I might call the natural branch of the inner trajectory I followed in my search for the ultimate consistence of the universe." [740] Teilhard goes on to define his vision of Omega as, "the complex unit in which the organic sum of the reflective elements of the World becomes irreversible within a *transcendent Super-ego*." [741]

In his lecture delivered at the French embassy in Peking in 1946, Teilhard discusses the importance of the *point Omega* concept, its perceptual observation by mystics, and its importance in the terraforming of a planetary consciousness:

> Let us suppose that from this universal centre, this Omega point, there constantly emanate radiations hitherto only perceptible to those persons whom we call "mystics." Let us further imagine that, as the sensibility or response to mysticism of the human race increases with planetisation, the awareness of Omega becomes so widespread as to warm the earth psychically. [742]

The metaphor of warmth, expressed here by Teilhard, is no accident. An important element of Teilhard's model of

---

[740] Teilhard, "The Heart of Matter," 39. Essay written in 1954.

[741] Ibid. Italic emphasis added.

[742] Teilhard, "Life and the Planets," 122. Essay written in 1944.

human energy lies in his understanding that consciousness can be expressed in thermodynamic terms. In the essay "Human Energy," in a section with the title, "V. THE MAINTENANCE OF HUMAN ENERGY AND 'THE COSMIC POINT OMEGA,'" Teilhard describes how an axial form of this heat energy powers the current of conscious human energy. Teilhard describes the generation of this current:

> Considered in its organic material zones, human energy obeys the laws of physics and draws quite naturally on the reserves of heat available in nature. But studied in its axial, spiritualized form, it is found to be fed by a particular current (of which thermodynamics might well be, after all, no more than a statistical echo), which, for want of a better name, we will call "tension of consciousness."[743]

Teilhard here once again links thermodynamics to the phenomenon of consciousness, and he goes on to refute the widespread scientific paradigm of consciousness as a mere epiphenomenon of the material universe:

> We still persist in regarding the physical as constituting the "true" phenomenon in the universe, and the psychic as a sort of epiphenomenon ... we should consider the whole of thermodynamics as an unstable and ephemeral by-effect of the concentration on itself of what we call "consciousness."[744]

---

[743] Teilhard, "Human Energy," 138.

[744] Teilhard, "The Activation of Human Energy," 393.

It is reasonable to consider Teilhard's Omega Point, resolved down to the smallest possible dimension known to physics, as equivalent to a "Planck holosphere," as discussed in Chapter 5.

In one of his last essays, "The Nature of the Point Omega," Teilhard states that it is in the noosphere that all is truly preserved, for it is here that all experience is gathered and saved eternally:

> In convergent cosmogenesis, as I have said, everything happens as if the preservable contents of the world were gathered and consolidated, by evolution, at the centre of the sphere representing the universe . . . a cosmic convergence . . . to bind objectively to the real and already existing centre.[745]

Here again can be seen a congruence between Teilhard's process viewed as a convergent cosmogenesis, and Bohm's process seen as an enfolding of the explicate into an implicate domain.

Teilhard concludes the essay "Human Energy" with a highly optimistic observation revealing once again his lifelong fascination with the concept of the human personality's mode of survival beyond biological death:

> The principle of the conservation of personality signifies that each individual nucleus of personality, once formed, is for ever constituted as "itself"; so that, in the supreme personality that is the crown of the universe, all elementary personalities that have appeared in the course of evolution must be present again in a distinct (though super-personalized) state . . . each

---

[745] Teilhard, "The Nature of the Point Omega," 272–73.

elementary person contains something *unique and untransmittable* in his essence.[746]

"Centrology: An Essay in the Dialectic of Union"

During the occupation of China by the Japanese, Teilhard's anthropological work was severely curtailed, and he found himself with time to go deeply into the development of his more abstract ideas, which he expressed systematically and in great detail in his 1944 essay, "Centrology," written under somewhat stark wartime conditions during his Peking confinement. At the beginning of his essay he boldly states what he considers to be the scientific nature of this essay: "It is not an abstract metaphysics, but a realist ultraphysics of union."[747]

Teilhard opens his essay with an immediate discussion of "Centres and Centro-Complexity," describing how in living elements of the biosphere we find a continuation of the "granular (atomic molecular)" structure of the universe, and that, in fact, the human body "is simply a 'super-molecule.'" [748] However, unlike conventional physicists, who see cosmic particles as sources or centers of radiation and then map that radiation in the space–time domain, Teilhard places the focus of his inquiry on the "within" of each so-called particle. According to Teilhard, the space–time particles are not only centers of origination of radiation but each one of them also "has" a within, and "is" a within, a within that is a mode of consciousness, a

---

[746] Teilhard, "Human Energy," 162.

[747] Teilhard, "Centrology," 99.

[748] Ibid., 100.

psychic centre. In other words, Teilhard says, consciousness is a universal molecular property.

Teilhard goes further to claim that an increase in consciousness can be found associated with an increase in "centro-complexity," and he defines "the coefficient of centro-complexity" as "the true absolute measure of being in the beings that surround us."[749] Teilhard describes biology as "simply the physics of very large complexes."[750]

He points out that the atomic complexity of a virus is of the order of 10^5 atomic particles, and this complexity increases dramatically by the time we reach the size of a cell at 10^{10}, but in the brains of large mammals, has reached the great complexity of 10^{20} particles.[751]

Teilhard states that "if the universe is observed in its true and essential movement through time, it represents a system which is in a process of internal *centro-complexification*," and asserts a definition of evolution to be "*a transition from a lower to a higher state of centro-complexity*."[752]

In "Man's Place in the Universe," Teilhard had argued that existence entails three infinities: the infinite large, the infinite small, and the infinite complex, and he illustrates this with the chart reproduced in Figure 47, "Teilhard's Natural Curve of Complexities."[753]

---

[749] Ibid., 102.

[750] Ibid., 102, n1.

[751] Ibid. 102.

[752] Ibid., 103.

[753] Teilhard, "Man's Place in the Universe," 226. Essay written in 1942.

Using data from objects in nature Teilhard plots a curve (reproduced in Fig. 47) with two axes: a vertical y-axis scaled in *Size* (length in centimeters), and a horizontal x-axis on which is measured increases in *Complexity* (total number of atoms per object). Note that both scales are calibrated in base 10 logarithms. The curve plots size vs. complexity for various natural entities, named on both axes.

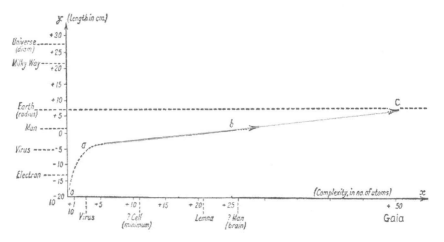

Figure 47. Teilhard's natural curve of complexities.[754] Reprinted with permission.

Points "a" and "b" on the plot indicate where Teilhard believes "state changes of consciousness" have occurred. Point "a" marks the emergence of life, and point "b" indicates the emergence of reflective consciousness (i.e., thought, being able to think about thinking).

While Teilhard does not discuss the arrow extending the curve to the right, the implication is clear if we mentally plot the value for the *Complexity* of Earth, which has been

---

[754] Ibid., 226.

estimated to consist of 1.33 x 10^{50} atoms.[755] Accordingly we have increased the width of Teilhard's horizontal axis scale, which in his own notebook stops at the human brain's +25 atoms, and have doubled the x range, to the Earth's +50 atoms. At +50 the curve in Fig. 47 has been extrapolated to intersect Teilhard's converging curve at point "c," marking a planetary change of state, a state described here by Teilhard as an awakening of a consciousness common to the whole earth:

> We can see it only as a *state of unanimity*: such a state, however, that in it each grain of thought, now taken to the extreme limit of its individual consciousness, will simply be the incommunicable, partial, elementary expression of a total consciousness which is common to the whole earth, and specific to the earth: *a spirit* [consciousness] *of the earth*.[756]

Elsewhere Teilhard has described the importance of the concept of reflection (alternately translated into English as reflexion), and this is associated with point "b" on the complexity chart, the concept also applies to a projected point "c" which would be a change of state for the consciousness of the planet, a noospheric "reflection":

> "Reflection," as the word itself indicates, is the power acquired by a consciousness of turning in on itself and taking possession of itself *as an*

---

[755] Calculated by Drew Weisenberger, a detector scientist at the Department of Energy's Thomas Jefferson National Accelerator Facility. See Weisenberger, "Jefferson Lab Questions and Answers," para. 2.

[756] Teilhard, "The Atomism of Spirit," 40.

object endowed with its own particular consistency and value: no longer only to know something but to know *itself*; no longer only to know, but to know that it knows.[757]

Teilhard's chart thus supports the first general conclusion in his essay on "Centrology," that the universe is in a state of internal "centro-complexification," and that in this "transition from a lower to a higher state of centro-complexity," we see a concomitant increase in complexity-consciousness, in a process that Teilhard terms cosmogenesis through centrogenesis.[758]

Form his earliest essays, Teilhard sees the planet itself as an evolving, larger entity, out of which humanity has sprung and to which humanity is adding new capabilities. Teilhard presents geological and zoological evidence of the planet Earth as an evolving lifeform,[759] a global being in the transitional process of awakening into a planetary state of reflective self-consciousness. He identifies a distinct axis of successive forms, layers of increasing complexity and centrification running from geogenesis through biogenesis and beyond, into psychogenesis; this axis, he insists, can be seen continuing in the present noetic awakening that it is life itself that is engendering the birth of a new mode of planetary consciousness, comprising an entity which he himself has named, the noosphere.[760]

---

[757] Teilhard, *The Human Phenomenon*, 110.

[758] Teilhard, "Centrology," 103.

[759] Teilhard, "Universalization and Union," 91. Essay written in 1953.

[760] Teilhard, "Centrology," 120.

He speculates that eventually "life might use its ingenuity to force the gates of its terrestrial prison . . . by establishing a connection psyche to psyche with other focal points of consciousness across space," and "the possibility of 'centre-to-centre' contacts between perfect centres."[761]

But it is not only the planet itself that is evolving for Teilhard, he also views consciousness in humanity as evolving and thus sees the human species accelerating toward an evolutionary threshold, where it will experience the nature of energy and self-reflection in ever newer ways, while feeling itself drawn magnetically toward new states of greater cohesion and complexity, not only of radiant physical energy, which he terms "the tangential component," but of an increasingly conscious, psychic flow, the spiritual or "radial component" of energy.[762] He even senses an imminent transformation in the biophysical gateway, the human brain, in which he foresees form and function itself complexifying past the point of isolated self-reflection:

> Is there not in fact, beyond the isolated brain, a still higher possible complex: by that I mean a sort of "brain" of associated brains? . . . . From this point of view, the natural evolution of the biosphere is not only continued in what I have called Noosphere, but assumes in it a strictly convergent form which, towards its peak, produces a point of maturation (or of collective reflection).[763]

---

[761] Ibid., 110.

[762] Ibid.

[763] Teilhard, "Outline of a Dialectic of Spirit," 144.

Another term used by Teilhard in describing this process is "convergence." He states that, "In the organo-psychic field of centro-complexity, the world is convergent; the isospheres are simply a system of waves which as time goes on (and it is they which measure time) close up around Omega point"; the world, according to Teilhard, is moving continuously in "a transition from a lower to a higher state of centro-complexity."[764]

Centrogenesis

Teilhard coins a new term, "centrogenesis," to encapsulate this process. In "Centrology," Teilhard begins his discussion of centrogenesis by claiming that the universe is made up of psychic nuclei, similar to the theory of monads developed by Gottfried Wilhelm Leibniz; monads were described by Leibniz as being the most basic, fundamental entities of which the cosmos is constructed (a idea seen here as a precursor to the model of holospheres in the holoplenum), however in his theory the monads are completely independent of one another, though in complete harmony.[765] Unlike the monads of Leibniz, Teilhard's nuclei are interconnected in three simultaneous ways.[766] These relationships are as follows:

- Tangentially—"on the surface of an isosphere"

---

[764] Teilhard, "Centrology," 103.

[765] Rescher, *G. W. Leibniz's Monadology.*

[766] Teilhard, "Centrology," 104.

- Radially—"through nuclei of lower centro-complexity" (n^1, n^2, etc.)

- Radially—"inwardly, creating an isosphere of a higher order" ($n + 1$)

Teilhard describes these elementary cosmic centres as "partially themselves," and "partially the same thing." In Fig. 48 can be seen four drawings presented by Teilhard at the beginning of his essay on "Centrology."

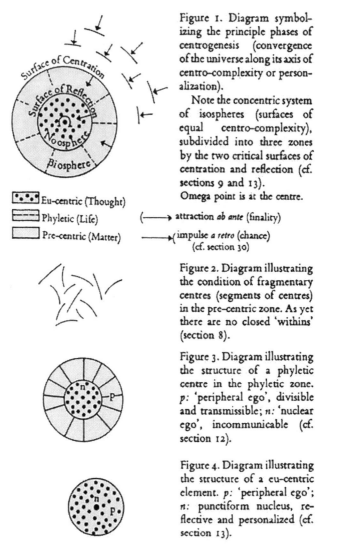

Figure 1. Diagram symbolizing the principle phases of centrogenesis (convergence of the universe along its axis of centro-complexity or personalization).

Note the concentric system of isospheres (surfaces of equal centro-complexity), subdivided into three zones by the two critical surfaces of centration and reflection (cf. sections 9 and 13).

Omega point is at the centre.

(⟶ attraction *ab ante* (finality)

⟶(impulse *a retro* (chance)
(cf. section 30)

Eu-centric (Thought)
Phyletic (Life)
Pre-centric (Matter)

Figure 2. Diagram illustrating the condition of fragmentary centres (segments of centres) in the pre-centric zone. As yet there are no closed 'withins' (section 8).

Figure 3. Diagram illustrating the structure of a phyletic centre in the phyletic zone. *p*: 'peripheral ego', divisible and transmissible; *n*: 'nuclear ego', incommunicable (cf. section 12).

Figure 4. Diagram illustrating the structure of a eu-centric element. *p*: 'peripheral ego'; *n*: punctiform nucleus, reflective and personalized (cf. section 13).

Figure 48. Teilhard's Figures 1 through 4 in "Centrology."[767] Printed with permission.

Three of Teilhard's images (Figures 2, 3, and 4) depict the three stages of centrogenesis. In Teilhard's Figure 2 can be seen the condition of "fragmentary centres (segments of

---

[767] Ibid., 100.

centres)," not yet enclosed in isospheric configurations, and still devoid of what Teilhard calls "personality." Thus Figure 2 presents elements that are termed "pre-centric" fragments, having no "withins."[768]

More evolved is the image of Teilhard's Figure 3, which reveals *phyletic centricity*, a change of state brought about by the self-closing of numerous fragmentary centers, which he defines as "life," and which manifests as phylum.[769] In regarding this state, Teilhard brings up two questions: (1) He asks, "how can we conceive the passage and communication of a 'within' from mother-cell to daughter-cell?", and (2) "Under what conditions is the phylum provided the greatest possible richness and variety for the evolutionary transmission of successful properties?"[770]

To answer the first question, Teilhard observes that there are "two sorts of ego in each phyletic centre, a nuclear ego . . . and a peripheral ego."[771] The *peripheral ego* is incompletely individualized, separate, and according to Teilhard, it is therefore divisible and can be shared through replication or association. Teilhard's then explains how the second ego, the *nuclear ego*, communicates:

> It is in virtue of the arrival at zero of its centric diameter that the living centre, in its turn, attains

---

[768] Ibid., 105.

[769] Ibid., 106.

[770] Ibid., 107.

[771] Ibid., 108.

the condition and dignity of a 'grain of thought."[772]

Thus the particular phyletic centre (consisting of a peripheral ego and a nuclear ego) retains access to all of the information ever associated with the particular phylum through resonance among phyletic isospheres (nuclear egos).

This is in agreement with both Sheldrake's theory of morphic resonance and Bohm's quantum cosmology as it provides a mechanism whereby speciation information may be shared through resonance, transferred into the explicate domain via the implicate domain, and vice versa.[773] Since the implicate order of the nuclear ego is nondual (outside of the space–time domain), it has random access to information generated in *all time* and *all space* and is thereby able to apply total information in its processing. Reflective consciousness is also a characteristic of this phyletic center, and the typical human personality can be here identified with Teilhard's "peripheral ego," while Omega provides a guiding force via centrogenesis (Bohm's quantum potential function, Q).

To answer his second question, (how does the phylum provided the greatest possible richness and variety for evolutionary growth?), Teilhard identifies a "two-fold complexity," one spatial, and the other temporal. Spatial complexity refers to the spread of the phylum over the surface of its isosphere, the creation of a population of phyletic centres that gather experience and mutate in the

---

[772] Ibid., 109.

[773] Sheldrake, *A New Science of Life: The Hypothesis of Morphic Resonance.*

356

ever-changing environment. At the same time, the action of temporal complexity provides the vast number of "trials" over the myriads of generations of which the phylum's ancestors represent the total sum.[774]

At the bottom of Fig. 48 we see Teilhard's final figure, the "structure of a eu-centric element," as a major, and perhaps ultimate, "change of state" in the emerging process, a reflection of consciousness in the noosphere, a reflective connection with Omega.[775] In the typical human grain of thought "reflection" has not yet reached a resonance with Omega. However it is possible to effect, in the individual, as Teilhard says, a "eu-centered, 'point-like' focus . . . and this is enough to allow the appearance of a series of new phenomena in the later advances of centrogenesis."[776] It is not difficult to assume that the "point-like focus" recommended here by Teilhard is a reference to his own direct experience in effectuating such a focus, his own participatory experience of consciousness.

Teilhard laments that while humans are generally reflective, only a few have yet been able to integrally connect with the punctiform nucleus, Omega; but those able to connect for any duration find that they now "posses the sense of irreversibility," a conviction that makes "an escape from total death . . . possible for a personalized being."[777] At this point, says Teilhard, "Welded together in this way, the noosphere, *taken as a whole*, begins to behave tangentially,

---

[774] Teilhard, "Centrology," 109.

[775] Ibid.

[776] Ibid.

[777] Ibid., 110.

like a single megacentre...ontogenesis of collective consciousness and human memory." [778] Here, Teilhard makes a prediction, stating that the evolution of human society on the planet will eventually lead to the following:

> ...the accelerated impetus of an earth in which preoccupation with production for the sake of well-being will have given way to the passion for the discovery for the sake of fuller being—the super-personalization of a super-humanity that has become super-conscious of itself in Omega. [779]

In a psychically convergent universe, the process of a reflective connection of the peripheral, phyletic ego with the central, eu-centric ego leads ultimately to a "final concentration upon itself of the noosphere," Omega.

> "Omega appears to us fundamentally as the centre which is defined by the final concentration upon itself of the noosphere—and indirectly, of all the isospheres that precede it." [780]

"All the isospheres that precede it" in time and space, of course, are the isospheres that are ourselves, our ancestors, and other centers of phyletic centro-complexity. When a locus of fragmentary centers closes, joining together to form a phyletic center, the newly formed noosphere experiences a state change and awakens. From that point, moving forward in space and time, the phyletic noosphere

---

[778] Ibid.

[779] Ibid., 110–11.

[780] Ibid., 111.

evolves through a series of internal noospheres, growing higher in energy and complexity, until it reaches its ultimate "final concentration" at Omega, as Teilhard states, "In Omega then, a *maximum complexity*, cosmic in extent, coincides with a *maximum cosmic centricity*."[781] In other words, at the heart of matter, at the Omega point, Teilhard tells us that maximum complexity equals maximum centricity.

Teilhard refers to the centre as "a quantum of consciousness," and tells us that each degree of consciousness at a given moment only exists as "an introduction to a higher consciousness."[782] He says that this general process is irresistible and irreversible.[783]

> The initial quantum of consciousness contained in our terrestrial world is not formed merely of an aggregate of particles caught fortuitously in the same net. It represents a correlated mass of infinitesimal centres structurally bound together by the conditions of their origin and development.[784]

Moving forward in his essay on centrology, Teilhard goes on to describe four attributes of Omega as:

- Personal

- Individual

---

[781] Ibid.

[782] Teilhard, "The Phenomenon of Spirituality," 100.

[783] Ibid., 99.

[784] Teilhard, *The Phenomenon of Man*, 73–74.

- Already partially actual (space–time energy)

- Partially transcendent (implicate order holoflux energy)[785]

It is personal "since it is centricity that makes beings personal," and, "Omega is supremely centred."[786] It is individual because it is "distinct from (which does not mean cut off from) *the lower personal centres* which it super-centres."[787] These lower centres are the various phyletic, peripheral egos, each of which is uniquely individual, yet can join with Omega without losing their individuated personality; in fact it is in the relationship, the resonance with Omega, that the very uniqueness of the individual is highlighted (i.e., "union differentiates").

Omega is both "partially actual" and partially transcendent." The relationship is one Teilhard characterizes as, "a 'bi-polar' union" of the emerged and the emergent. It is partially transcendent beyond the very center of space–time, within the Bohmian implicate order. There, all is "partially transcendent of the evolution that culminates in it." And it is there that all space–time experience is gathered, in the partially transcendent, in continuous communication via a mathematically dynamic process. Otherwise, Teilhard tell us, there would not "be the basis for the hopes of irreversibility."[788]

---

[785] Teilhard, "Centrology," 112.

[786] Ibid.

[787] Ibid.

[788] Ibid., 113.

And it is Omega that provides the momentum for centrogenesis.

> Drawn by its magnetism and formed in its image, the elementary cosmic centres are constituted and grow deeper in the matrix of their complexity. Moreover, gathered up by Omega, these same centres enter into immortality from the very moment when they become eu-centric and so structurally capable of entering into contact, centre to centre.[789]

Centrology and Complexity: Being and Union

At this point in his essay, Teilhard inserts what he calls "A Note on the 'Formal Effect' of Complexity" in which he examines the underlying roots of his assertion that consciousness *increases* with complexity in union (centro-complexity), and he states that an understanding of this phenomenon has come to him "experientially."[790] Teilhard sets forth, in two Latin propositions, the fundamental ontological relationship between being and union:

1. The one passive: *"Plus esse est a* (or ex) *pluribus uniri."*

2. The other active: *"Plus esse est plus plura unire."*

Plus esse can be translated as "more being," "growth in being," or "being increases," but from the context of this essay the phrase *plus esse* might be translated as

---

[789] Ibid.

[790] Ibid.

"consciousness increases."[791] Thus Teilhard describes a bi-modal process of an increasing conscious in the universe: actively and passively.

In the first proposition, the verb *uniri* is in the passive voice, "be united," and in context can be translated, "become one, become a center." The *a/ex* prepositions, often used interchangeably in Latin, indicate "out of" and "from." Thus *a pluribus* can be translated "out of many, from many," and accordingly, the first proposition may be translated as, "A new conscious center grows by many being joined."

In the second proposition, however, the verb *unire* is in the active voice, (i.e., "unite"), which in context can be translated "make a centered unity" of *plura* (literally, "more/many things"). Thus the second proposition can be translated as "A new consciousness center grows by many uniting."

Teilhard next applies these two propositions to the following stages of centro-complex evolution:

1. The appearance of life through association of fragments of centres.

2. The deepening of phyletic centres.

3. The emergence of reflective centres.

In the first instance, for a state change occurring in the domain of pre-life, Teilhard again formulates a metaphysical axiom in Latin: *Centrum ex elementis centri*, which translates as, "The Center out of elements of the

---

[791] Assistance with these Latin translations was provided by Fr. Thomas Matus, PhD, a Camaldolese Benedictine monk, in an e-mail message to author, August 27, 2015.

center." In this domain Centres are "built up additively, through the fitting together and gradual fusing of 'segments' of centres."[792] This is a passive growth.

In the second stage, Teilhard says, "being born from an egg (*centrum a centro*) complexifies upon itself by cellular multiplication." Here, each centre complexifies itself by increasing its own depth of complexity.[793] Here the active growth emerges, a growth in part directed by the centre. A similar pattern can be seen in Bohm's quantum potential function, a guiding energy from within the implicate order, within Teilhard's Omega point.

Finally, it is in the eu-centric that this quantum potential metaphysical process becomes superactive, and as Teilhard says, it is from "the noospheric centre, Omega," that there emerges "*Centrum super centra*," translated as "a new Centre emerges from an old centre."[794] Teilhard is saying here that Omega is not simply the sum of components, but something *new*, a unique entity bursting forth:

> In the eu-centric domain, the noospheric centre Omega, is not born from the confluence of human "egos," but emerges from their organic totality, like a spark that leaps the gap between the transcendent side of Omega and the "point" of a perfectly centered universe.[795]

---

[792] Teilhard, "Centrology," 114.

[793] Ibid.

[794] Ibid.

[795] Ibid.

Teilhard describes how, for individual human phyletic "egos," it may be possible to go beyond the present general evolutionary stage of consciousness, developed through the general societal drift of hominization through time. Teilhard explains how such an evolutionary leap might be accomplished:

> This can be envisaged in two ways, either by *connecting up neurones* that are already ready to function but have not yet been brought into service (as though held in reserve), in certain already located areas of the brain, where it is simply a matter of arousing them to activity; or, who can say?, by direct (mechanical, chemical or biological) stimulation of new arrangements.[796]

In his phrase, "direct stimulation," we can imagine a range of approaches which might be used to catalyze the evolutionary growth and transformation of consciousness within an individual, who would then experience what Teilhard terms, an "Ultra-hominization," of reflective consciousness, evolutionarily beyond that of the currently conventional ranges of human experience.

His first suggestion, "connecting up neurones that are already ready to function," might be seen as a catalysis by birth (genetic predisposition), accidental circumstances (serendipitous encounters with the sublime), or specific psycho-physical techniques (e.g., prayer, yoga, physical exercises, special diets, fasting, sweat lodges, etc.); but Teilhard goes even further to suggest that the evolutionary process might be boosted within the individual human

---

[796] Teilhard, "The Formation of the Noosphere II," 111. Essay written in 1949.

personality "by direct (mechanical, chemical, or biological) stimulation," and here we are reminded of exploration and critical experimentation with psychotropic drugs (psilocybin mushrooms, LSD, cannabis, ayahuasca, etc.), or through direct energy-stimulation devices found in the recent technologies of transcranial magnetic stimulation, or transcranial direct current stimulation.[797]

Similarly, but moving from neuronal to human level, Teilhard forecast's the connecting up of a network of individual consciousness via "a direct tuning:"

> In nascent super-humanity . . . the thousands of millions of single-minded individuals function in a nuclear way, by a direct tuning and resonance of their consciousness.[798]

At the close of "Centrology," Teilhard sets forth his "Corollaries and Conclusions." He begins by summarizing, in a sequence of five stages, the evolution of consciousness, and defining five points on the arc of centro-complexity at which occur categorically distinct evolutionary changes of state:

1. The appearance of life through association of fragments of centres.

2. The deepening of phyletic centres.

3. The emergence of reflective centres.

---

[797] Booth, Koren, and Persinger, "Increased Feelings of the Sensed Presence During Exposures to Weak Magnetic Fields."

[798] Teilhard, "Centrology," 114–15.

4. The birth of mankind (and reflective thought).

5. The dawn of Omega.[799]

In each of these five steps can be seen the effect of an increase in union, the creative energy of union causing changes of state, not simply due to some rearrangement or summation of parts, but, as Teilhard says, "doing so under the influence of the radiation of Omega."[800] The holoflux theory analog of Teilhard's "radiation," of course, is Bohm's quantum potential function, "Q," radiating from the implicate order to emerge within space–time. Teilhard's "Omega point" can thus be viewed as a spherical portal, an analog of Bohm's "implicate order."

In discussing the transition from Stage 4 to Stage 5, the change of state from the "birth of thought" to the "dawn of Omega," Teilhard insists that there should be *no* concern that such a change of state would mean a loss of personality, or a death of our uniquely distinct egos; on the contrary, says Teilhard, the noosphere is comprised of an effective *re-union* of all individual "savable elements" of each personality. Even more, it serves to effect an even higher, more complete integration of *each* individual experience, a heightening of individual personality, "a cosmic personalization, the fruit of centrogenesis."[801] It is, stresses Teilhard, through each sub personality center-to-center contact *within* the noosphere (through the centre), that

---

[799] Ibid., 116.

[800] Ibid., 115.

[801] Ibid., 119.

each individual personality is "super-personalized."[802] This center-to-center contact, Teilhard tells us, is a perceptual condition of each individual center merging into the noosphere, and it *is not an epiphenomenon* of such a union, but that it is a *requirement* for reaching full integral personalization:

> Something (someone) exists, in which each element gradually finds, by reunion with the whole, the completion of all the savable elements that have been formed in its individuality; thus the interior equilibrium of what we have called the Noosphere requires the presence *perceived by individuals* of a higher polar centre that directs, sustains and assembles the whole sheaf of our efforts.[803]

This process can be seen as a cybernetic feedback loop: the "higher polar centre" receives input from all of the "savable elements" of each "individuality," and, working with this information, the higher personality ("polar center") "sustain and assembles the whole sheaf of our efforts." In this way evolution proceeds through a continuous cyclic process of individual centres developing in space–time, merging into their respective centres through the directional "drift" of centro-complexity, *but not being lost* in the merger.

> To the extent that the grain of consciousness is *personalized*, it becomes released from its material support in the phylum . . . detached

---

[802] Ibid., 116.

[803] Teilhard, "Hominization," in *The Vision of the Past*, 78.

from the matrix of complexity, and meets the ultimate pole of all convergence.[804]

Finally, the fifth stage in the process of centro-complexity, "the dawn of Omega," occurs at the point where *thought* transforms into omni-contact with all other centres, as well as with the "higher" (n+1) center of personality, at which point there is a flaring forth into a categorically new mode of reflective consciousness, effecting a major change in state. Teilhard concludes that, "Far from tending to be confused together, the reflective centres intensify their *ego* the more they concentrate together."[805]

Isospheres

A key concept developed in "Centrology" is Teilhard's model of "isospheres," which he defines as "surfaces of equal centro-complexity."[806] He sees evolution catalyzed on these isospheres when "a maximum density of particles with a corresponding maximum of tentative gropings is produced on each isosphere." Listed in Table 8 are "isospheres" which have been defined for the planet earth, arranged in radial order.

These various regions of the planet each have their own unique and identifiable physical characteristics (temperature, density, etc.), and each might be considered as an isosphere of the planet.

---

[804] Teilhard, "Centrology," 122.

[805] Ibid., 116–17.

[806] Ibid., 100.

Teilhard's use of the word "isosphere" is focused less upon the physics of geology, and more upon the physics of metaphysics, a topology of consciousness, as he states in "Centrology":

> Thus there emerges the pattern of a *centred universe*—elements of equal complexity (and hence of equal centricity) being spread out over what we may call isospheres of consciousness.[807]

Table 8

Isospheres of Planet Earth

Scientific designation	Above/below sea level (miles)
Exosphere	310–620 mi.
Ionosphere or Plasmasphere	37–271 mi.
Thermosphere	56–311 mi.
Mesosphere	31–53 mi.
Stratosphere	10–30 mi.
Troposphere	4–12 mi.
Hydrosphere	0 to -5 mi.
Lithosphere or "rocky crust" (upper layer, crustal rocks) (0°–870° C.)	-275 mi.
Mantle (870°–3700° C) Upper Mantle (870° C) Asthenosphere (100–250 km deep) Inner Mantle (semi rigid, 870°–3700° C)	-21 to -1793 mi.
Outer Core (molten, 3700°–5000° C, 1370 miles thick)	-1800 mi.
Inner Core (Crystalline iron/nickel) (5000°–7200° C, 750 mile sphere)	-2170 mi.

Note. Data adapted from Tarbuck and Lutgens, *Earth Science,* 61. Author's table.

---

[807] Teilhard, "Centrology," 102.

Figure 49 depicts a holoflux topology of nested isospheres surrounding Teilhard's Omega. According to Teilhard, these isospheres of consciousness are concentric, "the radius of each sphere diminishing as the complexity increases."[808]

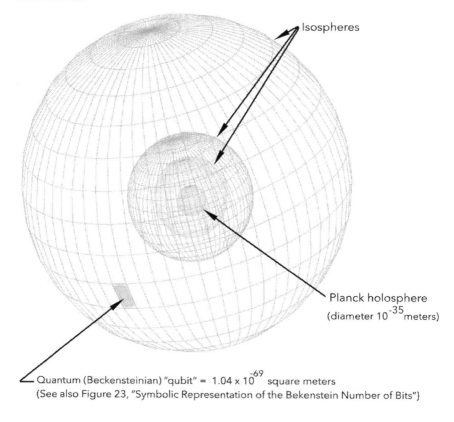

Isospheres

Planck holosphere
(diameter 10^{-35} meters)

Quantum (Beckensteinian) "qubit" = 1.04×10^{-69} square meters
(See also Figure 23, "Symbolic Representation of the Bekenstein Number of Bits")

Figure 49. Isospheres surrounding Planck holosphere.
Graphic by author.

Here Teilhard has clearly indicated the direction in which he sees increased consciousness: toward the centre, in the direction of Omega. According to holoflux theory, the

---

[808] Ibid.

radial distance between any two nested isospheres may be no less than the Planck length, and this leads us to visualize an enormous yet finite series of isospheres in space–time, nested like Russian dolls, or perhaps like separate capacitor plates in in an electronic circuit, beginning at the boundary of the Planck holosphere (enclosing Omega, the implicate order), and reaching an outer limit at the current (continuously expanding) diameter of the universe.

In this cosmological topology of nested three-dimensional isospheres, electrons would not travel in planar, two-dimensional, circular orbits, as depicted in Bohr's model; in the holoflux model, electron movements are seen as tangential flowing processes over three-dimensional shells, spherical movements over the surface regions of isosphere.[809]

As we move outward from the central Planck holosophere into isospheres of higher radial dimensions, each holosophere must be separated, minimally, by one Planck length. The manifestation of these isospheres in space–time would provide the geometric capacity for storing multiple qubits of information, as previously developed by John Wheeler in considering the event horizon of a black hole. Thus we may envision quantum states in a series of holospheric shells extending from the central Planck holosophere to the current boundary of the universe, spheres rather than rings. The universe here can be seen to consist of an almost infinite holoplenum of intersecting concentric shells of implicate order holospheres throughout space–time.

As seen in Bohr's model, to move from one shell to another shell, the electron can not move *continuously*

---

[809] Goswami, *The Visionary Window.*

through some intervening space–time gap, but instead is seen to execute a quantum leap to another level, possibly moving from one isospheric shell to another during a single Planck time cycles of 5×10^{-44} seconds, to appear at the next holosphere shell at a "clock-speed" of light, yet not moving *in* space–time as normally understood, but moving in and out of the explicate and implicate orders.

Viewed from the perspective of holoflux theory, a transformation of information flowing into the implicate order (frequency domain) occurs, cycling feedback "radiation" (Bohm's quantum potential function, "Q") into space–time, nudging every centre in an ever-so-slightly new direction in their evolutionary arcs in space–time.

Such a transformation might also be identified with Jean Gebser's "mutation of consciousness," the evolutionary mutation into what Gebser calls "integral consciousness."[810] In full agreement with Teilhard's assertion that evolution precludes loss of experienced personality, Gebser assures us that in evolving structures of consciousness, previous properties and potentialities do indeed survive:

> In contrast to biological mutations, these consciousness mutations do not assume or require the disappearance of previous potentialities and properties, which, in this case, are immediately integrated into the new structure.[811]

Like Gebser, Teilhard observes that all personalities are incomplete, that they are continually evolving, however

---

[810] Gebser, *The Ever-Present Origin*, 37.

[811] Ibid., 39.

slowly, and compares our individual personalities to the fragments of centres that seek for one another in the pre-living zones of matter, reminding us that, "at our level of evolution we are still no more than rough drafts."[812] Teilhard here states with emphasis, *"the personal—considered quantitatively no less than qualitatively—is continually on the upgrade in the universe."*[813]

It is clear that in his writings Pierre Teilhard de Chardin, the trained anthropologist, regarded his theories of hyperphysics not as philosophy or metaphysics, but as an extension of physical science. He argues for a convergence of physics and metaphysics, but not a union, and in a topological, geodesic-like metaphor, defends his hyperphysics as being distinct yet parallel to existing categories of inquiry:

> Just like meridians as they approach the pole, so science, philosophy, and religion necessarily converge in the vicinity of the whole. They converge, I repeat, but without merging, and never ceasing to attack the real from different angles and levels right to the end.... It is impossible to attempt a general scientific interpretation of the universe without *seeming* to intend to explain it right to the end. But only take a closer look at it, and you will see that this hyperphysics still is not metaphysics.[814]

---

[812] Teilhard, "Centrology," 117.

[813] Ibid.

[814] Teilhard, *Human Phenomenon*, 2.

Breaking Teilhard's "Death-Barrier"

One of Teilhard de Chardin's mature conclusions is that our entire consciousness is *not* snuffed out when our material bodies die. If consciousness manifests as some mode of holoflux energy, then following Einstein's observation, that "Energy cannot be created or destroyed, it can only be changed from one form to another," any energy of consciousness must follow the same pattern.[815] While there may be a transformation of energy, there can be no absolute destruction, energy (even modulated energy) cannot suddenly vanish.

By the very logic of evolution, in order for the species to learn, adapt, and preserve experiences gathered in the space–time domain, evolution at the human stage must break the "Death-Barrier," a term Teilhard develops in one of his final essays, "The Death-Barrier and Co-Reflection," completed January 1, 1955, three months before his own death, on Easter Sunday, April 10, 1955:

> When biological evolution has reached its *reflective* stage ("self-evolution") it can continue to function only in so far as man comes to realize that there is some *prima facie* evidence that the death-barrier *can* be broken.[816]

Teilhard had written previously of his own participatory experiences supporting his belief in an immortality of consciousness in a letter to his paleontologist colleague and friend, Helmut de Terra:

---

[815] Einstein, *Autobiographical Notes*, 17.

[816] Teilhard, "The Death-Barrier and Co-Reflection," 403.

My visible actions and influence count for very little beside my secret self. My real treasure is, *par excellence*, that part of my being which the centre, where all the sublimated wealth of the universe converges, cannot allow to escape. The reality, which is the culminating point of the universe, can only develop in partnership with ourselves by keeping us within the supreme personality: we cannot help finding ourselves personally immortal.[817]

Teilhard assumes that if there is a part, or region, or mode, or domain of our consciousness, that continues beyond our bodies, beyond the death of our bodies, as he says in "Breaking the Death-Barrier," then should we not then be motivated to know and even to explore that domain? That is the real treasure he is sharing with us: once specific memories are gone, the personality lives on, "keeping us within the supreme personality," within the implicate order, at the center, everywhere. But this "personality of the transcendent" can be seen, by mystics at least, even before the approach of the Death-Barrier.[818]

Not only does Teilhard categorically reject the majority of contemporary humankind's tacit assumption that death is "the end" (i.e., the end of individual consciousness), but he worries that such an erroneous stance might delay what he saw as the natural emergence of a noosphere, cultivated and powered by human conscious energy, a collective holoflux of homo sapiens.[819]

---

[817] de Terra, *Memories of Teilhard de Chardin*, 42.

[818] Teilhard, "The Death-Barrier and Co-Reflection," 402.

[819] Ibid., 403.

Chapter 7: Summary and Conclusions

This book has presented a theory that the ground of consciousness, consciousness itself, manifests as a continuously-transforming flow of energy in a two-way inward/outward flow between two domains whose boundaries are omni-present. This energy flux is encoded with both information and meaning, flowing alternately between the explicate domain of space–time and the nonspatial, nontemporal transcendent domain which David Bohm termed the implicate order, a domain that exists within the center, everywhere, of space–time. To express the interconnectedness of this energy flux, spanning a wholeness that embraces both space-time phenomena as well as transcendent phenomena, we have selected the term *holoflux*, from the root term holism, defined here as:

> the fundamental interconnectedness of all phenomena, and within this fundamental interconnectedness not only is each entity, relationship, experience and phenomenon a hollow or whole, in its own right, but all wholes are held together by a great unifying force.[820]

The Holoflux Theory of Consciousness

The holoflux theory of consciousness has been constructed upon three underlying concepts: Pribram's holonomic brain theory, Bohm's ontological interpretation of quantum theory, and Teilhard's centro-complexification of consciousness. These theories have been discussed here and shown to be congruent, supported and knit together by

---

[820] Collister, *A Journey in Search of Wholeness and Meaning*, 69.

376

established principles of electrical engineering. The holoflux theory proposed here can be categorized as a cosmological ontological process structured as follows:

- A CENTERED COSMOS: In agreement with the theory of general relativity, the holoflux theory is founded upon the notion that the universe has a center, and that center is everywhere.

- HOLOFLUX: Dark energy of the implicate order, outside of space–time; Karl Pribram's theorized flux within David Bohm's implicate order; it is an energy of sentient awareness that views the outwardly explicate world of space–time from within an implicate order.

- QUANTUM BLACK HOLES: Quantum black holes, *Planck holospheres* of the Bohmian implicate order; bounded by spherical shells of Planck length diameter 10^{-35} meters.

- THE HOLOPLENUM: An invariant *holoplenum* of close-packed holospheres, or *Teilhardian isospheres*, underlying and from which is projected the explicate order; the holoplenum fills a continuum of isospheres everywhere in the physical universe from the center of each position in space–time; the concept had been intuited by Leibniz in his theory of the monads.

- RESONANCE: Holoflux frequency resonance connects the explicate order (the outside world), with the implicate order (the inside world); holoflux communication occurs everywhere between the implicate order (frequency-phase flux in the implicate order, f_i) and resonating isospheres of the explicate order in spherical shells. These holo-shells must be separated at corresponding distances, λ_i, from each central Planck holosphere, to maintain the relationship, $f_i \lambda_i = c$, where c is the speed of light in a vacuum, 3×10^8 m/sec.

- CYCLIC PROCESS: A flowing movement, an *electromagnetic-holoflux* movement of energy continually cycles between the implicate order and the explicate order; the flow can be mathematically modeled through Fourier transforms and the Bohm quantum potential wavefunctions.

- A COSMIC CLOCK: Granular units of Planck time (t_P), vibrate at a "clock-cycle" rate of 5.39106×10^{44} cycles per second synchronizing the flow between alternating manifestations of implicate and explicate frequency information; in Cartesian coordinates, this can be pictured as a square wave, a Planck-time clock.

- BOHM'S QUANTUM POTENTIAL FUNCTION: Conceptional computations within the implicate order are "expressed" in space–time (the explicate order) via the effect of Bohm's quantum potential, Q.

- A FOURIER LENS: A Fourier-type mathematical transform can be seen to act as a lens through which the implicate "views" or "cognizes" the explicate order of space–time; this Fourier lensing is the process by which the implicate order retrieves, observes, and experiences information generated within the explicate order.

A diagram of these assumptions is presented in Fig. 50, "Solving the Hard Problem of Consciousness," in which the relative positions of essential concepts from the following five philosophers have also been indicated:

- David Chalmers' "structure of awareness" is posited to be synonymous with the implicate order, and his "structure of consciousness" accordingly is shown within the explicate order.[821]

- Ned Block's "A-consciousness" lies in the implicate order, and his "B-consciousness" in the explicate order.[822]

- David Bohm's "meaning" lies in the implicate order, and his "information" in the explicate order.[823]

- Pierre Teilhard de Chardin's "Omega" lies in the implicate order, and his "centro-complexity" in the explicate order.[824]

- László's "A-dimension" lies in the implicate order, and his "B-dimension" lies in the explicate order.[825]

---

[821] Chalmers, "Facing Up to the Problem of Consciousness."

[822] Block, *Consciousness, Function, and Representation.*

[823] Bohm, *Wholeness and the Implicate Order.*

[824] Teilhard, "The Nature of the Point Omega."

[825] László , *The Self–Actualizing Cosmos.*

The process can be visualized as shell-like waves of radiant information-embedded energy spreading out and intersecting with the myriad of the other expanding shells of active information from all of the other "particle/holospheres" in the holoplenum-filled cosmos. The intersection of these waves and their condensation, where the density of intersection is maximum, is regarded in classical physics as "matter," but this can also be seen as a process, an on-going holographic extrusion of information *from* the implicate order *into* the explicate order, where the manifestations in space–time are holographically projected.

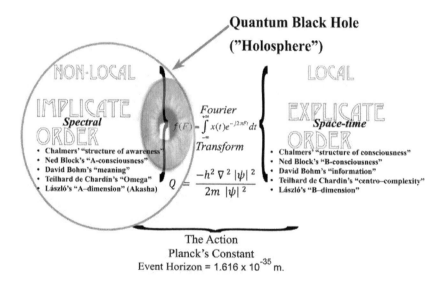

Figure 50. Solving the hard problem of consciousness.

In the diagram, an iris-like lens at the Planck length aperture, between David Bohm's implicate order and the explicate order, mirrors Karl Pribram's 1991 conceptualization in *Brain and Perception*:

> These two domains characterize the input to and output from a lens that performs a Fourier

transform. On one side of the transform lies the space–time order we ordinarily perceive. On the other side lies a distributed enfolded holographic-like order referred to as the frequency or spectral domain.[826]

Note that the image of an iris in fig. 50 appears at the edge of the event horizon of a quantum black hole, or implicate order holosphere. The iris symbolizes consciousness looking out from the implicate order into space–time via a Fourier transform lensing process. This can also be understood as the observer observing the observed, as in the context of Wheeler's "Self-observing U."[827] Two equations can be seen in the center of the figure, depicting Pribram's holonomic Fourier transform, and Bohm's quantum potential function Q. These illustrate the ongoing mathematical lensing-flow of conscious energy between the local (explicate) and nonlocal (implicate) regions of reality.

In projecting the cosmos, nonlocal holoflux energy in the spectral domain resonates actively with electromagnetic plasma in the space–time domain; thus the nonlocal affects the local, explicate order. This information emerges as electromagnetic energy at the Planck wavelength, moving outwardly from the implicate center in spherical waves of electromagnetic energy, into the explicate.

The flow of holoflux energy into space–time can also be expressed in electrical engineering imagery,

---

[826] Pribram, *Brain and Perception*, 70.

[827] Wheeler, *Geons, Black Holes, and Quantum Foam*, 339; also see fig. 21.

topologically, as a variation of Ampere's "left-hand rule." [828] The three domains can be visualized with the thumb, index finger, and middle finger of the left hand held mutually perpendicular to indicate the three orthogonal fields: the electric domain (e_d), the magnetic domain (m_d), and the frequency flux domain (f_d). We hypothesize that all three domains have equally valid ontological reality, but that only two of them, the magnetic and the electric, manifest explicitly in the space–time domain. Conversely, the third domain, the frequency flux domain (f_d), manifests "within" the implicate domain, transcendent of space and time.

Such a hypothesis appears to be consistent with Teilhard's theories of centrology, in which the entire universe "is made up of psychic nuclei" which operate at right angles to one another, a tangential and a radial. [829] These two modes of consciousness, Teilhard tells us, "operate at different levels." [830]

One level might be seen in a tangential electrical field operating in the system that powers the "meat-mind" of neuronal fibers in brain and nervous systems during waking cognitive consciousness. The other mode of consciousness, operating at right angles to the electric, would then be seen as magnetic, radial or axial energy in various degrees of resonant connection with the implicate center. Thus two systems of consciousness are seen to coexist simultaneously.

If we try to substantiate Teilhard's claimed observation of two different modes of psychic nuclei, then

---

[828] Nilson and Hornung, *Practical Radio Communication*, 54.

[829] Teilhard, "Centrology," 104.

[830] Teilhard, "The Activation of Human Energy," 393. Essay written in 1952.

we are drawn to consider a magnetic system of consciousness in the locus of the cardiovascular system. The entire system of magnetically polarized molecules in the bloodstream, throughout the more than 25,000 miles of veins and capillaries, might act as a fully connected waveguide system at infrared light frequencies.[831] A parallel can be seen in twenty-first-century internet technology, where glass fiber optic cables interconnected over hundreds of thousands of miles act as waveguides for networks at visible light frequencies. Thus an entire system, a pathway of information-modulated consciousness, might exist, in addition to the electrical nervous system distributed throughout the brain and body in a neuronal electrical network.

Strategies for Testing the Holoflux Hypothesis

If consciousness is manifesting as energy flow in electromagnetic-frequency fields, then one should be able to determine experimentally the location of high bandwidth network channels within human physiology, channels by which electromagnetic information interchange guides the growth process, effects repair, and catalyzes evolutionary mutation. The widespread assumption of material science has been that consciousness emerges from neuron activity in the human brain only as an epiphenomenon. [832] Accordingly, where then might a neurophysicist search, outside of neuronal linkages?

---

[831] Zimmer, "Origins: On the Origin of Eukaryotes," 667.

[832] Dennett, *Consciousness Explained*, 406.

Dimensional evidence indicates that good candidate ranges for testing the electromagnetic field component of consciousness can be found in the infrared spectrum. This region lies just below the threshold of the visible spectrum that is picked up by eye cone structures.[833] Human core body temperatures, ranging from 36.3 C to 37.5 C on a diurnal cycle, indicate that, applying Wien's Law, we should search the infrared spectrum in a bandwidth between 9.36425 microns and 9.32808 microns, near the middle of the infrared.

The range of human body temperature associated with human consciousness spans an exceptionally wide frequency band. Fig. 51 displays this range as spanning 9.88 to 9.11 microns, charted as corresponding wavelength.

Human EMF Wavelength

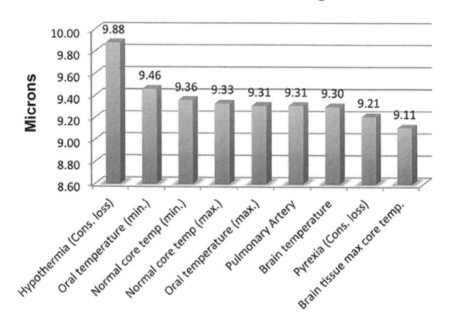

---

[833] Oyster, *The Human Eye: Structure and Function.*

Figure 50. Human electromagnetic wavelength.[834]
Graphic by author.

Human body temperature ranges from a minimum of 68.0 F (hypothermia with loss of consciousness) to a maximum of 106.7 F (maximum core brain temperature before death).

Converting from wavelength, this range is equivalent to a frequency range of 30.3 gigahertz to 32.0 gigahertz, an enormously wide band compared to, for example, the FM radio frequency band, ranging from 87.0 to 88.1 MHz. Over 1000 equivalent FM radio stations could be easily broadcast within the human infrared radiation band, with no overlapping interference.[835]

Assuming that electromagnetic energy in the infrared range networks consciousness within the human body, where might we search to detect such activity? One approach in the search for an infrared component of consciousness would be to monitor the dynamics of an infrared spectrum emanating from and external to the human body in an attempt to detect information laden photons escaping the body as modulated infrared radiation.

Interestingly, because biologic materials are transparent to light in the near-infrared region of

---

[834] Data from Geiger, Aron, and Todhunter, *The Climate Near the Ground*, 452.

[835] Calculations in this paragraph use Wien's Law to convert wavelength to frequency.

the light spectrum, transmission of photons through organs is possible.[836]

Another approach would be to search for infrared energy signals flowing as patterns within physiological waveguide channels within the human body. The ubiquitous blood capillary system, for example, with typical inner diameters of 10 microns, is a likely candidate to be acting as an electromagnetic waveguide. Capillaries provide a ready-made network infrastructure within which the flow and resonance of a modulated infrared energy plasma might be discovered.

Other bandwidths than the infrared should not be ignored in the search for an electromagnetic energy mode of conscious activity. If we consider the much smaller microtubules which are embedded within the neurons, we find them to be excellent candidates to act as waveguides for electromagnetic frequency propagation at an even higher frequency band. In July 2015, Stuart Hameroff provided the following update on his research in the area of microtubules and anesthesiology, and new support for Pribram's holonomic brain/mind theory:

> Actually, the brain is looking more like an orchestra, a multi-scalar vibrational resonance system, than a computer. Brain information patterns repeat over spatiotemporal scales in fractal-like, nested hierarchies of neuronal networks, with resonances and interference beats. . . .Holograms encode distributed information as multi-scalar interference of coherent vibrations, e.g. from lasers. Pribram lacked a proper coherent source, a laser in the

---

[836] Cohn, *Near-Infrared Spectroscopy: Potential Clinical Benefits in Surgery*, 323.

brain, but evidence now points to structures inside brain neurons called microtubules as sources of laser-like coherence for the brain's vibrational hierarchy? . . .microtubules have quantum resonances in gigahertz, megahertz and kilohertz frequency ranges (the work of Anirban Bandyopadhyay and colleagues at National Institute of Material Science in Tsukuba, Japan). . . .These coherent "fractal frequencies" in microtubules apparently couple to even faster, smaller-scale terahertz vibrations among intra-tubulin "pi electron resonance clouds," and to slower ones, e.g. by interference "beats" giving rise to larger scale EEG.[837]

Applying Wien's Law to the inner diameter of a typical microtubule results in a wavelength in the ultraviolet band, quite a bit higher in frequency than the infrared, but just on the other side of the "visible spectrum" band used by eye rods and cones during normal daylight visual reception. In 2010, a team exploring microtubule resonance at the University of Pavia's Nano-Biotechnology laboratory verified the existence of electromagnetic resonance of microtubules at a frequency of approximately 1510 MHz.[838] The team concluded the following:

> The analysis of the results of bi-refringence experiment highlights that the microtubules react to electromagnetic fields . . . at a frequency of 1510 MHz . . . . Considering the nanoscopic size of microtubules, the resonance analysis

---

[837] Hameroff, "Is Your Brain Really a Computer, or Is It a Quantum Orchestra?", para. 5, 6, 8, 9.

[838] Pizzi et al., "Evidence of New Biophysical Properties of Microtubules," 1.

would be more effective if carried out on much higher frequencies (up to 100 GHz), with suitable instrumentation. The presence of a small but sharp resonance effect at a low frequency could be the hint of a much more evident effect at even higher frequencies.[839]

Confirmation of the generation of such electromagnetic frequencies is described in a similar study completed in the following year at another research laboratory as reported in the *Journal of Theoretical Biology*, which describes additional evidence for high frequency electromagnetic field oscillations associated with microtubules:

> The electromagnetic radiation and field characteristics of the whole cellular microtubule network have not been theoretically analyzed previously. The results indicate that macroscopic detection system (antenna) are not suitable for measurement of cellular electrodynamic activity in the radiofrequency region since the radiation of single cells is very low (lower than 10^{-20} Watts). Low noise nanoscopic detection methods with high spatial resolution, enabling measurements in the cell vicinity, would be desirable, in order to measure cellular electrodynamic activity reliably.[840]

Some interest has already been shown in the function of microtubules as antennas, for example in ciliogenesis.

---

[839] Ibid., 13.

[840] Havelka et al., "High-Frequency Electric Field and Radiation Characteristics of Cellular Microtubule Network," 31.

Cilia are present on almost every cell type in the human body and are composed of a microtubule-based core structure, that have been seen to "act as antennae" to sense extracellular signals, such as hormones, odorants, and changes in the local environment.[841]

Several possible ranges for electromagnetic networks of consciousness are indicated in Fig. 52, "Eight Feasible Bands for Consciousness." Note that while microtubules are 40 nm in diameter, even smaller is the average 20 nanometers synaptic cleft width, which would make the interstitial space between synapses resonant in the ultraviolet range.

---

[841] Ishikawa and Marshall, "Ciliogenesis: Building the Cell's Antenna," 222.

Eight Feasible Bands for Consciousness

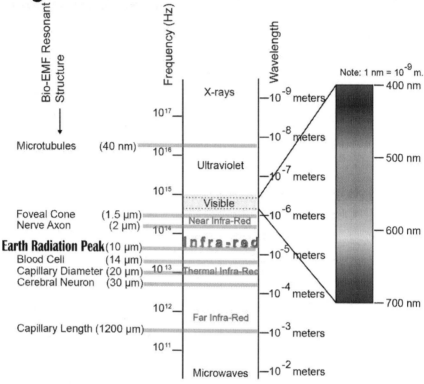

Figure 51. Eight feasible bands for consciousness. Annotations added by author to graphic by Jahoe (2012). Reprinted under the terms of a Creative Commons Attribution ShareAlike 2.5 Generic license. Image retrieved from Wikimedia Commons.

The adult human brain is estimated to contain "approximately 20 billion neocortical neurons, with an average of 7,000 synaptic connections each," making these structures possible candidates for involvement in processing and memory storage; every cubic centimeter of cerebral cortex contains roughly a trillion synapses.[842]

---

[842] Drachman, "Do We Have Brain to Spare?", 1.

To test whether consciousness modulates electromagnetic field activity, we should begin with the monitoring, recording, and frequency domain analysis of electromagnetic spectra radiating from biological structures. We should also measure, record, and analyze what has previously been regarded only as signal "noise" in the infrared energy radiating through the blood capillary system.

Further analysis should search for modulated patterns encoded within these spectral recordings that might indicate that they carry information. This would be similar to the research methodology conducted by John Lilly in the 1950s, in a research project funded by the National Science Foundation during which Lilly's team monitored and recorded audible dolphin/human communications, and applied Fourier frequency domain analysis in the search for super audible information patterns.[843]

Uploading Consciousness from Wetware to Hardware

In conclusion, it is possible to speculate on practical implications of this holoflux theory for future technologies. Identification of an electromagnetic energy field manifesting information characteristics in biological systems would support the feasibility that, in principle, major components of consciousness might eventually be stored, maintained, and manipulated using hardware (e.g., fiber optics and silicon) instead of wetware (biological tissue). An intriguing implication would be that

---

[843] Lilly, *The Mind of the Dolphin: A Nonhuman Intelligence.*

consciousness might be uploaded from wetware into such a hardware environment, and vice versa.

On the other hand, if the theories of Teilhard de Chardin are correct, human wetware consciousness is even now being uploaded into a planetary geomagnetic noosphere, tuned to human species-specific wavelengths, on a continual basis, fed by over 7 billion beating human hearts. This would be the source of a radiant holoflux energy feeding into an evolving planetary noosphere, part of the ever higher centro-complexities predicted in Teilhard's theories of hyperphysics.

REFERENCES

Aczel, Amir D. 2007. *The Jesuit and the Skull: Teilhard de Chardin, Evolution, and the Search for Peking Man.* New York: Riverhead.

Aetheling. 2012. "File:World-Population-1800-2100.svg" (graphic file). November 22, 2015. Wikimedia Commons. Retrieved from https://commons.wikimedia.org/wiki/File:World-Population-1800-2100.svg.

Aigner, Dennis J. 2000. *The Swastika Symbol in Navajo Textiles.* Laguna Beach, California: DAI Press.

Alabiso, Carlo, and Ittay Weiss. 2015. *A Primer on Hilbert Space Theory: Linear Spaces, Topological Spaces, Metric Spaces, Normed Spaces, and Topological Groups.* New York: Springer.

Alkari. 2012. "File:Yin_yang.svg" (graphic file). November 28, 2015. Wikimedia Commons. Retrieved from https://commons.wikimedia.org/wiki/File:Yin_yang.svg.

Allaby, Michael, and Ailisa Allaby, eds. 1999. "Telluric Current." In *A Dictionary of Earth Sciences.* 2nd ed. New York: Oxford University.

Amuecki. 2008. "File:Resonance.png" (graphic file). November 11, 2015. Wikimedia Commons. Retrieved from https://commons.wikimedia.org/wiki/File:Resonance.png.

Association for Asian Studies, Southeast Conference. 1979. *Annals. Volumes 1–5.* Durham, NC: Duke University Press.

Aur, Dorian, and Mandar S. Jog. 2010.
*Neuroelectrodynamics: Understanding the Brain
Language.* Amsterdam: IOS Press.

Averse. 2007. "File:Diplexer1.jpg" (graphic file). November
13, 2015. Wikimedia Commons. Retrieved from
https://en.wikipedia.org/wiki/Microwave#/media/F
ile:Diplexer1.jpg.

Baggott, Jim. 2011. *The Quantum Story: A History in 40
Moments.* New York: Oxford University.

Bailes, K. E. 1990. *Science and Russian Culture in an Age of
Revolutions: V.I. Vernadsky and His Scientific
School, 1863–1945.* Bloomington: Indiana
University.

Bailey, Alice A. 1927. *The Light of the Soul: The Yoga Sutras
of Patanjali.* New York: Lucis Publishing.

Bain, George Grantham. 2011.
"File:Niels_Bohr_Date_Unverified_LOC.jpg"
(graphic file). November 28, 2015. Wikimedia
Commons. Retrieved from
https://commons.wikimedia.org/wiki/File:Niels_Bo
hr_Date_Unverified_LOC.jpg.

Becker, Robert O. 1990. *Cross Currents: The Perils of
Electropollution and the Promise of Electromedicine.*
New York: Jeremy Tarcher.

Becker, Robert O., and Gary Selden. 1985. *The Body
Electric: Electromagnetism and the Foundation of
Life.* New York: Harper.

Bekenstein, Jacob D. 1973. "Black Holes and Entropy."
Physical Review 7 (8): 2333–46.

Bell, E. T. 1937. *Men of Mathematics.* New York: Simon and
Schuster.

Bell, J. S. 1987. *The Speakable and Unspeakable in Quantum Mechanics*. Cambridge: Cambridge University.

Benenson, Walter, John W. Harris, Horst Stocker, and Lutz Holger, eds. 2006. *Handbook of Physics*. New York: Springer Science.

Berg, Jerome S. 2008. *Broadcasting on the Short Waves, 1945 to Today*. London: McFarland & Company.

Bergson, Henri. 1911. *Creative Evolution*. Translated by Arthur Mitchell. New York: Henry Holt.

Bisson, Terry. 1990. "They're Made Out of Meat." *Omni Magazine* 13 (7): 42–45. New York: General Media.

Blakeslee, Douglas, ed. 1972. *The Radio Amateur's Handbook*. Newington, CT: The American Radio Relay League.

Blinkov, S. M. and I. I. Glezer. 1968. *The Human Brain in Figures and Tables. A Quantitative Handbook*. New York: Plenum.

Block, Ned. 2007. *Consciousness, Function, and Representation*: *Collected Papers, Vol. 1*. Cambridge: The MIT Press.

Bohm, David. 1951. *Quantum Theory*. New York: Prentiss-Hall.

———. 1952. "A Suggested Interpretation of the Quantum Theory in Terms of 'Hidden Variables,' Vol. 1." *Physical Review* 85 (2): 166–93. Retrieved from http://fma.if.usp.br/~amsilva/Artigos/p166_1.pdf.

———. 1965. *The Special Theory of Relativity*. Philadelphia: John Benjamins.

———. 1978. "The Enfolding-Unfolding Universe: A Conversation with David Bohm." In *The Holographic Paradigm and Other Paradoxes: Exploring the Leading Edge of Science*, edited by Ken Wilber, 44–104. Boulder, CO: Shambhala.

———. 1980. *Wholeness and the Implicate Order*. London: Routledge.

———. 1985. *Unfolding Meaning: A Weekend of Dialogue with David Bohm*. London: Routledge.

———. 1986. "The Implicate Order and the Super-Implicate Order." In *Dialogues with Scientists and Sages: The Search for Unity*, edited by Renée Weber, 23–49. New York: Routledge.

———. 1987a. "Hidden Variables and the Implicate Order." In *Quantum Implications: Essays in Honour of David Bohm*, edited by B. J. Hiley and F. David Peat, 33–45. London: Routledge.

———. 1989. "Meaning and Information." In *The Search for Meaning: The New Spirit in Science and Philosophy*, edited by Paavo Pylkkänen, 43–85. Northamptonshire, England: The Aquarian Press.

———. 1990. *Beyond Limits: A Full Conversation with David Bohm*. Interview by Bill Angelos for Dutch public television. Posted March 5, 2011. Retrieved from http://bohmkrishnamurti.com/beyond-limits/

———. 1990. "A New Theory of the Relationship of Mind and Matter." *Philosophical Psychology* 3 (2): 271–86.

Bohm, David, and Basil J. Hiley. 1993. *The Undivided Universe: An Ontological Interpretation of Quantum Theory*. London: Routledge.

Bohm, David, and J. Krishnamurti. 1985. *The Ending of Time: Where Philosophy and Physics Meet*. New York: Harper Collins.

Bohm, David, and J. Krishnamurti. 1999. *The Limits of Thought: Discussions between J. Krishnamurti and David Bohm*. London: Routledge.

Bohm, David, and F. David Peat. 1987. *Science, Order, and Creativity*. London: Routledge.

Bohm, David, and R. Weber. 1982. "Nature as Creativity." *ReVision* 5 (2): 35–40.

Booth, J. C., S. A. Koren, and Michael A. Persinger. 2005. "Increased Feelings of the Sensed Presence and Increased Geomagnetic Activity at the Time of the Experience During Exposures to Transcerebral Weak Complex Magnetic Fields." *International Journal of Neuroscience* 115 (7): 1039–65.

Born, Irene, trans. 1971. *The Born–Einstein Letters: Friendship, Politics and Physics in Uncertain Times*. New York: Macmillan.

Borsellino, A., and T. Poggio. 1972. "Holographic Aspects of Temporal Memory and Optomotor Responses." *Kybernetik* 10 (1): 58–60.

Brigham, E. O. 2002. *The Fast Fourier Transform*. New York: Prentice-Hall.

Broughton, S. A., and K. Bryan. 2008. *Discrete Fourier Analysis and Wavelets: Applications to Signal and Image Processing*. New York: Wiley.

Browder, Andrew. 1996. *Mathematical Analysis: An Introduction*. New York: Springer-Verlag.

Bruskiewich, Patrick. 2014. *Max Planck and Black-Body Radiation*. Vancouver: Pythagoras Publishing.

Carr1, Bernard J. and Steven B. Giddings. 2005. "Quantum Black Holes." *Scientific American* 292 (5): 30–35.

Cazenave, Michel, ed. 1984. *Science and Consciousness: Two Views of the Universe, Edited Proceedings of the France-Culture and Radio-France Colloquium, Cordoba, Spain*. Oxford: Pergamon.

Chalmers, David J. 1995. "Facing Up to the Problem of Consciousness." *Journal of Consciousness Studies* 2 (3): 200–19.

———. 2010. *The Character of Consciousness*. New York: Oxford University.

Chaudhuri, Haridas. 1954. *The Philosophy of Integralism: The Metaphysical Synthesis in Sri Aurobindo's Teaching*. Pondicherry, India: Sri Aurobindo Ashram Trust.

———. 1960. "The Integral Philosophy of Sri Aurobindo." In *The Integral Philosophy of Sri Aurobindo: A Commemorative Symposium*, edited by Haridas Chaudhuri and Frederic Spiegelberg, 17–34. London: George Allen & Unwin.

———. 1969. *The Integral Philosophy of Sri Aurobindo*. London: George Allen & Unwin.

Chen, Frances F. 2006. *Introduction to Plasma Physics and Controlled Fusion: Vol 1. Plasma Physics*. 2nd ed. New York: Springer.

Cheney, Brainard. 1965. "Has Teilhard de Chardin 'Really' Joined the Within and the Without of Things?" *The Sewanee Review* 73 (2): 217–36.

Cheney, Margaret. 1981. *Tesla: Man Out of Time*. New York: Dorset Press.

Chomsky, Noam. 2000. *New Horizons in the Study of Language and Mind*. Cambridge, England: Cambridge University.

Clark, Walter. 1939. *Photography by Infrared—Its Principles and Applications*. New York: John Wiley & Sons.

Cohn, Stephen M., 2007. "Near-Infrared Spectroscopy: Potential Clinical Benefits in Surgery." *Journal of the American College of Surgeons* 205 (2): 322–32. doi: http://dx.doi.org/10.1016/j.jamcollsurg.2007.02.024

Collister, Rupert Clive. 2010. *A Journey in Search of Wholeness and Meaning*. New York: Peter Lang.

Cook, David M. 2002. *The Theory of the Electromagnetic Field*. Englewood Cliffs, NJ: Prentice-Hall.

Corte, Nicolas. 1960. *Pierre Teilhard de Chardin: His Life and Spirit*. New York: Macmillan.

Crease, Robert P. 2008. *The Great Equations: Breakthroughs in Science from Pythagoras to Heisenberg*. New York: W. W. Norton.

Cuénot, Claude. 1965. *Teilhard de Chardin: A Biographical Study*. London: Burnes & Oates.

Darekk2. 2012. "File:Water_infrared_absorption_coefficient_large.gif" (graphic file). November 28, 2015. Wikimedia Commons. Retrieved from https://en.wikipedia.org/wiki/File:Water_infrared_absorption_coefficient_large.gif.

Darling, David J. 2004. *The Universal Book of Mathematics: From Abracadabra to Zeno's Paradoxes*. Hoboken, NJ: Wiley.

Dawson, Lorne L. 2006. *Comprehending Cults: The Sociology of New Religious Movements*. New York: Oxford University.

Deacon, Terrence W. 2010. "What Is Missing from Theories of Information." In *Information and the Nature of Reality: From Physics to Metaphysics*, edited by Paul Davies and Niels Henrik Gregersen, 123–42. Cambridge, England: Cambridge University.

———. 2012. *Incomplete Nature: How Mind Emerged from Matter*. New York: W. W. Norton.

de Lubac, Henri. 1967. *The Religion of Teilhard de Chardin*. Translated by René Hague. New York: Desclée.

de Terra, Helmut. 1964. *Memories of Teilhard de Chardin*. Translated by J. Maxwell Brownjohn. New York: Harper & Row.

De Valois, Karen K., and Russell L. De Valois. 1988. *Spatial Vision*. New York: Oxford University.

Dennett, Daniel C. 1991. *Consciousness Explained*. New York: Back Bay Books.

Dewey, B. 1985. *The Theory of Laminated Spacetime*. Inverness, CA: Bartholomew.

Dewynne, Dustin. 2012. "File:Dualism-vs-Monism.png" (graphic file). November 27, 2015. Wikimedia Commons. Retrieved from https://commons.wikimedia.org/wiki/File:Dualism-vs-Monism.png.

Differenxe. 2010. "File:Sawtooth_Fourier_Analysys.svg" (graphic file). October 22, 2015. Wikimedia Commons. Retrieved from http://commons.wikimedia.org/wiki/File:Sawtooth_Fourier_Analysys.svg.

Dorf, Richard C., ed. 1997. *The Electrical Engineering Handbook*. 2nd ed. Boca Raton, FL: CRC Press.

Drachman, David A. 2005. "Do We Have Brain to Spare?" *Neurology* 64 (6): 2004–5. doi: http://dx.doi.org/10.1212/01.WNL.0000166914.38327.BB.

Dunwell, Frances F. 1980. *The Hudson: America's River*. New York: Columbia University.

Edelman, Gerald M., and Giulio Tononi. 2000. *A Universe of Consciousness: How Matter Becomes Imagination*. New York: Basic Books.

Edmondson, Amy C. 1987. *A Fuller Explanation: The Synergetic Geometry of R. Buckminster Fuller*. Boston: Birkhäuser.

Einstein, Albert. 1979. *Autobiographical Notes*. Peru, IL: Carus.

Eliot, Thomas Stearns. 1943. *Four Quartets*. New York: Harcourt Brace.

———. 1976. *Collected Poems 1909–1962*. New York: Harcourt Brace.

Fechner, Gustav Theodor. 1946. *Religion of a Scientist: Selections from Gustav Theodor Fechner*, New York: Pantheon.

Fellmann, E. A. 2007. *Leonhard Euler*. Translated by E. Gautschi. Basel, Germany: Birkhauser.

Ferrer, Jorge, and Jacob Sherman, eds. 2008. *The Participatory Turn: Spirituality, Mysticism, Religious Studies*. Albany: State University of New York.

Feuerstein, Georg. 1987. *Structures of Consciousness: The Genius of Jean Gebser—An Introduction and Critique*. Lower Lake, CA: Integral.

Feynman, Richard, Robert Leighton, and Matthew Sands. 1964. *The Feynman Lectures on Physics, Vol. 1*. Reading, MA: Addison-Wesley.

Fields, R. Douglas. 2009. *The Other Brain*. New York: Simon & Schuster.

Flanagan, Owen. 1997. "Conscious Inessentialism and the Epiphenomenalist Suspicion." In *The Nature of Consciousness: Philosophical Debates*, edited by Ned Block, Owen Flanagan, and Güven Güzeldere, 357–73. Cambridge, MA: MIT Press.

Fourier, Jean Baptiste Joseph. 1822. *The Analytic Theory of Heat*. Paris: Firmin Didot Père et Fils.

Fulvio314. 2013. "File:Coat_of_Arms_of_Niels_Bohr.svg" (graphic file). November 28, 2015. Wikimedia Commons. Retrieved from https://commons.wikimedia.org/wiki/File:Coat_of_Arms_of_Niels_Bohr.svg.

Gabor, Dennis. 1946. "Theory of Communication." *Journal of the Institute of Electrical Engineers* 93: 429–41.

Gao, Shan. 2014. *Dark Energy: From Einstein's Biggest Blunder to the Holographic Universe*. 2nd ed. Seattle, WA: Amazon Kindle Direct.

Garay, Luis J. 1995. "Quantum Gravity and Minimum Length." *International Journal of Modern Physics* 10 (2): 145–65.

Gebser, Jean. 1949. *The Ever-Present Origin: Part One: Foundations of the Aperspectival World.* Translated by J. Keckeis. Stuttgart, Germany: Deutsche Verlags-Anstalt.

———. 1956 (1996). "Cultural Philosophy as Method and Venture." Translated by Georg Feuerstein. *Integrative Explorations: Journal of Culture and Consciousness* 3 (1): 77–82. Retrieved from http://static1.squarespace.com/static/535ef5d8e4b0 ab57db4a06c7/t/541f74a0e4b0394ddbf5a040/14113 47616917/integrative_explorations_3.pdf.

Geiger, Rudolf, Robert H. Aron, and Paul Todhunter. 2003. *The Climate Near the Ground.* Lanham, MD: Rowman and Littlefield.

Gidley, Jennifer. 2007. "The Evolution of Consciousness as a Planetary Imperative: An Integration of Integral Views." *Integral Review* 3 (5): 4–226. Retrieved from http://integral-review.org/pdf-template-issue.php?pdfName=issue_5_gidley_the_evolution_ of_consciousness_as_a_planetary_imperative.pdf.

Glatzmaier. 2007. "File:Geodynamo_Between_Reversals.gif" (graphic file). November 12, 2015. Wikimedia Commons. Retrieved from https://commons.wikimedia.org/wiki/File:Geodyna mo_Between_Reversals.gif.

Globus, Gordon G. 2006. *The Transparent Becoming of World: A Crossing Between Process Philosophy and Quantum Neurophilosophy.* Philadelphia: John Benjamins.

Goswami, Amit. 2000. *The Visionary Window: A Quantum Physicist's Guide to Enlightenment*. Wheaton, IL: Quest Books.

Gott, J. Richard III, Mario Jurić, David Schlegel, and Fiona Hoyle. 2005. "A Map of the Universe." *The Astrophysics Journal* 624 (2): 463–514.

Gray, Henry. 1918. "File:Gray754.png" (graphic file). October 31, 2015. Wikimedia Commons. Retrieved from https://commons.wikimedia.org/wiki/File:Gray754.png.

Haas, Jonathan. 2012. "File:Neurons_uni_bi_multi_pseudouni.svg" (graphic file). October 31, 2015. Wikimedia Commons. Retrieved from http://commons.wikimedia.org/wiki/File:Neurons_uni_bi_multi_pseudouni.svg.

Haisch, Bernard. 2010. *The Purpose-Guided Universe: Believing in Einstein, Darwin, and God*. Pompton Plains, NJ: New Page Books.

Hameroff, Stuart R. 2015. "Is Your Brain Really a Computer, or Is It a Quantum Orchestra?" *Huffington Post*, July 9. Retrieved from http://www.huffingtonpost.com/stuart-hameroff/is-your-brain-really-a-co_b_7756700.html.

Hameroff, Stuart, and Roger Penrose. 1996. "Conscious Events as Orchestrated Space-Time Selections." *Journal of Consciousness Studies* 3 (1): 35–53.

Hameroff, Stuart R., Travis J. A. Craddock, and Jack A. Tuszynski. 2014. "Quantum Effects in the Understanding of Consciousness." *Journal of Integrative Neuroscience* (13) 2: 229–52. doi:10.1142/S0219635214400093.

Harnad, Stevan. 1994. "Why and How We Are Not Zombies." *Journal of Consciousness Studies* 1 (1): 18–23.

Havelka, D., M. Cifra, O. Kucera, J. Pokorny, and J. Vrba. 2011. "High-frequency Electric Field and Radiation Characteristics of Cellular Microtubule Network." *Journal of Theoretical Biology* 286 (7): 31–40.

Heehs, Peter. 2008. *The Lives of Sri Aurobindo*. New York: Columbia University.

Herculano-Houzel, Suzana. 2009. "The Human Brain in Numbers: A Linearly Scaled-up Primate Brain." Frontiers in Human Neuroscience (3) 31: 1–11. doi: 10.3389/neuro.09.031.2009

Hertz, Heinrich. 1893. *Electric Waves: Being Researches On the Propagation of Electric Action with Finite Velocity Through Space*. London: MacMillan.

Hiley, B. J., and F. David Peat, eds. 1987. *Quantum Implications: Essays in Honour of David Bohm*. London: Routledge.

Hiley, B. J., and F. David Peat, eds. 1987. "The Development of David Bohm's Ideas from the Plasma to the Implicate Order." In *Quantum Implications: Essays Honour of David Bohm*, edited by B. J. Hiley and F. David Peat, 1–32. London: Routledge.

Horne, Alistair. 1962. *The Price of Glory: Verdun 1916*. New York: St. Martin's Press.

Howell, Kenneth B. 2001. *Principles of Fourier Analysis*. Boca Raton, FL: Chapman & Hall.

Ishikawa, Hiroaki, and Wallace F. Marshall. "Ciliogenesis: Building the Cell's Antenna." *Nature Reviews Molecular Biology* 12 (4): 222-34. dos:10.1038/nrm3085

Jahoe. 2012. "File:Electromagnetic-Spectrum.png" (graphic file). November 28, 2015. Wikimedia Commons. https://commons.wikimedia.org/wiki/File:Electrom agnetic-Spectrum.png.

Jbarta. 2014. "File:Max_Planck_1878.GIF" (graphic file). November 28, 2015. Wikimedia Commons. Retrieved from https://commons.wikimedia.org/wiki/File:Max_Pla nck_1878.GIF.

Jibu, Mari, and Kunio Yasue. 1995. *Quantum Brain Dynamics and Consciousness.* Philadelphia: John Benjamins.

———. 2003. "Quantum Brain Dynamics and Quantum Field Theory." In *Brain and Being: At the Boundary Between Science, Philosophy, Language and Arts,* edited by Gordon Globus, Karl Pribram, and Giuseppe Vitiello, 267–90. Philadelphia: John Benjamins.

Johnston, Sean F. 2006. *Holographic Visions: A History of New Science.* New York: Oxford University.

Jung, C. G. 1968. *Psychology and Alchemy.* Vol. 12 of *The Collected Works of C. G. Jung.* Edited and translated by Gerald Adler and R. F. C. Hull. 2nd ed. Princeton, NJ: Princeton University.

———. (1946) 1969. "On the Nature of the Psyche." In Vol. 8 of *The Collected Works of C. G. Jung,* translated by R. F. C. Hull, 159–234. 2nd ed. Princeton, NJ: Princeton University.

Kachris, Christoforos, Keren Bergman, and Ioannis Tomkos. 2012. *Optical Interconnects for Future Data Center Networks*. New York. Springer.

Kafatos, Menas, Rudolph E. Tanzi, and Deepak Chopra. 2011. "How Consciousness Becomes the Physical Universe." *Journal of Cosmology* (14): 1318–1328. Retrieved from http://journalofcosmology.com/Consciousness140.html.

King, Ursula. 1996. *Spirit of Fire: The Life and Vision of Teilhard de Chardin*. New York: Orbis Books.

———. 1999. *Pierre Teilhard de Chardin: Writings Selected with an Introduction by Ursula King*. New York: Orbis Books.

Köhler, Wolfgang. 1940. *Dynamics in Psychology: Vital Applications of Gestalt Psychology*. New York: W. W. Norton.

———. 1969. *The Task of Gestalt Psychology*. New Jersey: Princeton University.

Köhler, Wolfgang, and Mary Henle. 1971. *The Selected Papers of Wolfgang Köhler*. New York: W. W. Norton.

Kropf, Richard W. 2014. "Searching for Soul: Teilhard, De Lubac, Rahner, and the Evolutionary Quest for Immortality." *Teilhard Studies* 69 (4): 1–28.

Kuehn, Kerry. 2014. *A Student's Guide Through the Great Physics Texts, Vol. 1: The Heavens and The Earth*. New York: Springer.

Kuo, Franklin. 1962. *Network Analysis and Synthesis*. New York: John Wiley & Sons.

Lashley, Karl. 1951. "An Examination of the Electric Field Theory of Cerebral Integration." *Psychological Review* 58: 123–36.

———. 1950. "In Search of the Engram." *Symposium of the Society for Experimental Biology* 4: 454–82.

László, Ervin. 2006. *Science and the Re-Enchantment of the Cosmos: The Rise of the Integral Vision of Reality.* Rochester, VT: Inner Traditions.

———. 2007. *Science and the Akashic Field: An Integral Theory of Everything.* Rochester, VT: Inner Traditions.

———. 2014a. *The Immortal Mind: Science and the Continuity of Consciousness beyond the Brain.* Rochester, VT: Inner Traditions.

———. 2014b. *The Self-Actualizing Cosmos: The Akasha Revolution in Science and Human Consciousness.* Rochester, VT: Inner Traditions.

Leckie, Robert. 1987. *Delivered from Evil: The Saga of World War II.* New York: Harper & Row.

Leith, Emmet N., and J. Upatnieks. 1962. "Reconstructed Wavefronts and Communication Theory." *Journal of the Optical Society of America* 52 (10): 1123–30.

———. 1965. "Photography by Laser." *Scientific American* 212 (6): 24–35.

Leroy, Pierre. 1960. "Teilhard de Chardin: The Man." Introduction to *The Divine Milieu,* by Teilhard de Chardin, 13–42. New York: Harper & Row.

Lilly, John. 1967. *The Mind of the Dolphin: A Nonhuman Intelligence.* New York: Doubleday.

———. 1977. *The Deep Self: Consciousness Exploration in the Isolation Tank.* New York: Simon & Schuster.

Livio, Mario. 2003. *The Golden Ratio: The Story of Phi, the World's Most Astonishing Number.* New York: Broadway Books.

Lundqvist, Stig, ed. 1992. *Nobel Lectures, Physics 1971–1980.* Singapore: World Scientific.

Lyon, Richard F. "File:Sine_wavelength.svg" (graphic file). November 22, 2015. Wikimedia Commons. Retrieved from https://commons.wikimedia.org/wiki/File:Sine_wavelength.svg.

MacKenna, Stephen. 1992. *Plotinus: The Enneads.* New York: Larson Publications.

Malinski, Tadeusz. 1960. *Chemistry of the Heart.* Ohio: Biochemistry Research Laboratory. Retrieved from http://hypertextbook.com/facts/2003/IradaMuslumova.shtml

Mandelbrot, Benoit. 1986. "Fractals and the Rebirth of Iteration Theory." In *The Beauty of Fractals: Images of Complex Dynamical Systems*, by H.-O. Peitgen and P. H. Richter, 151–60. Berlin: Springer-Verlag.

McCraty, Rollin. 2003. *The Energetic Heart: Bioelectromagnetic Interactions Within and Between People.* Boulder Creek, CA: Institute of HeartMath.

McCraty, Rollin, M. Atkinson, D. Tomasino, and R. T. Bradley. 2009. "The Coherent Heart: Heart–Brain Interactions, Psychophysiological Coherence, and the Emergence of System-Wide Order." *Integral Review* 5 (9): 10–115.

McCraty, Rollin, Annette Deyhle, and Doc Childre. 2012. "The Global Coherence Initiative: Creating a Coherent Planetary Standing Wave." *Global Advances in Health and Medicine* 1 (1): 64–77. Retrieved from https://www.heartmath.org/assets/uploads/2015/01 /gci-creating-a-coherent-planetary-standing-wave.pdf.

McFadden, Johnjoe. 2002a. "The Conscious Electromagnetic Information (CEMI) Field Theory: The Hard Problem Made Easy." *Journal of Consciousness Studies* 9 (8): 45–60.

———. 2002b. "Synchronous Firing and Its Influence on the Brain's Electromagnetic Field: Evidence for an Electromagnetic Field Theory of Consciousness." *Journal of Consciousness Studies* 9 (4): 23–50.

———. 2006. "The CEMI Field Theory." In *The Emerging Physics of Consciousness*, edited by Jack A. Tuszynski, 385–404. Berlin: Springer-Verlag.

———. 2007. "Conscious Electromagnetic Field Theory." *NeuroQuantology* 5 (3): 262–70.

McGinn, Colin. 1997. "Consciousness and Space." In *Explaining Consciousness: The Hard Problem*, edited by Jonathan Shear, 97–108. Boston: MIT.

McIntosh, Steve. 2007. *Integral Consciousness and the Future of Evolution*. St. Paul, MN: Paragon House.

Merrell-Wolff, Franklin. 1973. *The Philosophy of Consciousness Without an Object: Reflections on the Nature of Transcendental Consciousness*. New York: Julian Press.

Milonni, Peter W., and Joseph E. Eberly. 2010. *Laser Physics*. Hoboken, NJ: John Wiley & Sons.

Morgan, Conway Lloyd. 1978. *Emergent Evolution: Gifford Lectures, 1921–22*. New York: Simon & Schuster.

Morin, Edgar. 1999. *Seven Complex Lessons in Education for the Future*. Translated by Nidra Poller. Paris: UNESCO.

Mysid. 2008. "File:Atmospheric_electromagnetic_opacity.svg" (graphic file). November 28, 2015. Wikimedia Commons. https://commons.wikimedia.org/wiki/File:Atmospheric_electromagnetic_opacity.svg.

National Multiple Sclerosis Society. n.d. "Cerebrospinal Fluid (CSF)." Retrieved from http://www.nationalmssociety.org/Symptoms-Diagnosis/Diagnosing-Tools/Cerebrospinal-Fluid-(CSF).

Netter, F. H. 1972. *A Compilation of Paintings of the Normal and Pathologic Anatomy of the Nervous System*. Summit, NJ: CIBA.

Neville, Katherine. 1992. "Saral and David Bohm, Prague, June 1992" (photograph). Retrieved from http://www.karlpribram.com/photos/.

Nilson, Arthur R., and J. L. Hornung. 1943. *Practical Radio Communication: Principles, Systems, Equipment, Operation, Including Very High and Ultra High Frequencies and Frequency Modulation*. 2nd ed. New York: McGraw-Hill.

Nishikawa, K., and M. Wakatani. 2000. *Plasma Physics*. Berlin: Springer-Verlag.

Nunez, Paul L. 2010. *Brain, Mind, and the Structure of Reality*. New York: Oxford University.

Oates, B. 1971. *Celebrating the Dawn: Maharishi Mahesh Yogi and the TM Technique.* New York: Putnam Books.

Ouspensky, P. D. 1949. *In Search of the Miraculous: Fragments of an Unknown Teaching.* London: Harcourt.

Oyster, Clyde W. 1999. *The Human Eye: Structure and Function.* Sunderland, MA: Sinauer Associates.

Peat, F. David. 1997. *Infinite Potential: The Life and Times of David Bohm.* Reading, MA: Addison-Wesley.

Pelekanos. (1478) 2007. "File:Serpiente_alquimica.jpg" (graphic file). File uploaded April 10 by Carlos Adanero. Wikimedia Commons. Retrieved from https://commons.wikimedia.org/wiki/File:Serpiente_alquimica.jpg.

Penfield, Wilder. 1975. *The Mystery of the Mind: A Critical Study of Consciousness and the Human Brain.* Princeton, NH: Princeton University.

Penrose, Sir Roger. 1989. *The Emperor's New Mind: Concerning Computers, Minds and the Laws of Physics.* New York: Oxford University.

Penrose, R., Stuart Hameroff, and S. Kak, eds. 2011. *Consciousness and the Universe: Quantum Physics, Evolution, Brain & Mind* (Contents selected from Volumes 3 and 14, *Journal of Cosmology*). Cambridge: Cosmology Science.

Persinger, Michael A. 2014. "Schumann Resonance Frequencies Found Within Quantitative Electroencephalographic Activity: Implications for Earth-Brain Interactions." *International Letters of Chemistry, Physics and Astronomy* 30: 24–32. doi:10.18052/www.scipress.com/ILCPA.30.24.

Pizzi, Rita, Giuliano Strini, Silvia Fiorentini, Valeria
    Pappalardo, and Massimo Pregnolato. 2010.
    "Evidences of New Biophysical Properties of
    Microtubules." In *Artificial Neural Networks*, edited
    by Seoyun J. Kwon. New York: Nova Science
    Publishers, 1–17. Retrieved from
    https://air.unimi.it/retrieve/handle/2434/167480/1
    68890/evidences.pdf.

Planck, Max. 1901. "On the Law of Distribution of Energy in
    the Normal Spectrum." *Annalen der Physik*. 309 (3):
    553–63.

Pockett, Susan. 2000. *The Nature of Consciousness: A
    Hypothesis*. Lincoln, NE: Writers Club.

———. 2007. "Difficulties with the Electromagnetic Field
    Theory of Consciousness: An Update."
    NeuroQuantology 5 (3): 271–75. Retrieved from
    http://www.neuroquantology.com/index.php/journa
    l/article
    /view/136/136 (login required).

Pribram, Karl H. 1962. "The Neuropsychology of Sigmund
    Freud." In *Experimental Foundations of Clinical
    Psychology*, edited by Arthur J. Bachrach, 442–68.
    New York: Basic Books.

———. 1971. *Languages of the Brain: Experimental
    Paradoxes and Principles in Neuropsychology*.
    Englewood Cliffs, NJ: Prentice-Hall.

———. 1982. "What the Fuss is All About." In *The
    Holographic Paradigm and Other Paradoxes*, edited
    by Ken Wilber, 27–34. Boulder: Shambhala.

———. 1984. "Mind, Brain and Consciousness: The Organization of Competence and Conduct." In *Science and Consciousness: Two Views of the Universe*, edited by Julian Davidson and Richard Davidson, 115–32. New York: Springer.

———. 1990. "Prolegomenon for a Holonomic Brain Theory." In *Synergetics of Cognition*, edited by H. Haken, 150–84. Berlin: Springer-Verlag.

———. 1991. *Brain and Perception: Holonomy and Structure in Figural Processing*. Hillsdale, NJ: Lawrence Erlbaum.

———. 1994. "What Is Mind that the Brain May Order It?" In *Proceedings of Symposia in Applied Mathematics: Proceedings of the Norbert Wiener Centenary Congress, Vol. 52*, edited by V. Mandrekar and P. R. Masani, 301–29. Providence, RI: American Mathematical Society.

———. 2004a. "Brain and Mathematics." In *Brain and Being: At the Boundary Between Science, Philosophy, Language and Arts*, edited by Gordon Globus, Karl Pribram, and Giuseppe Vitiello, 215–40. Philadelphia: John Benjamins.

———. 2004b. "Consciousness Reassessed." *Mind and Matter* 2 (1): 7–35.

———. 2011. "Karl Pribram: Bibliography." Retrieved from http://www.karlpribram.com/bibliography/.

———. 2013. *The Form Within: My Point of View*. Westport, CT: Prospecta Press.

Pribram, Karl H., A. Sharafat, and C. Beckman. 1984. "Frequency Encoding in Motor Systems." In *Human Motor Actions: Bernstein Reassessed*, edited by H. T. A. Whiting, 121–56. Amsterdam: Elsevier Science Publishers.

Prigogine, Ilya. 2015. *Modern Thermodynamics: From Heat Engines to Dissipative Structures*. Hoboken, NJ: John Wiley & Sons.

Pylkkänen, Paavo. 2007. *Mind, Matter, and the Implicate Order*. New York: Springer.

Radhakrishnan, Sarvepalli, ed. 1952. *History of Philosophy Eastern and Western, Vol. 2*. London: George Allen & Unwin.

Ramon y Cajal, Santiago. 2007. "File: Purkinje_cell_by_Cajal.png" (graphic file). January 30, 2016. Wikimedia Commons. Retrieved from https://commons.wikimedia.org/wiki/File:Purkinje_cell_by_Cajal.png.

Raven, Charles E. 1962. *Teilhard de Chardin: Scientist and Seer*. London: William Collins Sons.

Rendek, Kimberly N., Raimund Fromme, Ingo Grotjohann, and Petra Fromme. 2013. "Self-Assembled Three-Dimensional DNA Nanostructure." *Acta Crystallographica Section F: Structural Biology and Crystallization Communications* 69 (2): 141–46. doi:10.1107/S1744309112052128.

Rescher, Nicholas, ed. 1991. *G. W. Leibniz's Monadology: An Edition for Students*. Pittsburgh: University of Pittsburgh.

Ringbauer, M., B. Duffus, C. Branciard, E. G. Cavalcanti, A. G. White, and A. Fedrizzi. 2015. "Measurements On the Reality of the Wavefunction." *Nature Physics* 11 (2): 249–254. doi:10.1038/nphys3233.

Romanes, G. J., ed. 1964. *Cunningham's Textbook of Anatomy*. 10th ed. New York: Oxford University.

Romary. 2006. "File:Come pariou.jpg" (graphic file). January 29, 2016. Wikimedia Commons. Retrieved from https://commons.wikimedia.org/wiki/File:Come_pariou.jpg.

Rose, D. 2006. *Consciousness: Philosophical, Psychological and Neural Theories*. New York: Oxford University.

Ruhenstroth-Bauer, Gerhard. 1993. "Influence of the Earth's Magnetic Field on Resting and Activated EEG Mapping in Normal Subjects." *International Journal of Neuroscience* 73 (3): 331–49.

Runehov, Anne, and Luis Oviedo, eds. 2013. *Encyclopedia of Sciences and Religions*. Dordrecht, Netherlands: Springer Netherlands.

Ruppert, L. 1956. *History of the International Electrotechnical Commission*. Geneva: Central Bureau of the IEC.

Samson, Paul R., and David Pitt, eds. 1999. *The Biosphere and Noosphere Reader: Global Environment, Society and Change*. New York: Routledge.

Schrock, Karen. 2007. "An Opera Singer's Piercing Voice Can Shatter Glass." *Scientific American*, August 23. Retrieved from http://www.scientificamerican.com/article/fact-or-fiction-opera-singer-can-shatter-glass/

Sentman, Davis D. 1995. "Schumann Resonances." In *Handbook of Atmospheric Electrodynamics, Vol. 1,* edited by Hans Volland, 267–96. Boca Raton, FL: CRC Press.

Shannon, C. E. 1948. "A Mathematical Theory of Communication." *Bell System Technical Journal* 27: 623–56.

Sheldrake, Rupert. 1981. *A New Science of Life: The Hypothesis of Morphic Resonance.* Rochester, VT: Park Street.

———. 1988. *The Presence of the Past: Morphic Resonance and the Habits of Nature.* New York: Times Books.

———. 1989. *Morphic Resonance: The Nature of Formative Causation.* Rochester, VT: Park Street.

Skrbina, David. 2007. *Panpsychism in the West.* Cambridge, MA: MIT Press.

Smolin, Lee. 2013. *Time Reborn.* London: Penguin Books.

Speaight, Robert. 1967. *The Life of Teilhard de Chardin.* New York: Harper & Row.

Sperry, Roger W., N. Miner, and R.E. Myers. 1955. "Visual Pattern Perception Following Subpial Slicing and Tantalum Wire Implantations in the Visual Cortex." *Journal of Comparative and Physiological Psychology* 48 (1): 50–58.

Squire, Larry R., ed. 1998. *The History of Neuroscience in Autobiography, Vol. 2.* London: Academic Press.

Stanford Daily. 1977. "Scientists to Speak." 172 (2): 8.

Stapp, Henry P. 2009. *Mind, Matter, and Quantum Mechanics.* 3rd ed. New York: Springer-Verlag.

Steiner, Rudolf. 1959. *Cosmic Memory: Prehistory of Earth and Man*, translated by K. E. Zimmer. San Francisco: Harper & Row.

Stuart, C.I.J., Y. Takahashi, and H. Umezawa .1979. "Mixed System Brain Dynamics: Neural Memory as a Macroscopic Ordered State." *Foundations of Physics* (9): 301–7.

Susskind, Leonard. 2008. *The Black Hole War: My Battle with Stephen Hawking to Make the World Safe for Quantum Mechanics*. New York: Little, Brown and Company.

Svdmolen. 2005. "File:Red_White_Blood_cells.jpg" (graphic file). November 12, 2015. Wikimedia Commons. Retrieved from https://en.wikipedia.org/wiki/File:Red_White_Blood_cells.jpg.

Taimni, I. K. 1969. *Man, God and the Universe*. Madras, India: The Theosophical Society.

Talbot, Michael. 1992. *The Holographic Universe*. New York: Harper Collins.

Telsa, Faraday. 2014. "File:Assembly_of_microscale_beads_on_Faraday_waves.gif" (graphic file). February 7, 2016. Wikimedia Commons. https://upload.wikimedia.org/wikipedia/commons/4/40/Assembly_of_microscale_beads_on_Faraday_waves.gif.

Teilhard de Chardin, Pierre. (1916) 1968. "Cosmic Life." In *Writings in Time of War*, translated by René Hague, 14–71. London: William Collins Sons.

——— (1916) 1978. "Christ in Matter." In *The Heart of Matter*, translated by René Hague, 61–67. New York: Harcourt Brace Jovanovich.

———. (1917) 1978. "Nostalgia for the Front." In *The Heart of Matter*, translated by René Hague, 168–81. New York: Harcourt Brace Jovanovich.

———. (1918a) 1978. "The Great Monad." In *The Heart of Matter*, translated by René Hague, 182–95. New York: Harcourt Brace Jovanovich.

———. (1918b) 1978. "My Universe." In *The Heart of Matter*, translated by René Hague, 196–208. New York: Harcourt Brace Jovanovich. ———. (1923) 1966. "Hominization." In *The Vision of the Past*, translated by J. M. Cohen, 51–79. New York: Harper & Row.

———. (1931) 1969. "The Spirit of the Earth." In *Human Energy*, translated by J. M. Cohen, 93–112. New York: Harcourt Brace Jovanovitch.

———. (1937) 1969. "The Phenomenon of Spirituality." In *Human Energy*, translated by J. M. Cohen, 93–112. New York: Harcourt Brace Jovanovitch.

———. (1941) 1976. "The Atomism of Spirit." In *Activation of Energy*, translated by René Hague, 21–57. London: William Collins Sons.

———. (1942) 1976. "Man's Place in the Universe." In *The Vision of the Past*, translated by J.M. Cohen, 216–33. New York: Harper & Row.

———. (1943) 1969. "Human Energy." In *Human Energy*, translated by J. M. Cohen, 113–62. New York: Harcourt Brace Jovanovitch.

———. (1944) 1976. "Centrology: An Essay in a Dialectic of Union." In *Activation of Energy*, translated by René Hague, 97–127. London: William Collins Sons.

———. (1945) 1959. "Life and the Planets." In *The Future of Man*, translated by Norman Denny, 97–123. New York: Harper & Row.

———. (1946) 1976. "Outline of a Dialectic of Spirit." In *Activation of Energy*, translated by René Hague, 143–51. London: William Collins Sons.

———. (1948) 1975. "My Fundamental Vision." In *Toward the Future*, translated by René Hague, 163–208. London: William Collins Sons.

———. (1949) 1956. "The Formation of the Noosphere II." In *Man's Place in Nature: The Human Zoological Group*, translated by René Hague, 96–121. New York: Harper & Row.

———. (1950a) 1978. "The Heart of Matter." In *The Heart of Matter*, translated by René Hague, 15–79. New York: Harcourt Brace Jovanovich.

———. (1950b) 1976. "The Zest for Living." In *Activation of Energy*, translated by René Hague, 229–43. London: William Collins Sons.

———. (1951a) 1976. "The Convergence of the Universe." In *Activation of Energy*, translated by René Hague, 281–96. London: William Collins Sons.

———. (1951b) 1976. "A Mental Threshold Across Our Path: From Cosmos to Cosmogenesis." In *Activation of Energy*, translated by René Hague, 251–68. London: William Collins Sons.

———. (1951c) 1975. "Some Notes on the Mystical Sense: An Attempt at Clarification" In *Toward the Future*, translated by René Hague, 209–11. London: William Collins Sons.

———. (1953a) 1976. "The Activation of Human Energy." In *Activation of Energy*, translated by René Hague, 359–93. London: William Collins Sons.

———. (1953b) 1976. "The Energy of Evolution." In *Activation of Energy*, translated by René Hague, 359–72. London: William Collins Sons.

———. (1953c) 1976. "The Stuff of the Universe." In *Activation of Energy*, translated by René Hague, 375–83. London: William Collins Sons.

———. (1953d) 1976. "Universalization and Union." In *Activation of Energy*, translated by René Hague, 77–95. London: William Collins Sons.

———. (1954) 1956. "The Nature of the Point Omega." In *The Appearance of Man*, translated by J.M. Cohen, 271–73. New York: Harper & Row.

———. (1955) 1976. "The Death-Barrier and Co-Reflection, or the Imminent Awakening of Human Consciousness to the Sense of Its Irreversibility." In *Activation of Energy*, translated by René Hague, 395–406. London: William Collins Sons.

———. 1956. *The Appearance of Man*. Translated by J. M. Cohen. New York: Harper & Row.

———. 1959. *The Phenomenon of Man*. Translated by Bernard Wall. New York: Harper & Row.

———. 1960. *The Divine Milieu*. New York: Harper & Row.

———. 1961. *The Making of a Mind: Letters from a Soldier–Priest 1914–1919*. Translated by Rene Hague. New York: Harper & Row.

———. 1962. *Letters from a Traveler*. New York: Harper & Row.

———. 1965. *Building the Earth*. Translated by Noël Lindsay. Wilkes-Barre, PA: Dimension Books.

———. 1968. *Letters to Two Friends 1926–1952*. New York: New American Library.

———. 1969a. *Human Energy*. Translated by J. M. Cohen. New York: Harcourt Brace Jovanovitch.

———. 1969b. *Letters to Leontine Zanta*. Translated by Bernard Wall. New York: Harper & Row.

———. 1971a. *Christianity and Evolution: Reflections on Science and Religion*. Translated by René Hague. London: William Collins Sons.

———. 1971b. *Pierre Teilhard de Chardin: L'Oeuvre Scientifique*. Edited by Nicole and Karl Schmitz-Moormann. 10 vols. Munich: Walter-Verlag.

———. 1972. *Lettres Intimes de Teilhard de Chardin a Auguste Valensin, Bruno de Solages, et Henri de Lubac 1919–1955*. Paris: Aubier Montaigne.

———. 1976. *Activation of Energy*. Translated by Rene Hague. London: William Collins Sons.

———. 1978. *The Heart of Matter*. Translated by René Hague. New York: Harcourt Brace Jovanovich.

———. 2003. *The Human Phenomenon*. Translated and edited by Sarah Appleton-Weber. Portland, OR: Sussex Academic. First published 1955.

Tjlaxs. 2005. "File:YoungJamesClerkMaxwell.jpg" (graphic file). November 28, 2015. Wikimedia Commons. https://commons.wikimedia.org/wiki/File:YoungJamesClerkMaxwell.jpg.

Todeschi, Kevin J. 1998. *Edgar Cayce on the Akashic Records: The Book of Life.* Virginia Beach, VA: A. R. E. Press.

Turgeon, Mary Louise. 2004. *Clinical Hematology: Theory and Procedures.* Baltimore, MD: Lippincott Williams & Wilkins.

Tudzynski, P., T. Correia, and U. Keller. 2001. "Biotechnology and Genetics of Ergot Alkaloids." *Applied Microbiology and Biotechnology*, 57: 593–605. doi:10.1007/s002530100801.

Tuszyński, Jack A., ed. 2006. *The Emerging Physics of Consciousness.* New York: Springer-Verlag.

Van Dokkum, Pieter G., and Charlie Conroy. 2010. "A Substantial Population of Low-Mass Stars in Luminous Elliptical Galaxies." *Nature* 468 (7326): 940–42. doi:10.1038/nature09578.

Vejvoda, Stanislav. 2003. *17th International Conference on Structural Mechanics in Reactor Technology.* Prague, Czech Republic: Czech Standard Institute.

Vernadsky, Vladimir Ivanovich. 1998. *The Biosphere.* Translated by D. B. Langmuir. New York: Springer-Verlag.

Walker, J. Samuel. 2004. *Three Mile Island: A Nuclear Crisis in Historical Perspective.* Berkeley: University of California Press.

Warren, Stephen G., and Richard E. Brandt. 2008. "Optical Constants of Ice from the Ultraviolet to the Microwave: A Revised Compilation." *Journal of Geophysical Research*, 113 (D14): 1047–57.

Wasson, Tyler, and Gert Brieger. 1987. *Nobel Prize Winners: A Biographical Dictionary*. New York: H. W. Wilson.

Weber, Renée. 1982. "The Physicist and the Mystic—Is a Dialogue Between Them Possible?" In *The Holographic Paradigm and Other Paradoxes: Exploring the Leading Edge of Science*, edited by Ken Wilber, 187–214. Boulder, CO: Shambhala.

Weisenberger, Drew. n.d. "Jefferson Lab Questions and Answers: How Many Atoms Are There in the World?" Retrieved January 20, 2016 from http://education.jlab.org/qa/mathatom_05.html

Wheeler, John Archibald. 1990. *Information, Physics, Quantum: The Search for Links*. Austin, TX: University of Texas.

———. 1990. *A Journey into Gravity and Spacetime*. New York: Scientific American.

———. 1998. *Geons, Black Holes, and Quantum Foam: A Life in Physics*. New York: W. W. Norton.

Whicher, Ian. 1997. "Nirodha, Yoga Praxis, and the Transformation of the Mind." *Journal of Indian Philosophy* 25 (1): 1–67.

Whitehead, Alfred North. 1978. *Process and Reality: An Essay in Cosmology. Gifford Lectures*, 1927–28. New York: Simon & Schuster.

Wick, Manfred, Wulf Pinggera, and Paul Lehmann. 2003. *Clinical Aspects and Laboratory Iron Metabolism.* Vienna, Austria: Springer-Verlag.

Wiener, Norbert. 1948. *Cybernetics or Control and Communication in the Animal and the Machine.* Cambridge, MA: MIT Press.

Wilber, Ken, ed. 1982. *The Holographic Paradigm and Other Paradoxes: Exploring the Leading Edge of Science.* Boulder, CO: Shambhala.

———, ed. 1985. *Quantum Questions: Mystical Writings of the World's Great Physicists.* Boston: Shambhala.

———. 1996. *A Brief History of Everything.* Boston: Shambhala.

———. 1997. *Integral Spirituality: A Startling New Role for Religion in the Modern and Postmodern World.* Boston: Integral Books.

Wiltschko, Wolfgang, and Roswitha Wiltschko. 2008. "Magnetic Orientation and Magnetoreception in Birds and Other Animals." *Journal of Comparative Physiology A: Neuroethology, Sensory, Neural, and Behavioral Physiology* 191 (8): 675–93. doi:10.1007/s00359-005-0627-7.

Wiseman, Howard M., Fuwa Maria, Shuntaro Takeda, Marcin Zwierz, and Akira Furusawa. 2015. "Experimental Proof of Nonlocal Wavefunction Collapse for A Single Particle Using Homodyne Measurements." *Nature Communications* 6: 192–203. Retrieved from http://www.nature.com/ncomms/2015/150324/ncomms7665/full/ncomms7665.html.

Wong, Eva. 1997. *The Shambhala Guide to Taoism.* Boston: Shambhala.

Woolf, N. J. 2006. "Microtubules in the Cerebral Cortex: Role in Memory and Consciousness." In *The Emerging Physics of Consciousness*, edited by Jack A. Tuszyński, 49–94. New York: Springer-Verlag.

Yau, Shing-Tung, and Steve Nadis. 2010. *The Shape of Inner Space: String Theory and the Geometry of the Universe's Hidden Dimensions*. New York: Basic Books.

Zimmer C. 2009. "Origins: On The Origin of Eukaryotes." *Science* 325 (5941): 666–68.

Zizzi, Paola. 2006. "Consciousness and Logic in a Quantum Computing Universe." In *The Emerging Physics of Consciousness*, edited by Jack A. Tuszyński, 457–81. New York: Springer-Verlag.

APPENDIX:
The Holofield Theory of Ervin László

The holofield theory of Ervin László correlates well with an essential concept of the holoflux theory of consciousness developed in this book, specifically in the postulated existence of two domains or dimensions of reality, an "A-dimension" equivalent to Bohm's implicate order or Pribram's frequency flux domain, and an "M-dimension," equivalent to Bohm's explicate, space–time material domain. [844] A graduate of the Sorbonne and a professor of Philosophy, Systems Sciences, and Future Studies, László had been twice nominated for the Nobel Peace Prize; he writes of the universe, including human beings, appearing to be "nonlocally" coherent, part of a unified field of consciousness. [845]

In agreement with John Archibald Wheeler, who held that information is even more fundamental to the universe than energy, László describes an "information field," which he also calls the "A-field," lying outside of space–time and yet interacting dynamically with material manifesting in space and time. [846] In reference to this A-field, or A-dimension, László frequently uses the term *Akasha*, referencing the Sanskrit word (Ākāśa), described in Vedic texts in India as early as 5,000 BCE, in which Akasha is

---

[844] László, *Science and the Re-Enchantment of the Cosmos*, 34–35.

[845] László, *The Self-Actualizing Cosmos*, 44–45.

[846] László, *An Integral Theory of Everything*, 67.

closely associated with vibration. [847] In the Vedas its function is identified with *shabda*, the first vibration, the first ripple beginning our universe, and also with *spanda*, which has been described as "vibration/movement of consciousness."[848] The Akasha has been described by an Indian professor of inorganic chemistry, I.K. Taimni, as a sort of space out of which integrated energy vibrations emanate (much as holoflux emanates from out of an implicate domain into space–time as electromagnetic waves):

> There is ... a mysterious integrated state of vibration from which all possible kinds of vibrations can be derived by a process of differentiation. That is called *Nāda* in Sanskrit. It is a vibration in a medium called *Ākāśa* which may be translated as "space" in English. But the conception of *Ākāśa* ... is quite different from that of Science. It is not mere empty space but space which, though apparently empty, contains within itself an infinite amount of potential energy.... This infinite potentiality for producing vibrations of different kinds in any intensity or amount is due to the fact that at the back of *Ākāśa* or hidden within it, is consciousness.[849]

In László cosmology, the universe is the interaction of two dimensions, an "A-dimension" and an "M-dimension"

---

[847] Whicher, "Nirodha, Yoga Praxis, and the Transformation of the Mind," 67.

[848] Ibid.

[849] Taimni, *Man, God and the Universe*, 203.

428

("M" for "material"). The M-dimension contains that which manifests (i.e., the cosmos, the galaxies in space–time), and is that upon which material science has been primarily focused. The M-dimension can be seen as congruent with David Bohm's explicate order. László's other dimension is the A-dimension, his Akashic dimension outside of space–time, which can be identified with Bohm's implicate, enfolded order.[850] According to László, there is continual two-way interaction between the A-dimension and the M-dimension. In a cybernetic cycle, the A-dimension provides the blueprint for manifesting changes occurring in the timespace M-dimension, while information recording these changes flows back to and are recorded in the nontemporal vibrations of the A-dimension.[851]

In this model of an A-field and M-field interacting can be seen the functional properties to support Rupert Sheldrake's morphic field paradigm. Sheldrake describes his theory of the morphic field's memory as morphic resonance, and here relates it to the quantum vacuum field:

> All morphic fields have an inherent memory given by morphic resonance. Morphogenetic fields, the organizing fields of morphogenesis, are one kind of the larger category of morphic fields, rather like a species within a genus . . . . Morphic fields must in some way interact directly or indirectly with electromagnetic and quantum fields . . . . Another possible point of connection between morphic fields and modern physics is through the quantum vacuum field. According to standard

---

[850] Bohm, *Wholeness and the Implicate Order.*

[851] László, *The Self-Actualizing Cosmos*, 95.

quantum theory, all electrical and magnetic forces are mediated by virtual photons that appear from the quantum vacuum field and then disappear into it again.[852]

Sheldrake here states that some sort of memory information, stored in the morphic field outside of space–time, is interacting with electromagnetic fields within space–time.

László supports and extends Sheldrake's model to include a mechanism for morphic resonance, describing it as the effect of a long-term interaction of a species with the A-dimension.[853] Here is László's description of a species-specific pattern acting as a natural attractor for morphic resonance in the A-dimension.

> The information generated in this interaction is conserved in the A-dimension. The A-dimension is the memory of the M-dimension; it is the manifest world's Akashic record. The sea of Akashic information includes the species-specific pattern that is the natural "attractor" of healthy functioning in organism. This pattern results from the long-term interaction of a species with the A-dimension; it is the enduring memory of those interactions; and it codes the generic norms of viable species.[854]

László here parallels Sheldrake's description of morphic resonance, describing it as information transfer

---

[852] Sheldrake, *Morphic Resonance: The Nature of Formative Causation*, 158.

[853] László, *The Self-Actualizing Cosmos*, 57.

[854] Ibid.

from a morphic field (A-field) to a living organism (M-field), a sort of information blueprint for the living organism:

> According to the Akasha paradigm the information that coordinates the functions of a living organism is a specific pattern in the sea of A-dimensional information. This corpus of information governs action, interaction, and reaction throughout the manifest world. It also governs the functions of the living organism. It is a blueprint of normal organic functioning.[855]

Sheldrake's morphogenetic field thus mirrors László's A-dimensional field, but while Sheldrake makes explicit a possible relationship or interaction of morphic fields with electromagnetic fields, László fails the attempt to identify the A-field with any of the current fields known to physicists. Here he states that the "Akashic Field" is, as yet, unknown to the physical sciences:

> The evidence for a field that would conserve and convey information is not direct; it must be reconstructed in reference to more immediately available evidence. Like other fields known to modern physics, such as the gravitational field, the electromagnetic field, the quantum fields, and the Higgs field, the in-formation field cannot be seen, heard, touched, tasted, or smelled ... it seems evident that a further field is required. In my previous books I named the universal in-formation field the Akashic Field.[856]

---

[855] Ibid., 56.

[856] László, *Science and the Akashic Field*, 73.

László also puts forth in his theory that the A-field is the quantum vacuum itself, that the field is the fundamental energy and information-carrying field, interconnecting all things in and between all dimensions, nonlocally, in a multiverse. And László further describes the A-field, which he says is currently unknown to physics, as being a "vacuum-based holofield."[857] But László again declares, as did Bohm and Teilhard, that any such posited field must be firmly rooted in what science already knows about the nature of physical reality:

> The concept of such a field cannot be an ad hoc postulate, nor can it be an extra-scientific hypothesis. It must be rooted in what science already knows about the nature of physical reality.... We assume that the interaction of such a field with quanta and quanta-based systems—atoms, molecules, cells, organisms, ecologies, and systems even of cosmological dimension—produces nonlocal interaction within and among them.[858]

Unfortunately, while László states clearly that his concept must be rooted in science, he provides no clear connection between the A-field and the tenets of modern science, neither through mathematics nor physics, and this leaves his theory incomplete.

Nevertheless, László's intuited metaphor of the A-field being some sort of "blueprint" can be used to explain why evolution is not a random process. If we assume that through some mechanism the arc of the creating cosmos is

---

[857] László, *Science and the Re-Enchantment of the Cosmos*, 34.

[858] László, *The Self-Actualizing Cosmos*, 13–15.

guided by information stored in the A-field, then all of the "fine-tuned constants" discovered in our universe, and marveled at by cosmologists, might be more readily explained. If we assume that the A-field contains (and shares) information from billions upon billions of experimental attempts, in previously evolving space–time universes, to create new forms (new forms of particles, new forms of galaxies, new forms of matter, life, and consciousness), then it is the influx of this information collapsing from the A-field into the M-field that produces the exquisitely-tuned constants that are enjoyed in the structure of our particular universe. Such a viewpoint accords well with the recent ideas of the theoretical physicist Lee Smolin, that "for cosmology to progress, physics must abandon the idea that laws are timeless and eternal and embrace instead the idea that even they evolve in real time."[859]

László's theory brilliantly points the way towards a truly new paradigm for material science and future research directions, but it is unfortunate that his use of the Vedic term akasha and the Theosophist term "Akashic record" serves only to undermine his theory among the scientific community. His occasional use of the terms "spiritual" and "yoga" in his essays would seem also to limit the dissemination of his work within a broader scientific community, as seen here:

> Our bodily senses do not register Akasha, but we can reach it through spiritual practice. The

---

[859] Smolin, *Time Reborn*, 123.

ancient Rishis reached it through a disciplined, spiritual way of life, and through yoga.[860]

The "Akashic record" is a term invented and widely used by Theosophists in the mid-nineteenth century, in particular by Alice Bailey, in discussing Patañjali's *Yoga Sutras*, "The ākāshic record is like an immense photographic film, registering all the desires and earth experiences of our planet."[861]

The concept and term "Akashic record" is also frequently found in the early twentieth-century writings of the Austrian philosopher Rudolph Steiner, who identifies the Akashic records to be the source of information obtained through his supersensory perception into the history of the planet.[862] Steiner taught a theory, which he claimed to practice himself, through which, by conscious development of latent organs of perception, we can go beyond the ordinary space–time sensory systems into various modes by which we can directly access cosmic memory:

> Everything which comes into being in time has its origin in the eternal. But the eternal is not accessible to sensory perception. Nevertheless, the ways to the perception of the eternal are open . . . . We can develop forces dormant in us so that we can recognize the eternal . . . . In gnosis and in theosophy it is called the "Akasha Chronicle." Only a faint conception of this

---

[860] László, *Science and the Akashic Field*, 76.

[861] Bailey, *The Yoga Sutras of Patañjali*, 78

[862] Steiner, *Cosmic Memory: Prehistory of Earth and Man*.

chronicle can be given in our language. For our language corresponds to the world of the senses. . .The one who has acquired the ability to perceive in the spiritual world comes to know past events in their eternal character.[863]

More recently, the American clairvoyant Edgar Cayce (1877–1945), known as "the sleeping prophet," and writing in the mid-twentieth century, also used the term "akashic records" to describe the source of ideas with which he claimed to have connected during his deep trance and sleep states.[864]

László's theories find a great deal of support in these writings and traditions outside of the scientific field of inquiry, based as they are upon participatory, experiential data, which is not normally of interest in the material sciences. He is not averse to discussing such participatory experience of his own, and using it to extend his theory:

> When we enter an altered state of consciousness images, ideas, and intuitions flow into our consciousness that transcend the range of our sensory perceptions. These elements are part of the totality of the information in the cosmic matrix: The Akasha. This information is in a distributed form, as in a hologram.[865]

The idea of information distributed as a hologram accords well with Karl Pribram's research-based speculation on holographic memory processes; and, in the following

---

[863] Ibid., 39.

[864] Todeschi, *Edgar Cayce on the Akashic Records.*

[865] László, *The Self-Actualizing Cosmos,* 95.

passage, László's insistence on the importance of the need for understanding the whole, rather than exclusively separate parts, reminds us of David Bohm's explicate "whole," connected everywhere by the implicate order:

> The crucial feature of the emerging view is space and time transcending correlation. Space and time do not *separate* things. They *connect* things . . . information is conserved and conveyed in nature at all scales of magnitude and in all domains.[866]

László refers to the Akasha field as a "fifth dimension," and points out that it was seen in ancient culture, much as Bohm views the implicate order, to be the foundational basis of the cosmos:

> The *rishis* (seers) of India viewed the deep dimension as the fifth and most fundamental element in the cosmos; they called it by the Sanskrit term *Akasha*.[867]

László's A-field hypothesis indicates that a shift in the material science approach to consciousness is occurring, and a new paradigm may be emerging:

> a paradigm where information rather than matter is seen as the basic reality, and where space and time, and the entities that emerge and

---

[866] László, *Science and the Reenchantment of the Cosmos*, 35.

[867] László, *The Immortal Mind*, 113.

evolve in space and time, are manifestations of a deeper reality beyond space and time.[868]

---

[868] Ibid.

Made in the USA
Las Vegas, NV
26 December 2024

15340685R00259